SPOTLIGHT · ON LITERACY ·

Authors, Consultants, and Reviewers

MULTICULTURAL AND EDUCATIONAL
CONSULTANTS

Alma Flor Ada, Yvonne Beamer, Joyce Buckner,
Helen Gillotte, Cheryl Hudson, Narcita Medina,
Lorraine Monroe, James R. Murphy, Sylvia Peña,
Joseph D. Rubin, Ramon Santiago, Cliff Trafzer,
Hai Tran, Esther Lee Yao

LITERATURE CONSULTANTS

Ashley Bryan, Joan I. Glazer, Paul Janeczko,
Margaret H. Lippert

INTERNATIONAL CONSULTANTS

Edward B. Adams, Barbara Johnson,
Raymond L. Marshall

MUSIC AND AUDIO CONSULTANTS

John Farrell, Marilyn C. Davidson,
Vincent Lawrence, Sarah Pirtle, Susan R. Synder,
Rick and Deborah Witkowski, Eastern Sky Media
Services, Inc.

TEACHER REVIEWERS

Terry Baker, Jane Bauer, James Bedi, Nora Bickel,
Vernell Bowen, Donald Cason, Jean Chaney,
Carolyn Clark, Alan Cox, Kathryn DesCarpentrie,
Carol L. Ellis, Roberta Gale, Brenda Huffman,
Erma Inscore, Sharon Kidwell, Elizabeth Love,
Isabel Marcus, Elaine McCraney, Michelle Moraros,
Earlene Parr, Dr. Richard Potts, Jeanette Pulliam,
Michael Rubin, Henrietta Sakamaki,
Kathleen Cultron Sanders, Belinda Snow,
Dr. Jayne Steubing, Margaret Mary Sulentic,
Barbara Tate, Seretta Vincent,
Willard Waite, Barbara Wilson, Veronica York

Macmillan/McGraw-Hill

A Division of The McGraw-Hill Companies

Copyright © 1997 Macmillan/McGraw-Hill,
a Division of the Educational and Professional
Publishing Group of The McGraw-Hill Companies, Inc.

Macmillan/McGraw-Hill
1221 Avenue of the Americas
New York, New York 10020

Printed in the United States of America

ISBN 0-02-181009-5 / 4, L.10
6 7 8 9 R R W 02 01 00 99

Spotlight on Literacy

AUTHORS

ELAINE MEI AOKI • VIRGINIA ARNOLD • JAMES FLOOD • JAMES V. HOFFMAN • DIANE LAPP

MIRIAM MARTINEZ • ANNEMARIE SULLIVAN PALINCSAR • MICHAEL PRIESTLEY • CARL B. SMITH

WILLIAM H. TEALE • JOSEFINA VILLAMIL TINAJERO • ARNOLD W. WEBB • KAREN D. WOOD

Macmillan McGraw-Hill

NEW YORK • FARMINGTON

Unit 1

Make a Wish

4

Unit 2

Naturally!

6

Unit 3

That's What Friends Are For

Unit 4

PITCH IN!

Unit 5

Memories to Keep

Unit 6

Twice-Told Tales

15

Unit 1

Make a Wish

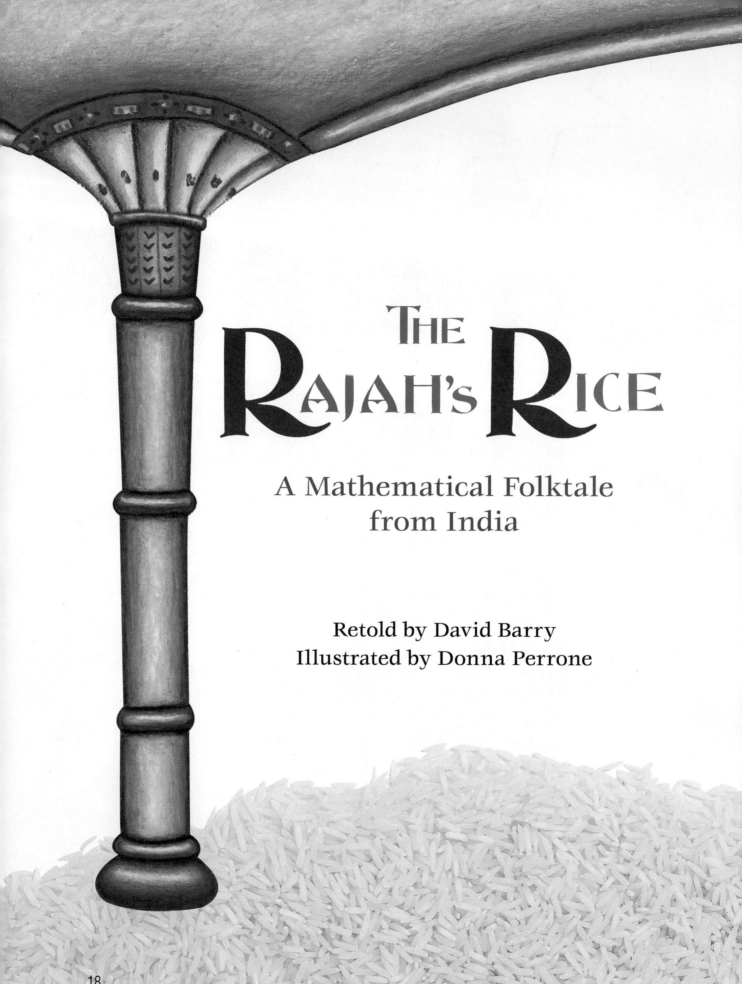

THE RAJAH'S RICE

A Mathematical Folktale from India

Retold by David Barry
Illustrated by Donna Perrone

Once upon a time a long time ago, a girl named Chandra lived in a small village in India. Chandra loved elephants. She also loved numbers. So of course she loved all numbers to do with elephants: two tusks to polish on each elephant, eighteen toenails to clean, a hundred scrubs on a side at each bath. Chandra had many chances to think about elephant numbers because she had a special job: She was the bather of the Rajah's elephants.

Chandra liked other numbers, too. As she walked past rice paddies, muddy after the harvest, she counted the snowy egrets that flew above her.

She passed through the marketplace at the edge
of the village and stopped to help the spice peddler
count change.

When she joined her friends where
they stood watching the Rajah's elephants parade
through the town square, she remembered every
elephant number she knew. Then she started thinking
about rice.

It was rent collection day, and bags bulging with
rice hung from the sides of the elephants.

No wonder the people looked sad. The Rajah
had taken so much rice for himself that the
whole village would be hungry.

But this was the way it had always been.
For thousands of years, the villagers had
farmed the Rajah's land. For thousands of
years, he had come with his elephants to
take most of the rice harvest.
    The whole thing made Chandra
angry, but what could she do?

23

On the elephants' next bath day, Chandra packed up her equipment and walked over the fields to the palace. She was about to enter the gates when the guard stopped her.

"You cannot come in this morning, Elephant Bather. The elephants have taken sick."

Chandra peered through the bamboo gate into the elephant yard. There she could see her elephants lying on the ground as still as felled trees. No amount of calling, singing, or cooing made them so much as raise their heads.

Over the days that followed Chandra sat watch over her precious elephants. She was not allowed inside, so she waited at the gate, watching medical men from all across the land come to cure the elephants.

The first doctor sat on cushions in the courtyard and feasted: he ate eight meat pastries, ten

chickpea dumplings, and twelve sand lobsters served on banana leaves at each meal. While he ate, the elephants got sicker.

Another doctor spent all day and most of the night in the elephant yard chanting and burning incense. The elephants got even sicker.

Seven more doctors came and went, but the elephants got still sicker.

One morning, the Rajah returned from a walk in the gardens to find Chandra at the gate, staring in at the elephants. "What are you doing here, Elephant Bather?" he asked.

"I worry about the elephants," she said. "I love them all and know them well. Maybe I can help them."

The Rajah thought for a moment. "Go ahead and try," he said. "I need those elephants. Without them, I will not be able to carry the rice to market on market day. If you can save them, you may choose your own reward."

The guard opened the gates, and Chandra and the Rajah walked in silence to the elephant yard. Chandra approached Misha, the Rajah's favorite elephant. She studied his

feet: the nails, the pads, the cuticles. She studied his tusks and the eight molars deep inside his mouth. She studied the lips, the tongue and the throat. She looked deep into his eyes.

When Chandra got to the first ear, she discovered a painful-looking infection inside the ear canal. The other ear was the same. So were the ears of the other elephants. Chandra cleaned their ears, sang the elephants a soothing song, and went home.

At dawn the next day, when Chandra returned, the elephants were walking unsteadily around their yard. They greeted her with joyful trumpeting.

The Rajah was overjoyed. He declared a festival day and invited everyone in the land to the palace.

The Rajah led Chandra to the ceremony room. Piled on a long table, next to the Rajah's chessboard, was a glittering array of gold necklaces, brilliant sapphires and rubies, diamond brooches, bags of gold rupees, and other treasures.

The guests began to arrive, and soon the ceremony room was crowded with villagers.

"Name your reward, Elephant Bather," said the Rajah.

Chandra looked at the beautiful jewels on the table before her. She thought about her elephants and the hundreds of sacks of rice they carried away from the village each year. And then she noticed the chessboard.

"The villagers are hungry, Rajah," she began. "All I ask for is rice. If Your Majesty pleases, place two grains of rice on the first square of this chessboard. Place four grains on the second square, eight on the next, and so on, doubling each pile of rice till the last square."

The villagers shook their heads sadly at Chandra's choice.

The Rajah was secretly delighted. A few piles of rice would certainly be far cheaper than his precious jewelry. "Honor her request," he boomed to his servants.

Two servants brought out a small bowl of rice and carefully placed two grains of rice on the first square of the board. They placed four grains on the second square. Then eight on the third square, sixteen on the fourth square, thirty-two on the fifth square, sixty-four on the sixth square, 128 on the seventh square, and finally 256 grains of rice on the eighth square at the end of the row.

Several servants snickered at Chandra's foolishness, for although the 256 grains filled the eighth square completely, they amounted to only a single teaspoon of rice.

At the first square of the second row, the servants stood awkwardly, not knowing how to count out the rice. The next number was 512, but that was too high to count quickly, and besides, it was too many grains of rice to fit on one square of the chessboard.

Chandra started to explain, "Since you had one teaspoon of rice at the end of the first row, why not just put two teaspoons—"

But the Rajah cut in. "Just keep doubling the rice," he ordered. "You don't need to count every grain."

So the servants put two teaspoons of rice into a bowl for the first square of the second row. For the second square, they put four teaspoons of rice in the bowl. Then eight teaspoons of rice for the third square, and so continued, doubling the number of teaspoons each square.

The eighth square on the second row needed 256 teaspoons of rice, which by itself filled another bowl.

On the third row, the servants started to count by teaspoons again, but the Rajah cut in. Showing off his knowledge of mathematics, he said, "If the sixteenth square takes one bowl of rice, then the seventeenth square takes two bowls of rice. You don't need to count by teaspoons anymore."

So the servants counted by bowls. Two bowlfuls for the first square, then four, then eight, then sixteen, and so on. The rice for the last square of the third row completely filled a large wheelbarrow.

Chandra's neighbors smiled at her. "Very nice," one of them said. "This would feed my family for a whole year."

As the servants worked through the fourth row, wheelbarrow by wheelbarrow, the Rajah paced back and forth, his eyes wide in amazement. His servants gathered around him. "Shall we bring rice from your royal storehouses?" they asked.

"Of course," was the reply. "A Rajah never breaks
a promise." The servants took the elephants and
headed out to the first storehouse to get more rice.

By late afternoon, the Rajah had collapsed onto his couch. As his attendants fanned him with palm fronds, the servants started on the fifth row of the chessboard, and soon they were emptying entire storehouses into the courtyard.

Within several squares, rice poured from the windows of the palace and into the gardens beyond. By the middle of the fifth row, all of the Rajah's storehouses were empty.

He had run out of rice.

The Rajah struggled to his feet and ordered the
rice to be loaded onto the elephants and taken to the
village. Then he approached Chandra.

"Elephant Bather," he said to her, "I am out of
rice and cannot fill the chessboard. Tell me what I
can give you to be released from my vow."

"You can give the people of the village the land they farm, and take only as much rice as you need for yourself," answered Chandra.

The Rajah gazed at the mountains of rice that filled his palace and gardens, then out beyond the gardens to the fields the villagers farmed, stretching as far as he could see. Then he looked back at Chandra, the elephant bather.

"It is done," he said.

That night the Rajah arrived in the village as Chandra and the other villagers prepared a celebration feast.

"Would you be so kind as to join me for a short walk, Chandra?" he asked. "I have a question for you."

As they strolled toward the village square, the Rajah spoke. "I am a very rich man, and it took all of the rice I owned to fill little more than one-half of the chessboard. How much rice would it have taken to fill the whole board?" he asked.

"If you had kept doubling the rice to the last square of the chessboard, all of India would be knee deep in rice," said Chandra, and smiled.

NOTE ON THE MATH

Powers of two, as mathematicians call doubling, are very powerful indeed. Taking the number 2 and doubling it 64 times (the number of squares on a chessboard) results in the number 18,446,744,073,709,551,616, enough grains of rice to fill the great volcano, Mt. Kilimanjaro.

Here is a chart that should give you a feel for how fast something will grow when you double it over and over.

Start with grains of rice.

grains   teaspoons   bowls   wheelbarrows   festival halls   palaces   World Trade Centers   Manhattans

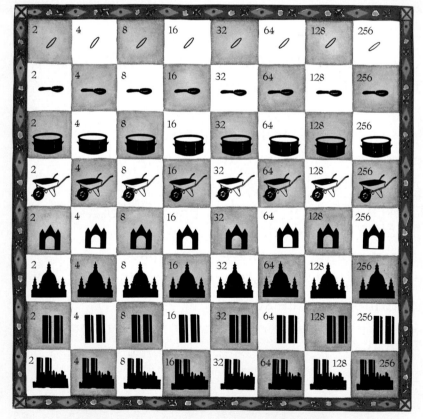

256 grains = 1 teaspoon

256 teaspoons = 1 bowl

256 bowls = 1 wheelbarrow

256 wheelbarrows = 1 festival hall full to the roof

256 festival halls = 1 palace of 256 rooms

256 palaces = 1 World Trade Center

256 World Trade Centers = 1 Manhattan island, covered 7 stories deep in rice

256 Manhattans = 1 Mt. Kilimanjaro full of rice

Add all 64 squares together and you get India, covered knee deep in rice.

Meet
DAVID BARRY

Next to words, David Barry says he likes nothing better than numbers. That is why he has always liked the math concepts in the tale of *The Rajah's Rice.*

Like Chandra, Barry understands the power of math. He explains, "It is a good starting point. If you're good in math, you can go anywhere, do anything."

Meet
DONNA PERRONE

Donna Perrone loves art from around the world. She travels to places she reads about in art books. Then she uses photographs she takes to recreate those places.

For *The Rajah's Rice,* she studied the use of detail in Indian art. You can see this detail in the lively market scene. This scene is Perrone's favorite.

Arturo Buys ~a Llama~

by David Barry

Once long ago, in the high mountains of Chile, a mother sent her son Arturo to buy a young llama. She gave him ten gold escudos, which was all the money she had saved up, and told him to keep the money safe. On his way to the market, Arturo stopped in the town square where two men were arguing.

A woodsman was bragging because he thought he would soon be rich.

"Oh, you think you'll be rich soon?" asked an old man called Tomás. "I'll make you rich right now! If you can run around the town square three times, I'll double your money each time!"

"Of course I'll do that," said the woodsman.

"But naturally I deserve some payment," said Tomás. "You don't expect this for nothing, do you? You need to pay me eight gold escudos each time."

"I'm not sure what you mean," said the woodsman.

"For example, if you have 20 escudos," said Tomás, "I'll double your 20, giving you 20 more. Then you'll have 40. You pay me 8, and then you'll have 32. I'll do that each time you round the square."

"I don't have 20 escudos, but I'll do it anyway," said the woodsman as he dashed off. But after his three rounds, the woodsman exclaimed, "Hey! I have nothing left!"

Arturo pushed his way through the crowd that had gathered and said to Tomás, "I'd like to take a chance!"

The old man chuckled at the young boy's foolishness and replied, "Sure. Give it a try."

The people called out, "Don't do it, Arturo! You're just a boy, and he'll trick you!"

Without listening, Arturo ran off around the town square. Three times he rounded the square. Each time he presented his money to Tomás. Each time Tomás reached deep into his money pouch, doubled Arturo's money, and took back eight escudos.

After the third trip around the square, Arturo paid Tomás and triumphantly declared, "I have 24 escudos!"

Arturo bought a llama and led it home. In his pocket were 14 gold escudos for his mother.

How did 10 escudos grow to 24 escudos?

How many escudos would it take for Arturo to gain?

How many escudos would it take for him to lose?

How many escudos did the woodsman start with?

Her Dreams

In her dreams

there are sometimes trees

on which hang ornaments

as tall as she

she lifts her arms

to touch them

if she can stretch

high enough to

claim them

they will become

the jewelled moments

of her life.

Eloise Greenfield

Mr. Amos Ferguson's folk painting of a young girl in the Bahamas was the inspiration for the poem by Eloise Greenfield.

Meet Marc Harshman

To Marc Harshman, writing a story is like solving a jigsaw puzzle. At first, he isn't sure what pieces he has or how they will fit together.

Harshman put together several puzzle pieces to write *A Little Excitement*. He remembered his car catching on fire and thought of the smoke and flames. That started him thinking about fires in houses. In rural West Virginia, where he lives, houses often catch fire because of the wood-burning stoves people use to heat their homes.

Marc Harshman had two pieces of a story—a fire and wood-burning stoves. When he added his memories of growing up on a farm, he completed the puzzle and created *A Little Excitement*.

Meet Ted Rand

Ted Rand lives in a rural area in Washington State. In his drawings for *A Little Excitement,* he captures the feeling of day-to-day life in the country, as well as the drama of a house in flames on a dark, snowy night.

Rand encourages children to draw and to enjoy the fun of it. He says, "Drawing is a second language to me and I hope it becomes that to you."

A LITTLE EXCITEMENT

by Marc Harshman
illustrated by Ted Rand

Winter on Pleasant Ridge had gone on long enough. Sure, I loved sledding and snowmen, snowballs and snowforts. But they can be boring, especially when you live so far in the country that your only companions are a pair of older sisters. Half the time they didn't even want to play, and the other half when they did, they were always too bossy. Mom said maybe I was too fussy. Anyway, I was tired of winter and tired of being bossed.

And what else was there? Not much. Get up. Go out in the dark and carry hay while Dad milked. Eat. Go to school. Go home and carry hay again. Eat. Study. And put up with Annie and Sarah. Not much fun I can tell you.

Annie and Sarah would tease me about the girl that the bus driver made me sit beside. When we played games, it was always them against me, and if I cheated—just to make it fair—they complained!

Mom tried. She'd offer to play checkers and sometimes we did. But you can't tell your friends when they ask what you did last night: "Oh, played checkers with Mom." I liked working with Dad but winter wasn't the fun time for that. Winter work was all mud and buckets and cow manure. And at night after chores, Dad could only slump in his chair, too tired to do much with any of us. I wondered if he would ever get his old summer strength back.

Some days it seemed all I could wish for was that something exciting might happen. One Sunday when we visited Grandma after church, I listened to her tell about her winters as a girl. She would ride to town on a sleigh behind two black mares. There were blizzards that topped the roof of the old porch. And sometimes her school would be closed for weeks at a time. It all sounded pretty good, and lots more exciting than my winter. But when I told her this, she said, "Be careful what you wish for, Willie, you might just get it."

Well, I didn't quite understand that. I didn't see why you'd have to be careful. I thought the best thing in the world that could happen to this winter would be a little excitement.

Mom heard the strange, loud roar first. She woke
up Dad and he ran down the stairs, switched on the
light, and saw the glow from the overheated stove.
Dad's weariness had caught up with him. When he
loaded up the stove with as much wood as it could
hold that cold night, he forgot to shut out the air. So,
instead of burning slowly, the fire swelled white hot
and ignited the tar built up inside the chimney. He
hollered everyone awake, but it was Sarah who yelled
at me, pulled off the covers, and stumbled beside me
down the stairs. Was this what I'd wished for?

I was cold and the snow lay deep on the hill. In our pajamas we stood shivering, and in the dark at the top of the roof, out of the red brick chimney, roared a red-thick fire. Dad ran back in and closed the stove and hoped enough air would be stopped to slow the burning.

As the blaze crackled and spit above us, Dad and Annie set up the ladder and I ran for buckets. The heat from the burning tar could crack the chimney and set the house on fire inside and we couldn't do anything about that. But outside we could at least make sure the roof didn't catch fire. We broke ice on the spring and hauled up—carefully, carefully—that black water to keep the roof safe from sparks and cinders. And while that dark, moonless night was lit by the fiery torch atop our helpless house, there were no jokes but lots of "hurry-up" and silence.

Side by side with Annie I worked, quietly and hard and quickly, to keep the buckets coming to Dad. Later I saw his hands bloody from fighting to keep a hold on that slippery roof. *Roar* and *whoosh* were the sounds the fire made, and I was more scared than excited.

While we worked with the water, Mom and Sarah braved the house to pack what we'd need if the worst happened, if the whole house burned. Everyone seemed brave that night. I kept thinking how Annie's hands must be frozen like mine but she never said a word.

Eventually the Piney Volunteer Fire Department gathered: Jimmy up from Adeline, and Harry from Dutch Fork, Bob from Clouston, and Dan Creary from Sleepy Creek Hollow. They all came in pickups since the pump truck was froze up solid over at Dixon's. Neighbors from across the valley and down the ridge would arrive, too, before it was over. But, of course, the first one there was Dad himself—he joked later that no one had ever been quicker than that to a fire, and if they had, he'd eat his Sunday pants.

The night was beautiful, all white and black
beyond the fire. Somewhere in that black a deer
must have lifted her nose from grass pawed clear of
snow, looked over our way, and wondered—too smart
and too quick to be scared. I felt better when I heard
Jimmy and Bob, Harry and Dan shouting and laughing, even when it seemed they shouldn't. But finally
we watched the orange flames fall back until one
hour after it had started, Bob Jackson shone his
flashlight down the flue and announced: "She's all
gone, folks! Get on in the house and get to bed."
And, of course, we didn't.

The firemen and the neighbors, as well as the furniture, crowded back indoors after Bob yelled, and oh, the talk and the food—they were better than Thanksgiving. Mom got coffee, while some of the neighbor ladies laid out cookies and a wedge of cake they had brought from home. We ate and laughed till we'd nearly forgotten it was early morning and that a little while ago we had been more scared than we knew. Annie and Sarah and I played without fussing or bossing. I figured now that maybe my fussing had earned me some of their bossing. I was going to remember how brave they were, too, and no boy should mind having brave friends, even if they are his sisters. Maybe, if the three of us put our heads together, we could even come up with our own excitement.

Sunrise came absolutely quiet to our hilltop farm. A new powder of snow had fallen sometime after we got back to sleep. The black ash and soot from the blaze had already disappeared under it. It felt good to see that everything was safe. I hoped when I saw Grandma that she wouldn't mention what she had said on Sunday. Besides, she wouldn't have to worry about reminding me. I'm not likely to forget.

"Hot. It's overwhelmingly hot. There's a tremendous amount of commotion. Guys yelling, glass breaking. It's chaos.... It's like the world coming to an end."

New York City Fireman

68

Dousing the Flames

Fire

"Fire" is an alarm cry that has struck terror in people's hearts for centuries. Once a blaze is underway, it can cut a swath of destruction in just seconds. That's why fire fighters are trained to react to a fire alarm with speed, skill, and bravery in the presence of great danger.

Fire Fighters of the Past

The Roman emperor Augustus formed one of the first fire brigades, the Vigiles. They were equipped with buckets, axes, ladders, and wet blankets. ▼

For centuries the best line of defense against a fire was the bucket brigade. Men and women formed lines to pass buckets from a stream or pump to the fire. ▼

Until the mid-19th century fire fighters had to pump water by hand. ▼

Fire Trucks

The tower ladder has a boom that can reach as high as 150 feet, or about 12 floors.

The main ladder on the rear mount aerial ladder truck can extend as high as 100 feet, or about 8 floors.

Equipped with a water tank, pump, and up to 1,000 feet of hose, the pumper can provide 1,000 gallons of water a minute.

A pole connects the different levels of a firehouse. Why? It's quicker to slide down a pole than race down a flight of stairs. ▶

Fireboats combat fires on other boats and along the waterfront. Water supply is no problem since these boats pump as much as 22,000 gallons of water a minute out of a river or harbor.

The tiller-rig is really two trucks joined in the middle. To help the truck negotiate narrow city streets, there are steering wheels in front and back.

Instead of water, the foam unit pumps a special foam to put out oil and chemical fires.

HELMET
4 LBS.

OXYGEN
TANK AND
FACE MASK
27 LBS.

COAT
7 LBS.

A Fire Fighter's Gear

AXES,
CROW BAR,
OTHER TOOLS
10 LBS.

BOOTS
6 LBS.
(3 EA.)

Stylish, intelligent, ▶ and easily trained, Dalmatians became the mascots of firehouses because they didn't bother the horses that once pulled fire trucks.

▶ Fireproof aluminum-coated suits allow fire fighters to walk right into the flames.

71

First Light by Sandy Wadlington.

If once you have slept on an island
    You'll never be quite the same;
You may look as you looked the day before
    And go by the same old name.

You may bustle about in street and shop;
    You may sit at home and sew.
But you'll see blue water and wheeling gulls
    Wherever your feet may go.

You may chat to the neighbors of this and that
    And close to your fire keep,
But you'll hear ship whistle and lighthouse bell
    And tides beat through your sleep.

Oh, you won't know why, and you can't say how
    Such change upon you came,
But—once you have slept on an island
    You'll never be quite the same!

RACHEL FIELD

THE Lost Lake

by Allen Say

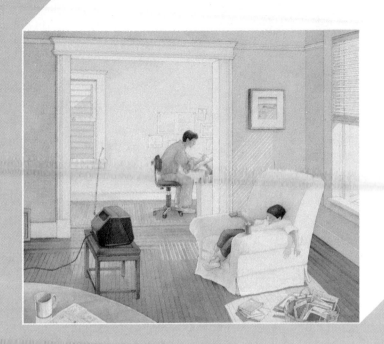

I went to live with Dad last summer.

Every day he worked in his room from morning to night, sometimes on weekends, too. Dad wasn't much of a talker, but when he was busy he didn't talk at all.

I didn't know anybody in the city, so I stayed home most of the time. It was too hot to play outside anyway. In one month I finished all the books I'd brought and grew tired of watching TV.

One morning I started cutting pictures out of old magazines, just to be doing something. They were pictures of mountains and rivers and lakes, and some showed people fishing and canoeing. Looking at them made me feel cool, so I pinned them up in my room.

Dad didn't notice them for two days. When he did, he looked at them one by one.

"Nice pictures," he said.

"Are you angry with me, Dad?" I asked, because he saved old magazines for his work.

"It's all right, Luke," he said. "I'm having this place painted soon anyway."

He thought I was talking about the marks I'd made on the wall.

That Saturday Dad woke me up early in the morning and told me we were going camping! I was wide awake in a second. He gave me a pair of brand-new hiking boots to try out. They were perfect.

In the hallway I saw a big backpack and a knapsack all packed and ready to go.

"What's in them, Dad?" I asked.

"Later," he said. "We have a long drive ahead of us."

In the car I didn't ask any more questions because Dad was so grumpy in the morning.

"Want a sip?" he said, handing me his mug. He'd never let me drink coffee before. It had lots of sugar in it.

"Where are we going?" I finally asked.

"We're off to the Lost Lake, my lad."

"How can you lose a lake?"

"No one's found it, that's how." Dad was smiling! "Grandpa and I used to go there a long time ago. It was our special place, so don't tell any of your friends."

"I'll never tell," I promised. "How long are we going to stay there?"

"Five days, maybe a week."

"We're going to sleep outside for a whole week?"

"That's the idea."

"Oh, boy!"

We got to the mountains In the afternoon.

"It's a bit of a hike to the lake, son," Dad said.

"I don't mind," I told him. "Are there any fish in the lake?"

"Hope so. We'll have to catch our dinner, you know."

"You didn't bring any food?"

"Of course not. We're going to live like true outdoorsmen."

"Oh . . ."

Dad saw my face and started to laugh. He must have
been joking. I didn't think we were going very far anyway,
because Dad's pack was so heavy I couldn't even lift it.

Well, Dad was like a mountain goat. He went straight
up the trail, whistling all the while. But I was gasping in no
time. My knapsack got very heavy and I started to fall behind.

Dad stopped for me often, but he wouldn't let me take off my pack. If I did I'd be too tired to go on, he said.

It was almost suppertime when we got to the lake.

The place reminded me of the park near Dad's apartment. He wasn't whistling or humming anymore.

"Welcome to the *Found* Lake," he muttered from the side of his mouth.

"What's wrong, Dad?"

"Do you want to camp with all these people around us?"

"I don't mind."

"Well, I do!"

"Are we going home?"

"Of course not!"

He didn't even take off his pack. He just turned and started to walk away.

Soon the lake was far out of sight.

Then it started to rain. Dad gave me a poncho and it kept me dry, but I wondered where we were going to sleep that night. I wondered what we were going to do for dinner. I wasn't sure about camping anymore.

I was glad when Dad finally stopped and set up the tent. The rain and wind beat against it, but we were warm and cozy inside. And Dad had brought food. For dinner we had salami and dried apricots.

"I'm sorry about the lake, Dad," I said.

He shook his head. "You know something, Luke? There aren't any secret places left in the world anymore."

"What if we go very far up in the mountains? Maybe we can find our own lake."

"There are lots of lakes up here, but that one was special."

"But we've got a whole week, Dad."

"Well, why not? Maybe we'll find a lake that's not on the map."

"Sure, we will!"

We started early in the morning. When the fog cleared we saw other hikers ahead of us. Sure enough, Dad became very glum.

"We're going cross-country, partner," he said.

"Won't we get lost?"

"A wise man never leaves home without his compass."

So we went off the trail. The hills went on and on. The mountains went on and on. It was kind of lonesome. It seemed as if Dad and I were the only people left in the world.

And then we hiked into a big forest.

At noontime we stopped by a creek and ate lunch and drank ice-cold water straight from the stream. I threw rocks in the water, and fish, like shadows, darted in the pools.

"Isn't this a good place to camp, Dad?"

"I thought we were looking for our lake."

"Yes, right..." I mumbled.

The forest went on and on.

"I don't mean to scare you, son," Dad said. "But we're in bear country. We don't want to surprise them, so we have to make a lot of noise. If they hear us, they'll just go away."

What a time to tell me! I started to shout as loudly as I could. Even Dad wouldn't be able to beat off bears. I thought about those people having fun back at the lake. I thought about the creek, too, with all those fish in it. That would have been a fine place to camp. The Lost Lake hadn't been so bad either.

It was dark when we got out of the forest. We built a fire and that made me feel better. Wild animals wouldn't come near a fire. Dad cooked beef stroganoff and it was delicious.

Later it was bedtime. The sleeping bag felt wonderful. Dad and I started to count the shooting stars, then I worried that maybe we weren't going to find our lake.

"What are you thinking about, Luke?" Dad asked.

"I didn't know you could cook like that," I said.

Dad laughed. "That was only freeze-dried stuff. When we get home, I'll cook you something really special."

"You know something, Dad? You seem like a different person up here."

"Better or worse?"

"A lot better."

"How so?"

"You talk more."

"I'll have to talk more often, then."

That made me smile. Then I slept.

Dad shook me awake. The sun was just coming up, turning everything all gold and orange and yellow. And there was the lake, right in front of us.

For a long time we watched the light change on the water, getting brighter and brighter. Dad didn't say a word the whole time. But then, I didn't have anything to say either.

After breakfast we climbed a mountain and saw our lake below us. There wasn't a sign of people anywhere. It really seemed as if Dad and I were all alone in the world.

I liked it just fine.

MEET
ALLEN SAY

ALLEN SAY

EL CHINO

ALLEN SAY

For Allen Say, who writes and illustrates many of his own stories, pictures always come first. When he makes up a story, he begins by drawing pictures without having words or even ideas to go with them. *The Lost Lake* grew out of pictures Say drew of a camping trip. He unexpectedly remembered hiking to a mountain lake many years before and finding the area completely ruined by litter.

Say has been an artist almost all of his life. He originally dreamed of being a cartoonist. At thirteen he already had a job drawing backgrounds for a famous cartoonist in Japan. Say eventually came to the United States. He never lost his interest in art and later began to write and illustrate stories.

Other books by this writer and illustrator that you might enjoy are *El Chino*, a book about Bill Wong, the first Chinese bullfighter, and *Tree of Cranes*, a book Say dedicated to the man he learned from and first worked for, the Japanese cartoonist Noro Shinpei.

The Falling

I saw a star slide down the sky,

Blinding the north as it went by,

Too burning and too quick to hold,

Too lovely to be bought or sold,

Good only to make wishes on

And then forever to be gone.

Sara Teasdale

illustrated by Burton Silverman

Sarah, Plain and Tall

AND

by Patricia MacLachlan

Anna and Caleb's mother died the day after Caleb was born. Papa and Anna miss Mama, and Caleb longs for a mother to love and care for him. When Papa decides to advertise for a wife, Sarah Elisabeth Wheaton answers the advertisement from Maine. After trading a few letters with Papa, Anna, and Caleb, Sarah decides to visit them in their prairie home for a month. She writes that they will recognize her at the train station because she is "plain and tall." Sarah brings Seal, her cat, and gifts from the ocean she loves so much. Papa, Caleb, and Anna wonder if Sarah will be content to stay and make her new home with them, so far from the sea.

The dandelions in the fields had gone by, their heads soft as feathers. The summer roses were opening.

Our neighbors, Matthew and Maggie, came to help Papa plow up a new field for corn. Sarah stood with us on the porch, watching their wagon wind up the road, two horses pulling it and one tied in back. I remembered the last time we had stood here alone, Caleb and I, waiting for Sarah.

Sarah's hair was in thick braids that circled her head, wild daisies tucked here and there. Papa had picked them for her.

Old Bess and Jack ran along the inside of the fence, whickering at the new horses.

"Papa needs five horses for the big gang plow," Caleb told Sarah. "Prairie grass is hard."

Matthew and Maggie came with their two children and a sackful of chickens. Maggie emptied the sack into the yard and three red banty chickens clucked and scattered.

"They are for you," she told Sarah. "For eating."

Sarah loved the chickens. She clucked back to them and fed them grain. They followed her, shuffling and scratching primly in the dirt. I knew they would not be for eating.

The children were young and named Rose and Violet, after flowers. They hooted and laughed and chased the chickens, who flew up to the porch roof, then the dogs, who crept quietly under the porch. Seal had long ago fled to the barn to sleep in cool hay.

Sarah and Maggie helped hitch the horses to the plow, then they set up a big table in the shade of the barn, covering it with a quilt and a kettle of flowers in the middle. They sat on the porch while Caleb and

Matthew and Papa began their morning of plowing.
I mixed biscuit dough just inside the door, watching.

"You are lonely, yes?" asked Maggie in her soft voice.

Sarah's eyes filled with tears. Slowly I stirred the dough.
Maggie reached over and took Sarah's hand.

"I miss the hills of Tennessee sometimes," she said.

Do not miss the hills, Maggie, I thought.

"I miss the sea," said Sarah.

Do not miss the hills. Do not miss the sea.

I stirred and stirred the dough.

"I miss my brother William," said Sarah.

"But he is married. The house is hers now. Not mine any longer. There are three old aunts who all squawk together like crows at dawn. I miss them, too."

"There are always things to miss," said Maggie. "No matter where you are."

I looked out and saw Papa and Matthew and Caleb working. Rose and Violet ran in the fields. I felt something brush my legs and looked down at Nick, wagging his tail.

"I would miss you, Nick," I whispered. "I would." I knelt down and scratched his ears. "I miss Mama."

"I nearly forgot," said Maggie on the porch. "I have something more for you."

I carried the bowl outside and watched Maggie lift a low wooden box out of the wagon.

"Plants," she said to Sarah. "For your garden."

"My garden?" Sarah bent down to touch the plants.

"Zinnias and marigolds and wild feverfew," said Maggie. "You must have a garden. Wherever you are."

Sarah smiled. "I had a garden in Maine with dahlias and columbine. And nasturtiums the color of the sun when it sets. I don't know if nasturtiums would grow here."

"Try," said Maggie. "You must have a garden."

We planted the flowers by the porch, turning over the soil and patting it around them, and watering. Lottie and Nick came to sniff, and the chickens walked in the dirt, leaving prints. In the fields, the horses pulled the plow up and down under the hot summer sun.

Maggie wiped her face, leaving a streak of dirt.

"Soon you can drive your wagon over to my house and I will give you more. I have tansy."

Sarah frowned. "I have never driven a wagon."

"I can teach you," said Maggie. "And so can Anna and Caleb. And Jacob."

Sarah turned to me.

"Can you?" she asked. "Can you drive a wagon?"

I nodded.

"And Caleb?"

"Yes."

"In Maine," said Sarah, "I would walk to town."

"Here it is different," said Maggie. "Here you will drive."

Way off in the sky, clouds gathered. Matthew and Papa and Caleb came in from the fields, their work done. We all ate in the shade.

"We are glad you are here," said Matthew to Sarah. "A new friend. Maggie misses her friends sometimes."

Sarah nodded. "There is always something to miss, no matter where you are," she said, smiling at Maggie.

Rose and Violet fell asleep in the grass, their bellies full of meat and greens and biscuits. And when it was time to go, Papa and Matthew lifted them into the wagon to sleep on blankets.

Sarah walked slowly behind the wagon for a long time, waving, watching it disappear. Caleb and I ran to bring her back, the chickens running wildly behind us.

"What shall we name them?" asked Sarah, laughing as the chickens followed us into the house.

I smiled. I was right. The chickens would not be for eating.

And then Papa came, just before the rain, bringing Sarah the first roses of summer.

The rain came and passed, but strange clouds hung in the northwest, low and black and green. And the air grew still.

In the morning, Sarah dressed in a pair of overalls and went to the barn to have an argument with Papa. She took apples for Old Bess and Jack.

"Women don't wear overalls," said Caleb, running along behind her like one of Sarah's chickens.

"This woman does," said Sarah crisply.

Papa stood by the fence.

"I want to learn how to ride a horse," Sarah told him. "And then I want to learn how to drive the wagon. By myself."

Jack leaned over and nipped at Sarah's overalls. She fed him an apple. Caleb and I stood behind Sarah.

"I can ride a horse, I know," said Sarah. "I rode once when I was twelve. I will ride Jack." Jack was Sarah's favorite.

Papa shook his head. "Not Jack," he said. "Jack is sly."

"I am sly, too," said Sarah stubbornly.

Papa smiled. "Ayuh," he said, nodding. "But not Jack."

"Yes, Jack!" Sarah's voice was very loud.

"I can teach you how to drive a wagon. I have already taught you how to plow."

"And then I can go to town. By myself."

"Say no, Papa," Caleb whispered beside me.

"That's a fair thing, Sarah," said Papa. "We'll practice."

A soft rumble of thunder sounded. Papa looked up at the clouds.

"Today? Can we begin today?" asked Sarah.

"Tomorrow is best," said Papa, looking worried. "I have to fix the house roof. A portion of it is loose. And there's a storm coming."

"We," said Sarah.

"What?" Papa turned.

"*We* will fix the roof," said Sarah. "I've done it before. I know about roofs. I am a good carpenter. Remember, I told you?"

There was thunder again, and Papa went to get the ladder.

"Are you fast?" he asked Sarah.

"I am fast and I am good," said Sarah. And they climbed the ladder to the roof, Sarah with wisps of hair around her face, her mouth full of nails, overalls like Papa's. Overalls that *were* Papa's.

Caleb and I went inside to close the windows. We could hear the steady sound of hammers pounding the roof overhead.

"Why does she want to go to town by herself?" asked Caleb. "To leave us?"

I shook my head, weary with Caleb's questions. Tears gathered at the corners of my eyes. But there was no time to cry, for suddenly Papa called out.

"Caleb! Anna!"

We ran outside and saw a huge cloud, horribly black, moving toward us over the north fields. Papa slid down the roof, helping Sarah after him.

"A squall!" he yelled to us. He held up his arms and Sarah jumped off the porch roof.

"Get the horses inside," he ordered Caleb. "Get the sheep, Anna. And the cows. The barn is safest."

The grasses flattened. There was a hiss of wind, a sudden pungent smell. Our faces looked yellow in the strange light. Caleb and I jumped over the fence and found the animals huddled by the barn. I counted the sheep to make sure they were all there, and herded them into a large stall. A few raindrops came, gentle at first, then stronger and louder, so that Caleb and I covered our ears and stared at each other without speaking. Caleb looked frightened and I tried to smile at him. Sarah

carried a sack into the barn, her hair wet and streaming down her neck. Papa came behind, Lottie and Nick with him, their ears flat against their heads.

"Wait!" cried Sarah. "My chickens!"

"No, Sarah!" Papa called after her. But Sarah had already run from the barn into a sheet of rain. My father followed her. The sheep nosed open their stall door and milled around the barn, bleating. Nick crept under my arm, and a lamb, Mattie with the black face, stood close to me, trembling. There was a soft paw on my lap, then a gray body. Seal. And then, as the thunder pounded and the wind rose and there was the terrible crackling of lightning close by, Sarah and Papa stood in the barn doorway, wet to the skin. Papa carried Sarah's chickens. Sarah came with an armful of summer roses.

Sarah's chickens were not afraid, and they settled like small red bundles in the hay. Papa closed the door at last, shutting out some of the sounds of the storm. The barn was eerie and half lighted, like dusk without a lantern. Papa spread blankets around our shoulders and Sarah unpacked a bag of cheese and bread and jam. At the very bottom of the bag were Sarah's shells.

Caleb got up and went over to the small barn window.

"What color is the sea when it storms?" he asked Sarah.

"Blue," said Sarah, brushing her wet hair back with her fingers. "And gray and green."

Caleb nodded and smiled.

"Look," he said to her. "Look what is missing from your drawing."

Sarah went to stand between Caleb and Papa by the window. She looked a long time without speaking. Finally, she touched Papa's shoulder.

"We have squalls in Maine, too," she said. "Just like this. It will be all right, Jacob."

Papa said nothing. But he put his arm around her, and leaned over to rest his chin in her hair. I closed my eyes, suddenly remembering Mama and Papa standing that way, Mama smaller than Sarah, her hair fair against Papa's shoulder. When I opened my eyes again, it was Sarah standing there. Caleb looked at me and smiled and smiled until he could smile no more.

We slept in the hay all night, waking when the wind was wild, sleeping again when it was quiet. And at dawn there was the sudden sound of hail, like stones tossed against the barn. We stared out the window, watching the ice marbles bounce on the ground.

And when it was over we opened the barn door and walked out into the early-morning light. The hail crunched and melted beneath our feet. It was white and gleaming for as far as we looked, like sun on glass. Like the sea.

It was very quiet. The dogs leaned down to eat the hailstones. Seal stepped around them and leaped up on the fence to groom herself. A tree had blown over near the cow pond. And the wild roses were scattered on the ground, as if a wedding had come and gone there. "I'm glad I saved an armful" was all that Sarah said.

Only one field was badly damaged, and Sarah and Papa hitched up the horses and plowed and replanted during the next two days. The roof had held.

"I told you I know about roofs," Sarah told Papa, making him smile.

Papa kept his promise to Sarah. When the work was done, he took her out into the fields, Papa riding Jack who was sly, and Sarah riding Old Bess. Sarah was quick to learn.

"Too quick," Caleb complained to me as we watched from the fence. He thought a moment. "Maybe she'll fall off and have to stay here. Why?" he asked, turning to me. "Why does she have to go away alone?"

"Hush up, Caleb," I said crossly. "Hush up."

"I could get sick and make her stay here," said Caleb.

"No."

"We could tie her up."

"No."

And Caleb began to cry, and I took him inside the barn where we could both cry.

Papa and Sarah came to hitch the horses to the wagon, so Sarah could practice driving. Papa didn't see Caleb's tears, and he sent him with an ax to begin chopping up the tree by the pond for firewood. I stood and watched Sarah, the reins in her hands, Papa next to her in the wagon. I could see Caleb standing by the pond,

one hand shading his eyes, watching, too. I went into the safe darkness of the barn then, Sarah's chickens scuttling along behind me.

"Why?" I asked out loud, echoing Caleb's question.

The chickens watched me, their eyes small and bright.

The next morning Sarah got up early and put on her blue dress. She took apples to the barn. She loaded a bundle of hay on the wagon for Old Bess and Jack. She put on her yellow bonnet.

"Remember Jack," said Papa. "A strong hand."

"Yes, Jacob."

"Best to be home before dark," said Papa. "Driving a wagon is hard if there's no full moon."

"Yes, Jacob."

Sarah kissed us all, even my father, who looked surprised.

"Take care of Seal," she said to Caleb and me. And with a whisper to Old Bess and a stern word to Jack, Sarah climbed up in the wagon and drove away.

"Very good," murmured Papa as he watched. And after a while he turned and went out into the fields.

Caleb and I watched Sarah from the porch. Caleb took my hand, and the dogs lay down beside us. It was sunny, and I remembered another time when a wagon had taken Mama away. It had been a day just like this day. And Mama had never come back.

Seal jumped up to the porch, her feet making a small thump. Caleb leaned down and picked her up and walked inside. I took the broom and slowly swept the porch. Then I watered Sarah's plants. Caleb cleaned out the wood stove and carried the ashes to the barn, spilling them so that I had to sweep the porch again.

"I *am* loud and pesky," Caleb cried suddenly. "You said so! And she has gone to buy a train ticket to go away!"

"No, Caleb. She would tell us."

"The house is too small," said Caleb. "That's what it is."

"The house is not too small," I said.

I looked at Sarah's drawing of the fields pinned up on the wall next to the window.

"What is missing?" I asked Caleb. "You said you knew what was missing."

"Colors," said Caleb wearily. "The colors of the sea."

Outside, clouds moved into the sky and went away again. We took lunch to Papa, cheese and bread and lemonade. Caleb nudged me.

"Ask him. Ask Papa."

"What has Sarah gone to do?" I asked.

"I don't know," said Papa. He squinted at me. Then he sighed and put one hand on Caleb's head, one on mine. "Sarah is Sarah. She does things her way, you know."

ANNA

"I know," said Caleb very softly.

Papa picked up his shovel and put on his hat.

"Ask if she's coming back," whispered Caleb.

"Of course she's coming back," I said. "Seal is here." But I would not ask the question. I was afraid to hear the answer.

We fed the sheep, and I set the table for dinner. Four plates. The sun dropped low over the west fields. Lottie and Nick stood at the door, wagging their tails, asking for supper. Papa came to light the stove. And then it was dusk. Soon it would be dark. Caleb sat on the porch steps, turning his moon snail shell over and over in his hand. Seal brushed back and forth against him.

Suddenly Lottie began to bark, and Nick jumped off the porch and ran down the road.

"Dust!" cried Caleb. He climbed the porch and stood on the roof. "Dust, and a yellow bonnet!"

Slowly the wagon came around the windmill and the barn and the windbreak and into the yard, the dogs jumping happily beside it.

"Hush, dogs," said Sarah. And Nick leaped up into the wagon to sit by Sarah.

Papa took the reins and Sarah climbed down from the wagon.

Caleb burst into tears.

"Seal was very worried!" he cried.

Sarah put her arms around him, and he wailed into her dress. "And the house is too small, we thought! And I am loud and pesky!"

Sarah looked at Papa and me over Caleb's head.

"We thought you might be thinking of leaving us," I told her. "Because you miss the sea."

Sarah smiled.

"No," she said. "I will always miss my old home, but the truth of it is I would miss you more."

Papa smiled at Sarah, then he bent quickly to un-hitch the horses from the wagon. He led them to the barn for water.

Sarah handed me a package.

"For Anna," she said. "And Caleb. For all of us."

The package was small, wrapped in brown paper with a rubber band around it. Very carefully I un-wrapped it, Caleb peering closely. Inside were three colored pencils.

"Blue," said Caleb slowly, "and gray. And green."

Sarah nodded.

Suddenly Caleb grinned.

"Papa," he called. "Papa, come quickly! Sarah has brought the sea!"

We eat our night meal by candlelight, the four of us. Sarah has brought candles from town. And nasturtium seeds for her garden, and a book of songs to teach us. It is late, and Caleb is nearly sleeping by his plate and Sarah is smiling at my father. Soon there will be a wedding. Papa says that when the preacher asks if he will have Sarah for his wife, he will answer, "Ayuh."

Autumn will come, then winter, cold with a wind that blows like the wind off the sea in Maine. There will be nests of curls to look for, and dried flowers all winter long. When there are storms, Papa will stretch a rope from the door to the barn so we will not be lost when we feed the sheep and the cows and Jack and Old Bess. And Sarah's chickens, if they aren't living in the house. There will be Sarah's sea, blue and gray and green, hanging on the wall. And songs, old ones and new. And Seal with yellow eyes. And there will be Sarah, plain and tall.

Meet PATRICIA MacLACHLAN

Although Patricia MacLachlan did not write as a child, she made up stories in her head. She imagined kings and queens, heroes and villains. When MacLachlan became an adult, kings and queens no longer captured her imagination. Instead, her children and the relatives she had known and heard about as a child became models for her characters.

MacLachlan becomes old friends with the people in her stories before she begins to write. "I . . . have all sorts of conversations with myself and with characters I make up. . . . I talk with characters in the car, over a sink full of dishes, in the garden."

MacLachlan's story ideas may begin with people, but she also thinks a lot about the setting. Because she was born in Wyoming and raised in Minnesota, she says, "the western landscape has always been a powerful force in my life."

In the Newbery Award-winning story *Sarah, Plain and Tall*, character and place cannot be separated. Sarah, a mail-order bride—like one of MacLachlan's distant relatives—leaves her home on the eastern seacoast to begin a new life in the West. To the prairie she brings her love of Maine and her longing for the sea.

Other books by MacLachlan that you might enjoy are *The Facts and Fictions of Minna Pratt* and *Arthur, for the Very First Time*.

DREAMS

Hold fast to dreams
For if dreams die
Life is a broken-winged bird
That cannot fly.

Hold fast to dreams
For when dreams go
Life is a barren field
Frozen with snow.

Langston Hughes

Naturally!

MEET
Richard and Jonah Sobol

Richard Sobol followed the battle to end the seal hunt for many years. On a trip to Canada, bad weather kept him from photographing the seals. He knew he would return.

On his next trip, Sobol took along his son Jonah. They spent a day on the ice with the seals. Jonah had many thoughts and questions. These ideas formed the heart of *Seal Journey*.

Sobol also created a book for children about the African elephant. He hopes his books will help children respect wildlife.

SEAL JOURNEY

by Richard and Jonah Sobol ■ photographs by Richard Sobol

The life cycle of the harp seal is one of the great wonders of nature. Each autumn the seals begin a remarkable journey that carries them over three thousand miles. At a steady flow throughout the winter months, hundreds of thousands of mature harp seals swim through iceberg-filled waters from their summer homes in the northwest Atlantic, just below the North Pole, to the solid ice packs in the Gulf of St. Lawrence in eastern Canada. Once they reach the great sheets of winter ice, each female harp seal will claim her own space on which to give birth to a single pup. Thousands upon thousands of harp seal pups, more than anyone could ever count, are born and nurtured here each spring, transforming this frozen wilderness into a vast nursery.

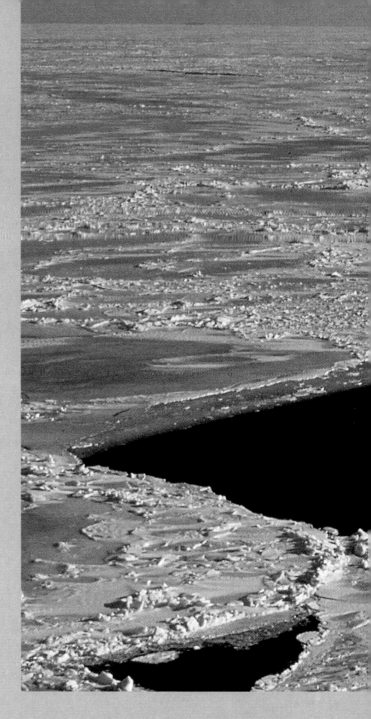

At the same time a second breeding population gathers on pack ice in the Barents Sea off the northern coast of Russia, while a third and smaller group comes together east of Greenland.

This year I had come to Charlottetown, Prince Edward Island, which is used as a base camp for scientists to observe the newborn harp seal pups. This was the third time that I had made this journey on assignment for a French photo agency. The first trip had been in 1981 when I set out to show the cruelty of the seal hunt that was then taking place. Now I was here to tell the story of the seals' survival and to photograph the beginnings of life out on the ice.

My eight-year-old son, Jonah, had been dreaming of seeing the seals, and I invited him to come along with me. "Can I really come with you?" he said in disbelief when I first asked. After that his questions were endless. "Will I get to see newborn seals?" "How cold will it be?" "How will we get onto the ice?" I answered as many questions as I could until finally I assured him that the best answers would come from his own observations out on the ice.

The seal colony was located about a hundred miles north of Prince Edward Island and the only way to reach it was by helicopter. Jonah sat in the front next to the pilot. After we took off, the pilot held up his map, showing Jonah the spot where we would find the

seals. The map, though, showed an ocean of blue, not miles and miles of white jagged ice, looking like a moonscape, that we had been flying over all this March morning. The snow-covered farmlands of Prince Edward Island had quickly faded from view. We now flew over wide swatches of packed ice sandwiched between small strips of open water. Searching the horizon, we eagerly waited for our first glimpse of the seals. The pilot smiled as he pointed outside and said, "Look down now, there they are. The seals have returned once again." Below us tiny brown specks dotted

the ice, first a few, then more and more, looking like chocolate sprinkles scattered on top of a huge bowl of vanilla ice cream.

As soon as we stepped out of the helicopter, we could hear the soft cries of hungry newborn pups. These were the only sounds that drifted through the stillness of this frozen landscape. It was springtime but the air was very cold—five degrees below zero. The wind bit into our skin. As we walked toward the seals, the snow swished and swirled under our clunky survival boots. We were careful to avoid the smooth round holes in the ice—bobbing holes—that the mother seals dive in and out of to return to the water to feed on small shrimp or fish, or just to swim.

Seals are great swimmers but, like other mammals, they require air to breathe. They are able to hold their breaths for long periods of time and dive deep into the water. Every few minutes they pop up through bobbing holes onto the ice to fill their lungs with air and to check on their pups.

As we walked closer to a small group of seals, we heard a sharp, deep cry, like a cat screeching in the night. We climbed along a large ridge of ice to get a better look. Up ahead, we spotted a female seal twisting one way,

then another, again and again. There was a sense of great excitement in her movements and cries. Jonah tugged at my sleeve and pointed to a newborn pup, only minutes old, that was lying beside the mother seal. It was still wet and yellow from its birth.

He did not look at all like the cuddly white ball of fur that we were expecting. It will take a day or two in the sun for this birth-stained scraggle to be transformed into a lush baby known as a "whitecoat." Jonah said he felt sorry for the tiny pup, outside on frozen ice, having just left the warmth of his mother's womb. Now, as the steam rose up from his scruffy, gooey coat the mother moved closer to him, to reassure him and share her warmth. As they nestled together in the warm glow of the sunlight, it was easy to see the dark markings on the mother seal's back. They were indeed the familiar curves of a harp, the musical instrument for which these seals are named.

To survive in this new world, harp seal pups are born with a small amount of baby fat which they immediately start to burn in order to give their bodies heat. But, they need their mothers' milk to grow the thick layer of blubber that will continue to protect them from the deep freeze that they are born into. We watched with wonder as the mother rolled onto her side, and the pup slid up toward her searching for the milk. The pup lay perfectly still, nursing without a break for ten minutes, as he would need to do five or six times each day.

The mother seals' milk is ten times richer than either cows' or humans' milk, and a well-fed pup will grow from twenty pounds at birth to almost eighty pounds by the time he is weaned at twelve days old.

Before the pup finished nursing, the mother rubbed noses with him. This "kiss of recognition" was her way of familiarizing herself with the smell of her pup. A mother seal is often surrounded by dozens of pups and she must be able to identify her own by its unique scent or it will not survive. She has only enough milk for one pup and she will only nurse her very own.

A few feet away we saw what appeared to be a mother seal giving her pup a swimming lesson. The mother nudged him toward the water, while the pup squealed and squealed. And then the pup

was in the water, floating and bobbing like a little cork. The pup had so much fat that he couldn't sink. "It's like he is wearing a life jacket," Jonah said, as the mother jumped in the water too. It was almost as if they were playing a game of tag. First the mother disappeared under the water. A few seconds later, she popped up in a different place. The pup squirmed and paddled to catch up to her. Then they rubbed noses.

Pups have to learn to swim well. Their home for most of the remainder of their lives is in the water, since harp seals spend only

four to six weeks a year on the ice. By the time the pup is two weeks old, it is weaned from its mother's milk and has to find its own food in the chilly waters of the Atlantic. The weaning is sudden—without any warning, the mother slides into the water between nursings as she normally does, only this time she leaves forever, never to return to her pup. The two of them will always be part of the same seal herd, but the pup must quickly adjust to life on its own.

While the pups are being born and nursed, the males keep their distance, gathering in groups around breaks of open water. Once the pups are weaned, the female harp seals join the males for mating. The complete cycle of birth, nursing, and mating takes place in about two weeks, incredibly fast for such a large animal.

In April when the ice melts and breaks up, the entire seal colony will join together again to journey back north to their summer feeding grounds in the Arctic seas. The young pups, having lost their fine white coats by now, will straggle behind the main herd, feeding as they go on small shrimp. As they grow stronger and their swimming skills improve, they will be able to dive and catch small fish to add to their diet. When fully grown, these harp seals will weigh up to three hundred pounds.

Home for the pups for the next few years will be in the North Atlantic feeding grounds, just below the Arctic Circle. The pups will feed, grow, and develop their swimming skills until they are old enough to mate. In their fifth or sixth year of life, when autumn comes, they will know that it is their time to join the mature seals on the long swim south. Together, they will return to the ice where they were born. By the time that their lives come to an end, some twenty-five years later, most harp seals will have travelled over 75,000 miles, round and round through the ocean.

Jonah and I saw hundreds of seals. We spent hours and hours exploring on the ice. The sky grew dark in the late afternoon, and the pilots started warming the helicopter engines. Our day would soon be over. But there was still one thing Jonah wanted to do. "Dad," he said in a quiet voice, "could I please hold one seal before we go?"

We should have headed toward our helicopter, but instead, we walked in the other direction, over the long sloping ice ridge, in search of a friendly pup. There we found her—a beautiful whitecoat, round and contented with her first week of life. Slowly, Jonah approached her. When he was close he lay down to pet her. I went over and picked the seal up and placed her on Jonah's lap. "I can feel her breathing," Jonah said through the wide smile that now covered his face. "Her whiskers tickle and the soft white fur is like a warm blanket covering me."

It is sad to think that this same fur was what the hunters were seeking when they stalked the ice to slaughter these seals. The fur that they stripped from the whitecoats was turned into slippers, gloves, and even dolls. For twenty years people who cared about saving seals came out onto the ice to challenge

the hunters and to make them stop. They let people throughout the world know about this cruelty and asked them not to buy anything made from seal fur. As more people knew what was happening to the seal pups they joined together and stopped buying seal products. The hunters had no place to sell the fur. Only then did the killing stop here. In other places though, some seal hunting does continue, as hunters still stain the ice with the blood of these lovely animals. These harp seal pups, born in the Gulf of St. Lawrence, are the lucky ones. Now protected by laws, for the first time in hundreds of years this seal nursery is filled only with the cries of the hungry pups and not the thuds of the hunters' clubs.

It was now time to go. Jonah gently put the seal back down and gave her a soft pat. As he walked away he turned back toward her for one final look.

"Good-bye, seal," he said. "Now I know that dreams can come true."

As we flew back toward Prince Edward Island and looked down at the ice, its sharp edges began to soften and the harsh white glare turned into water-color splashes of pink and gray in the fading light. Soon the ice will melt and the seals will return north. During the hot summer months people will be sailing and swimming in this same wide channel. Next winter the ice will form again, calling the harp seals back. The magic of nature will bring more people here, too. Each year more and more adventurous tourists are journeying out onto the ice to experience the beauty of the seals. During these few short weeks people and seals can bring their worlds together. Somehow these seals seem to know that the people they encounter now are their protectors and there is no need to be afraid. This is how it should be.

More Seal Facts

Harp seals belong to the mammal group called pinnipeds. Pinnipeds are divided into three families:

Family Otariidae, which includes fur seals and sea lions, also known as "eared seals."

Family Odobenidae, which includes the walrus.

Family Phocidae, which includes all true seals.

True seals are monk seals, elephant seals, Antarctic seals, and northern true seals. They have rear flippers that extend behind their bodies. They are also known as "earless seals." The openings to their ears are small holes on the sides of their heads.

Harp seals are classified as northern true seals and their scientific name is *Phoca groenlandicus.*
Average adult weight—300 pounds
Average adult length—5 1/2 feet
Average lifespan—30 years

Harp seals live in three areas in the North Atlantic—the east coast of Canada near Newfoundland, in the White Sea off the coast of Russia, and between Yan Mayan and Svalbard, east of Greenland. Estimates of world population today vary from 2.25 million to 3.5 million.

Sea Lion

Walrus

Elephant Seal

135

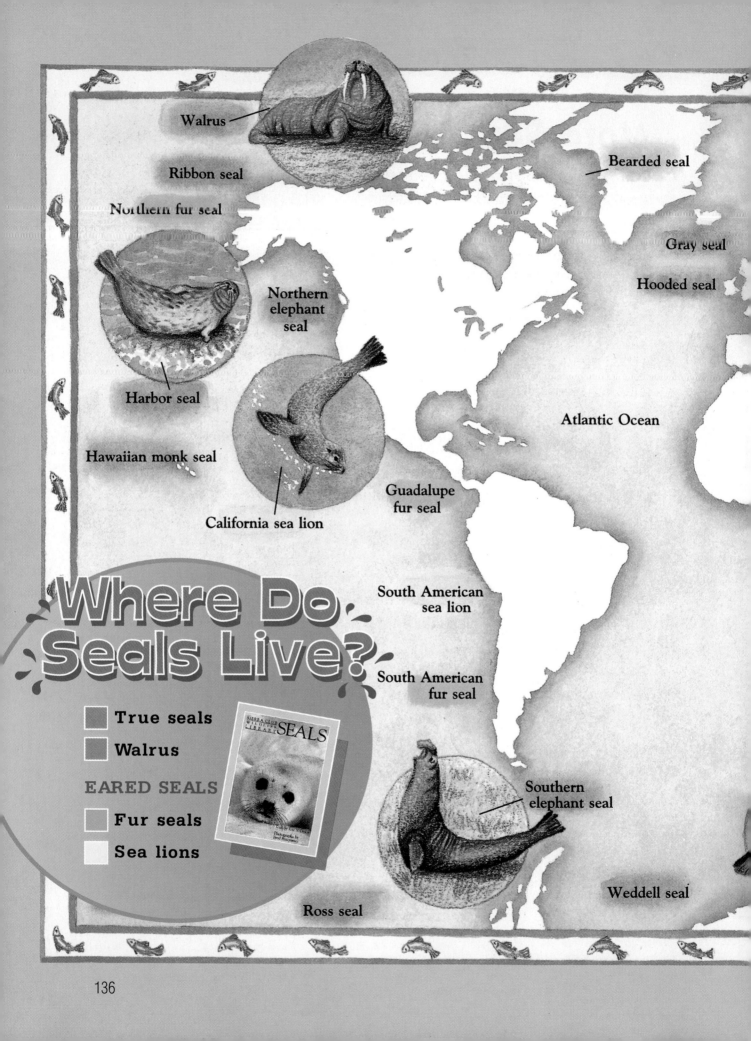

Where Do Seals Live?

Walrus

Bearded seal

Ribbon seal

Northern fur seal

Gray seal

Hooded seal

Harbor seal

Northern elephant seal

Hawaiian monk seal

California sea lion

Atlantic Ocean

Guadalupe fur seal

South American sea lion

South American fur seal

Southern elephant seal

Weddell seal

Ross seal

True seals

Walrus

EARED SEALS

Fur seals

Sea lions

SIERRA CLUB WILDLIFE LIBRARY SEALS

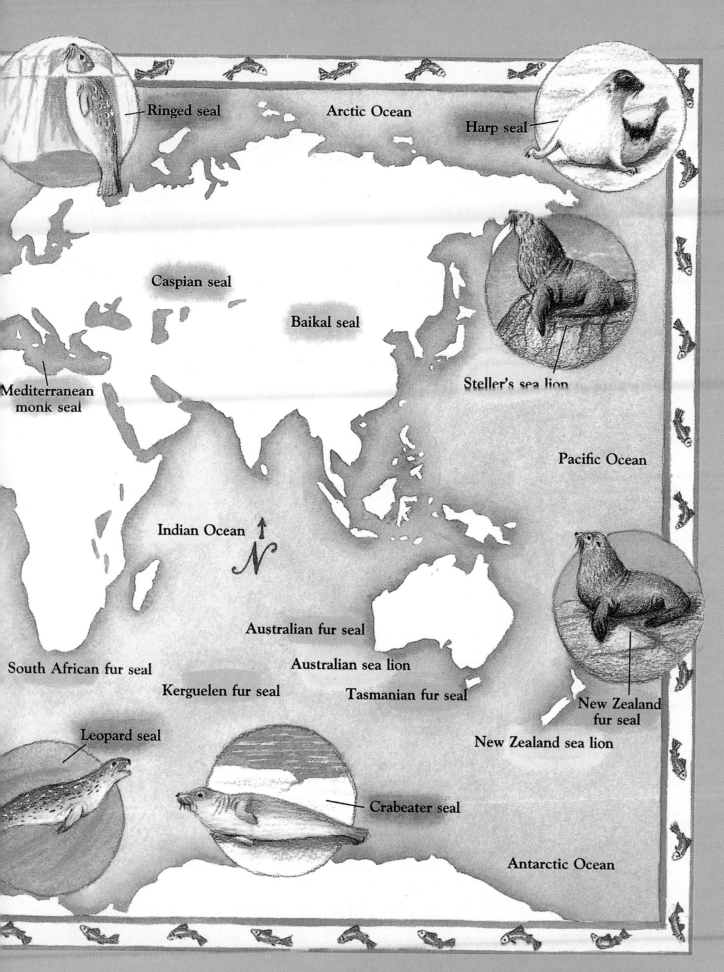

Ringed seal

Arctic Ocean

Harp seal

Caspian seal

Baikal seal

Steller's sea lion

Mediterranean
monk seal

Pacific Ocean

Indian Ocean

N

Australian fur seal

South African fur seal

Australian sea lion

Kerguelen fur seal

Tasmanian fur seal

New Zealand
fur seal

New Zealand sea lion

Leopard seal

Crabeater seal

Antarctic Ocean

I

How do they know—
the sparrows and larks—
when it's time to return
to the meadows and parks?

How do they know
when fall is still here
it's the "thing" to go south
that time of the year?

Do you think that a bird
is just smart, or, instead,
that he carries a calendar
'round in his head?

II

How do they know—
the hornets and bees—
what direction to take
through the woods and the trees,

How far they should go,
how long they should roam,
and which way to turn
when it's time to go home?

Do you think that a bee
knows north from northwest—
or has he a compass
tucked under his vest?

Aileen Fisher

139

DO NOT DISTURB

THE MYSTERIES OF
ANIMAL HIBERNATION AND SLEEP

BY MARGERY FACKLAM
ILLUSTRATED BY PAMELA JOHNSON

A 300-pound grizzly bear shuffled through a dry autumn meadow in Yellowstone National Park. She stopped to catch a mouse with one swat of her huge paw and then ambled on toward a clear stream. At the water's edge she stood on her hind legs to look around and sniff the air before she plunged into the cold water. In a moment she caught a salmon with a swoop of her paw and gulped it down. She devoured two more fish before she waded out and shook the water from her thick, gray-tipped "grizzled" fur, which glistened in the sun.

Day after day the grizzly loped through the meadows in avid search of insects, berries, and small rodents, stopping once for a real picnic when she found the carcass of an elk. Food seemed to be the only thing on her mind.

But as she grew fatter and the air grew colder, she began to search for something else—her winter den. Like other grizzlies, who are the largest land carnivores (meat-eaters) in the world and are part of the bigger family of brown bears, she looks for a fresh new den each year. When she found a place that suited her, on a steep north-facing slope at the base of a large fir tree, she began to dig. Dirt flew as she scooped out a tunnel with her long claws. It was a tight fit as she tunneled under the tree roots that would make a strong roof for her den, but she needed room enough only to squeeze through to her bedroom. In the spring, after four or five months of a deep sleep called hibernation, she would be much thinner.

The hollowed-out bedroom was just big enough for her to curl up in, head to tail. During her winter sleep, she would give birth to two tiny cubs, but they wouldn't take up much space. The cubs of a 300-pound grizzly bear are so small that they can both sit on a saucer.

For several weeks the grizzly crawled in and out of her den to arrange her bedding. Some bears use moss and grass, but this one liked the soft branches of a fir tree.

Late in November, when the temperature had dropped below freezing, the big grizzly no longer raced with the speed of a horse across the open meadow. Day after day she acted as though she were walking in her sleep. Her head drooped, and she dragged one foot after the other. Then one day, when the wind whipped the snow in swirls around her, the bear crawled into her den. All night it snowed, covering the opening to her tunnel until it disappeared. No one would be able to find it. The grizzly was safe for the winter, cozy and warm beneath the blanket of snow. She would not eat, drink water, urinate, or defecate until spring. Her heart rate would slow down from its usual 40 or 50 beats a minute to 10 or 12. Her temperature would drop a few degrees, and she would breathe slowly, just as a person in a deep sleep would do.

Like their grizzly cousins, the black bears also sleep through winter, but they don't tunnel or dig deep dens. Some scratch out a hollow at the base of a tree. Others like to sleep under a pile of brush and fallen logs, and still others curl up in small caves. They, too, build cozy beds of moss, leaves, pine needles, or bark and branches that will keep them as warm as down sleeping bags.

Although it is easy to find the winter dens of the black bears, it is almost impossible to find the well-hidden holes of the grizzlies. For many years scientists tracked the grizzlies in hopes of following them to their hibernation dens, but it never worked. They lost track of the bears in dense underbrush or blinding snowstorms.

Grizzlies are nearsighted. They can't easily recognize a person more than a hundred yards away, but they do have a keen sense of smell. If they catch the scent of a human, the bears may charge. Dr. Frank Craighead, Jr., who studies grizzlies with his brother Dr. John Craighead, had several close calls. "Our lives depended on detecting the bears before they detected us," he said.

The Craighead brothers, working in Yellowstone National Park, learned how to trap the bears and put them to sleep with tranquilizing drugs. Then they had to work fast in the short time a bear was unconscious. With a strong nylon rope net, they lifted and weighed the sleeping bear. One member of the team measured the bear while another took blood samples. They tattooed a number inside the bear's lip, checked its teeth, and attached a metal or plastic identification tag to the bear's ear. The Craighead team got to know the bears so well that they gave them names. There was Cutlip, Bigfoot, Scarface, Rip-nose, and Peg-leg, who limped on one stiff leg.

But no matter how carefully they watched these bears, they couldn't find their dens until they followed Marian. She was Number 40, and she became famous as the first grizzly to be tracked by radio.

In 1960 Marian was trapped and tranquilized. She weighed 300 pounds and was 65 inches long. The Craigheads put a bright red-and-yellow plastic collar around her 28-inch neck and attached a small battery-powered radio transmitter to the collar. The radio sent out beeps that the bear couldn't hear. But the Craigheads could hear the shrill beeping signal in the radio receivers they carried in their backpacks.

They followed Marian everywhere and finally solved the mystery of where grizzly bears hibernate. Since then, scientists have followed many bears and studied many dens. They found that bears, like people, have different ideas of comfort. The tunnel to Marian's den was only two feet long. One grizzly den in Alaska had an S-shaped tunnel 19 feet long, with a bedroom shaped like an ice-cream cone six feet across and nine feet high.

In the years since radio collars like Marian's were first used, newer ones have been made that work so well that bears can be tracked night and day in the most remote places. The continual beeping signal can be picked up by receivers in a satellite orbiting in space, in a helicopter flying overhead, or in a truck on a nearby road. Many of the bears' dens are even "bugged" with equipment that lets scientists know when the bear moves or when the temperature in the den changes.

One kind of transmitter is no bigger than a quarter. It can be easily implanted under the bear's skin after the animal has been tranquilized. When the bear wakes up, it doesn't seem to notice that it has become a walking radio station that sends messages every time its temperature or heart rate changes.

The Indians of the Northwest honored the grizzly bear and called it The Bear Who Walks Like a Man, Elder Brother, and Old Man with Claws. One of their legends says it was the grizzly who taught human beings how to survive in the woods.

And now it may be the grizzly who teaches humans how to survive in space. If people could learn how to hibernate, it would make long journeys beyond our galaxy safer and easier. Hibernating astronauts wouldn't have to eat. They wouldn't need to use precious fuel to heat the ship, and they wouldn't get bored.

But there are many questions and many years of research ahead before we find the answers. How does hibernation work? How can animals go without food and water for many months without starving to death? Why aren't they weak and sick when they wake up in the spring? Why don't they freeze in their snow-covered dens? What signals them to eat enough to add layers of fat for the winter? What tells them it's time to enter the den? And then how do they know it's time to wake up?

Do hibernating animals have some kind of "magic potion" that makes them hibernate?

MEET MARGERY FACKLAM

For as long as she can remember, Margery Facklam has found animals mysterious. And she has wanted to be near them. To work her way through college, she cared for a colony of porcupines. Later, she took jobs in zoos and science museums, where she taught others about animals.

As time passed, Facklam thought of another way to stay in touch with animals. She decided to write about them. In *Do Not Disturb: The Mysteries of Animal Hibernation and Sleep,* the author writes about animals that sleep through the winter. She wonders how hibernating animals can live without food or water for many months, why they don't freeze to death in even the coldest weather, and how they know when it's time to wake up. By writing about them, Facklam shares the mystery of animals with others.

Another book about animals by Margery Facklam that you might enjoy is *Partners for Life: The Mysteries of Animal Symbiosis.*

UNDER·THE GROUND

What is under the grass,
Way down in the ground,
Where everything is cool and wet
With darkness all around?

Little pink worms live there;
Ants and brown bugs creep
Softly round the stones and rocks
Where roots are pushing deep.

Do they hear us walking
On the grass above their heads;
Hear us running over
While they snuggle in their beds?

RHODA W. BACMEISTER

WHY FROG AND SNAKE NEVER PLAY TOGETHER

WRITTEN AND ILLUSTRATED BY
❖ ASHLEY BRYAN ❖

Mama Frog had a son. Mama Snake also had a son. One morning both children went out to play.

Mama Snake called after her child:

"Watch out for big things with sharp claws and teeth that gnaw. Don't lose your way in the bush, baby, and be back to the burrow before dark."

"Clawsangnaws," sang Snake as he went looping through the grass. "Beware of the Clawsangnaws."

Mama Frog called after her son:

"Watch out for things that peck or bite. Don't go into the bush alone, dear. Don't fight, and get home before night."

"Peckorbite," sang Frog as he went hopping from stone to stone. "Beware of the Peckorbite!"

Snake was singing his Clawsangnaws song, and Frog was singing of Peckorbites when they met along the way. They had never met before.

"Who are you?" asked Frog. "Are you a Peckorbite?" and he prepared to spring out of reach.

"**O**h no! I'm Snake, called by my Mama 'Snakeson': I'm slick, lithe and slithery. Who are you? Are you a Clawsangnaws?" and he got ready to move, just in case.

"No no! I'm Frog, called by my Mama 'Frogchild.' I'm hip, quick and hoppy."

They stood and stared at each other, then they said together:

"You don't look anything like me."

Their eyes brightened. They did not look alike, that's true, but some of their customs were alike. Both knew what to do when two say the same thing at the same time.

They clasped each other, closed their eyes and sang:

"You wish a wish
I'll wish a wish, too;
May your wish and my wish
Both come true."

Each made a wish then let go.

Just then a fly flew by, right past Frog's eyes. Flip! out went his tongue as he flicked in the fly.

A bug whizzed past Snake's nose. Flash! Snake flicked out his tongue and caught the bug.

They looked in admiration at each other and smiled. The two new friends now knew something of what each other could do. They felt at ease with each other, like old friends.

"Let's play!" said Frog.

"Hey!" said Snake, "that was my wish. Let's play in the bush."

"The bush! In the bush!" cried Frog. "That was my wish. If you go with me, it's all right 'cause Mama said I shouldn't go alone."

Frog and Snake raced to the bush and started playing games.

"Watch this," said Frog. He crouched down and counted, "One a fly, two a fly, three a fly, four!"

He popped way up into the air, somersaulted and came down, whop!

"Can you do that Snake?"

Snake bounded for a nearby mound to try the Frog-Hop. He got to the top of the slope, stood on the tip of his tail and tossed himself into the air. Down he came, flop! a tangle of coils. He laughed and tried again.

Sometimes Snake and Frog jumped together and bumped in midair. No matter how hard they hit, it didn't hurt. They had fun.

Then Snake said, "Watch this!" He stretched out at the top of the mound and counted, "One a bug, two a bug, three a bug, four!" Then swoosh! he slithered down the slope on his stomach.

"Try that Frog. It's called the Snake-Slither."

Frog lay on his stomach and slipped down the hill. His arms and legs flailed about as he slithered. He turned over at the bottom of the slope, *blump!* and rolled up in a lump.

Frog and Snake slithered down together, entangling as they went. Their calls and laughter could be heard all over the bush. One game led to another. They were having such a good time that the day passed swiftly. By late afternoon there were not two better friends in all the bush.

The sun was going down when Snake remembered his promise to his mother.

"I promised to be home before dark," he said.

"Me too," said Frog. "Good-bye!"

They hugged. Snake was so happy that he'd found a real friend that he forgot himself and squeezed Frog very tightly. It felt good, very, very good.

"Ow! easy!" said Frog. "Not too tight."

"Oh, sorry," said Snake loosening his hug-hold. "My! but you sure feel good, good enough to eat."

At that they burst out laughing and hugged again, lightly this time.

"I like you," said Frog. "Bye, Snake."

"Bye, Frog. You're my best friend."

"Let's play again tomorrow," they said together.

Aha! they clasped and sang once again:

> *"You wish a wish*
> *I'll wish a wish, too;*
> *May your wish and my wish*
> *Both come true."*

Off they went, Snake hopping and Frog slithering all the way home.

When Frog reached home, he knocked his knock, and Mama Frog unlocked the rock door. She was startled to see her child come slithering in across the floor.

"**N**ow what is this, eh?" she said. "Look at you, all covered with grass and dirt."

"It doesn't hurt," said Frog. "I had fun."

"Fun? Now what is this, eh? I can tell you haven't been playing in ponds or bogs with the good frogs. Where have you been all day? You look as if you've just come out of the bush."

"But I didn't go alone, Ma. I went with a good boy. He's my best friend."

"Best friend? Now what is this, eh?" said Mama Frog. "What good boy could that be, playing in the bush?"

"Look at this trick that he taught me, Ma," said Frogchild. He flopped on his stomach and wriggled across the floor, bungling up Mama Frog's neatly stitched lily-pad rug.

"That's no trick for a frog! Get up from there, child!" cried Mama Frog. "Now what is this, eh? Look how you've balled up my rug. Just you tell me, who was this playmate?"

"His name is Snakeson, Mama."

"Snake, son! Did you say Snake, son?"

"Yes. What's the matter, Mama?"

Mama Frog trembled and turned a pale green. She sat down to keep from fainting. When she had recovered herself, she said:

"**L**isten Frogchild, listen carefully to what I have
to say." She pulled her son close. "Snake comes from the
Snake family. They are bad people. Keep away from them.
You hear me, child?"

"Bad people?" asked Frog.

"Bad, too bad!" said Mama Frog. "Snakes are sneaks.
They hide poison in their tongues, and they crush you
in their coils."

Frogchild gulped.

"You be sure to hop out of Snake's reach if ever you
meet again. And stop this slithering foolishness. Slithering's not for frogs."

Mama Frog set the table muttering to herself:
"Playing with Snake! Now what is this, eh?" She rolled a
steaming ball of gleaming cornmeal onto Frogchild's plate.

"Sit down and eat your funji, child," said Mama Frog.
"And remember, I'm not fattening frogs for snakes, eh?"

Snake too reached home. He rustled the braided twig
hatch-cover to his home. His mother knew his rustle and
undid the vine latch. Snake toppled in.

"I'm hungry, Ma," he said, hopping all about.

"Eh, eh! Do good bless you! What a sight you are!"
said Mama Snake. "Just look at you. And listen to your
panting and wheezing. Where have you been all day?"

"In the bush, Mama, with my new friend. We played games. See what he taught me."

Snakeson jumped up on top of the table and leaped into the air. He came down on a stool, knocking it over and entangling himself in its legs.

"Eh, eh! Do good bless you. What a dangerous game that is," said Mama Snake. "Keep it up and see if you don't break every bone in your back. What new friend taught you that?"

She bent over and untangled her son from the stool.

"My frog friend taught me that. His name's Frogchild. It's the Frog-Hop, Mama. Try it. It's fun."

"Frog, child?" Mama Snake's jaws hung open showing her fangs. "Did you say Frog, child?"

"Yes," said Snakeson. "He's my best friend."

"You mean you played all day with a frog and you come home hungry?"

"He was hungry too, Mama, after playing the Snake Slither game that I taught him."

"Eh, eh! Well do good bless you! Come, curl up here son and listen carefully to what I have to tell you."

Snakeson curled up on the stool.

"Don't you know, son, that it is the custom of our house to eat frogs? Frogs are delicious people!"

Snakeson's small eyes widened.

"Ah, for true!" said Mama Snake. "Eating frogs is the custom of our house, a tradition in our family. Hopping isn't, so cut it out, you hear me?"

"Oh, Mama," cried Snakeson. "I can't eat frogs. Frog's a friend."

"Frog a friend! Do good bless you!" said Mama Snake. "That's not natural. Now you listen to me, baby. The next time you play with Frog, jump, roll and romp all you like. But when you get hungry, his game is up. Catch him and eat him!"

The next morning Snakeson was up early. He pushed off his dry-leaf cover and stretched himself. He remembered his mother's words, and the delicious feel of his frog friend when they had hugged. He was ready to go.

Mama Snake fixed her son a light breakfast of spiced insects and goldfinch eggs. Snakeson was soon on his way.

"Now don't you forget my instructions about frogs, do good bless you," Mama Snake called out after him. "And don't let me have to tell you again to watch out for big things with sharp claws and teeth that gnaw."

"Clawsangnaw," sang Snakeson. "Clawsangnaw."

He reached the bush and waited for his friend. He looked forward to fun with Frog, and he looked forward to finishing the fun with a feast of his fine frog friend. He lolled about in the sun, laughing and singing:

"You wish a wish
I'll wish a wish, too;
Can your wish and my wish
Both come true?"

The sun rose higher and higher, but Frog did not come.

"What's taking Frogchild so long?" said Snakeson. "Perhaps too much slithering has given him the bellyache. I'll go and look for him."

Snake found Frog's rock home by the pond. He rolled up a stone in his tail and knocked on the rock door.

"Anybody home?"

"Just me," answered Frogchild.

"May I come in?"

"Ah, it's you Snakeson. Sorry, my Mama's out, and she said not to open the door to anyone."

"Come on out then and let's play," said Snakeson. "I waited all morning for you in the bush."

"I can't," said Frog, "not now, anyway."

"Oh, that's too bad," said Snake. "My mother taught me a new game. I'd love to teach it to you."

"I'll bet you would," said Frog.

"You don't know what you're missing," said Snake.

"But I do know what you're missing," said Frog, and he burst out laughing.

"Aha!" said Snake. "I see that your mother has given you instructions. My mother has given me instructions too."

Snake sighed. There was nothing more to say or do, so he slithered away.

Frog and Snake never forgot that day when they played together as friends. Neither ever again had that much fun with anybody.

Today you will see them, quiet and alone in the sun, still as stone. They are deep in thought remembering that day of games in the bush, and both of them wonder:

"What if we had just kept on playing together, and no one had ever said anything?"

But from that day to this, Frog and Snake have never played together again.

You wish a wish
I'll wish a wish, too;
May your wish and my wish
Both come true.

MEET ASHLEY BRYAN

Ashley Bryan has been drawing and painting for as long as he can remember. "My first books, made in kindergarten, were illustrated *ABC* and counting books," he says.

The writer also remembers listening to music as he was growing up. His father played the saxophone, guitar, and banjo. His mother, he says, "sang from one end of the day to the other."

To Bryan, it seems natural to combine art and music to create books, as he did in *Walk Together Children* and *I'm Going to Sing.* For these songbooks, he chose music that has special meaning for him—African-American spirituals. Then he created striking woodcuts to go along with the songs.

African-American music is not the only part of Ashley Bryan's heritage that has inspired him. He also loves African folk tales. By retelling these tales, he hopes to pass on to readers "something of the rich oral tradition of storytelling." "African tales," he says, "are a beautiful means of linking the living Africa, past and present, to our own present."

Frogs Hopping Over Rocks by Sobun.

Haiku

An old silent pond ...
A frog jumps into the pond,
splash! Silence again.

BASHO

Frog-school competing
with lark-school at dusk softly
in the art of song ...

SHIKI

The old, plump bullfrog
held his ground and stared at me—
what a sour face!

ISSA

Japanese netsuke of a frog on a log.

167

Meet Jim Arnosky

Jim Arnosky hopes the outdoors will jump off the page when you open one of his books. He wants to bring the world of animals and nature to his readers.

Arnosky thinks of himself as a naturalist as well as an artist and a writer. In the middle of nature, he learns about the subjects that he puts into his books.

Arnosky writes mainly about his own life. "My books are autobiographical," he says, and explains that he has difficulty thinking of a story that doesn't come from a personal experience.

The subjects of *A Kettle of Hawks and Other Wildlife Groups,* however, are not people but groups of animals found in nature. The author explains that the names we use for animal groups are important. Each name tells us something about the animals in that group.

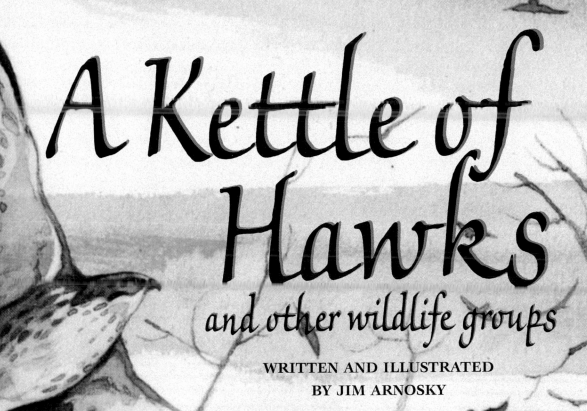

A Kettle of Hawks

and other wildlife groups

WRITTEN AND ILLUSTRATED
BY JIM ARNOSKY

Many of the names
we use for groups of
animals describe
something interesting
about the animals in each
group. These names
can be a starting point
for learning more
about wildlife.

Jim Arnosky

169

A Kettle of Hawks

Hawks silently soaring,
circling, climbing,
high in a kettle of hot air
A Kettle of Hawks in the sky.

Hawks fly alone much of the time, but in autumn and spring some travel great distances together. These seasonal movements are called migrations. To save energy, hawks will soar along using air currents or columns of hot air called thermals. The hot air in a thermal pushes the hawks high in the sky, giving them the altitude they need to peel away and glide for miles farther on their migration course.

When many hawks circle upward in the same thermal, they are said to be "kettling," because it looks as though the birds are boiling in a great kettle of air.

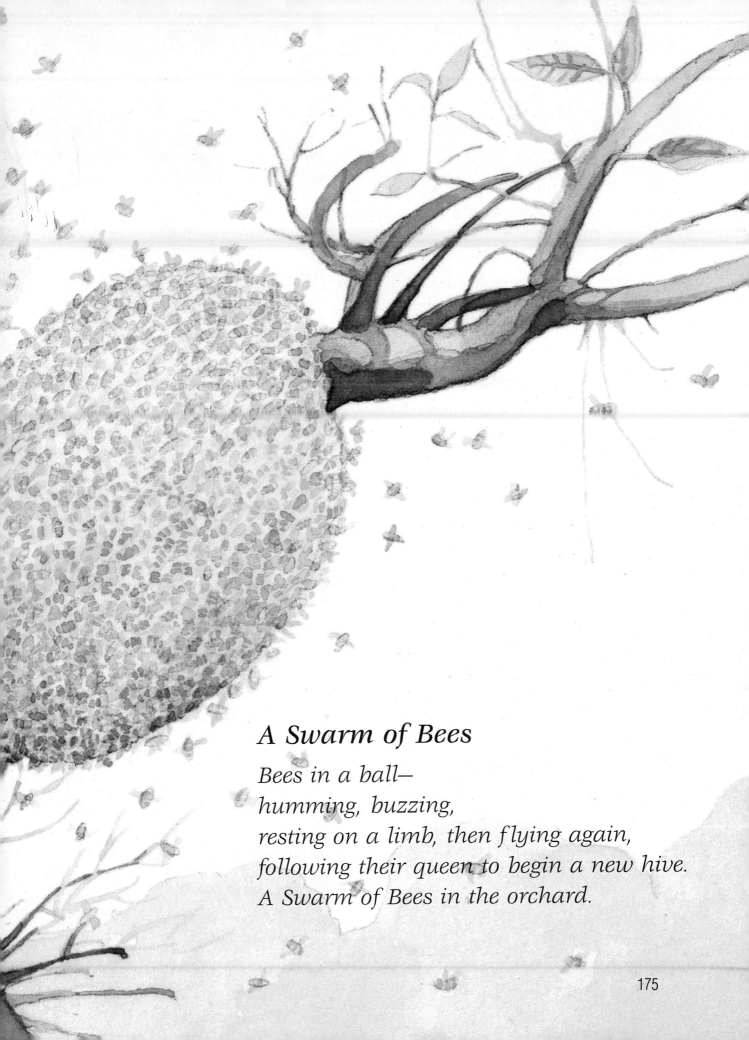

A Swarm of Bees

Bees in a ball—
humming, buzzing,
resting on a limb, then flying again,
following their queen to begin a new hive.
A Swarm of Bees in the orchard.

All activity in a beehive revolves around the queen bee. She is the mother of the hive, laying thousands of eggs that hatch into more bees—workers, drones, even new queen bees.

The worker bees are females. They gather pollen from flowers, bring it to the hive, and make it into beebread and honey. Worker bees also produce wax to make honeycomb.

Drones are male bees. They do not do any work. Drones mill about the hive, eating, growing fat, until one of them is singled out to mate with the queen. When that drone is chosen and mating is done, all the drones are driven from the hive. Since drones cannot feed themselves, they starve.

When the hive becomes over-crowded or a young queen takes control from an old queen, the bees will swarm. They leave the hive suddenly and go off, following one queen, to begin another hive in a new place. A swarm may contain thousands of bees—a buzzing cloud drifting through the air.

177

A School of Fish

Fish swimming,
darting together,
waving their fins in the water.
A School of Fish in the lake.

Minnows, bass, herring, and many other species of fish swim and feed in groups called schools. Imagine a group of classmates on a school trip, all facing in the same direction, staying close together. This gives you an idea of what a school of fish looks like underwater.

In the underwater world there is safety in numbers. A school of small fish may seem like one large fish to an enemy. Also, by grouping together, individual small fish are harder to locate than if they swam scattered all over.

Some species of fish swim in schools when they are very young and tiny and swim separately after they have grown bigger. Other species swim in schools all their lives.

A Gaggle of Geese

Geese in the distance,
honking, squawking,
landing in groups on the lake.
A Gaggle of Geese on a sandbar.

Even after a long journey geese are full of energy, flapping their wings, honking and gaggling noisily to one another. They are in top physical condition before, during, and after migration. This is due to their energy-saving system of flying in drafts. The leader of the flock breaks a trail through the air, and the rest of the geese follow behind. Each goose, flying a little to the side and rear of the goose ahead of it, is sucked along in the strong draft of air caused by the V-shaped flight formation. By "drafting" and taking turns leading the flock, the geese are able to pace themselves and conserve energy all through their long migration. And wherever they land, in a large flock or small groups called gaggles, they are never too tired to honk up a good goose conversation with their fellow travelers.

The next time you hear a name used to describe a group of animals, wonder about it. Find out if the name tells you something about the nature of the animals themselves. Anything you learn will add to the fun of watching wildlife.

*Here are some other animal groups
you can think about:*

A Bed of Clams

A Pod of Whales

A Paddle of Ducks

A Brood of Chickens

A Band of Coyotes

A Beaver Colony

A Wolf Pack

THE GREAT

PRETENDERS

by Nature's Images, Inc.

You must look closely to distinguish the viceroy (left) from the monarch butterfly. The viceroy's hind wing shows a black line across the middle.

The juniper inchworm caterpillar looks amazingly like the twigs it likes to eat.

The short-horned walkingstick is almost invisible among the desert grasses.

Some animal and plant species look a lot like what they are not. This may protect them from their enemies. Some do this by looking like part of their environment. This type of mimicry is called camouflage or *cryptic* (say CRIP-tick) coloration. Others look like toxic or bad-tasting species that predators avoid. This type of mimicry is called *Batesian* (say BAITS-ee-n) mimicry, named for its discoverer, Henry Bates, an English naturalist and explorer of the 1800s.

Camouflage is the most common type of mimicry in the animal and plant kingdoms. Many animal species look so much like their environment that they are invisible until they move. You must have a sharp eye to spot walkingsticks or juniper inchworms in the wild. Both these insects would be tasty meals for birds or lizards if they did not protect themselves by mimicking their background.

188

◀ The living rock cactus blends with its rocky desert environment.

▼ Baby killdeer depend on camouflage to avoid their enemies.

Pebbles? Rocks? Guess Again!

The young of ground-nesting birds, such as killdeer, would be easy prey without their excellent camouflage. They often improve their chances for survival by "freezing" motionless when danger approaches. Killdeer do not build a nest. Instead, they lay their eggs on the ground. The size and color of the eggs match the rocks. This helps protect them from animals such as raccoons or coyotes prowling for something to eat.

Animals aren't the only living things to use camouflage to improve their chances of survival. The well named "living rock cactus" found in the deserts of southwestern Texas and northern Mexico is almost invisible in its dry, rocky desert home. Lacking the spines of most cactus, this camouflage is particularly important to protect it from plant-eating animals looking for a juicy meal.

Do you remember Batesian mimicry? It is the resemblance of a harmless species to one that is dangerous or bad-tasting. We all know that bees and wasps can give a painful sting. Many species of flies depend on their resemblance to a bee or wasp as protection from predators.

189

A wasp can sting painfully. A wasp mimic, like the one at the right, looks so much like a real wasp that predators avoid it.

Bright Colors—Bad Taste

The brightly colored monarch butterfly is found throughout most of the United States. You have probably seen it near your home or garden. Because the caterpillar of the monarch butterfly feeds on toxic milkweed plants, the adult butterflies are distasteful to birds. Monarch butterflies advertise their bad taste with their brilliant colors.

Even though the viceroy butterfly is perfectly edible, birds leave it alone because it looks almost exactly like the foul-tasting monarch.

Insects are not the only creatures to advertise their bad taste with bright colors. When threatened, the red eft salamander produces a bad-tasting substance from its skin that can be deadly to small rodents or birds. The northern red salamander closely mimics the eft's appearance, but it is not a toxic species. By looking like the red eft, the northern rod salamander is protected from attack. Both these salamanders live in the moist forests of the eastern United States.

As you can see, different types of mimicry are used by animals and plants to protect themselves from being eaten. Can you think of other examples of mimicry that you have seen? Many are easy to find if you look closely at our wonderful world.

▲ The northern red salamander (above right) mimics the coloring of the bad-tasting red eft salamander (above left).

▼ The honey bee stings. The hover fly (below) does not. But who wants to find out? Probably not you!

A member of the Yakima
Nation dressed for a
powwow in Fort Hall, Idaho.

I WONDER

I wonder how it feels to fly
high in the sky...
like a bird.
I wonder how it feels to sit
on a nest...
like a bird.
I wonder how it feels to catch
a worm in the morning...
like a bird.
I feel funny...
maybe he is wondering
how it feels to be like a man.

*Native American of the
Yakima Nation*

193

Unit 3

That's
What
Friends
Are
For

MOM'S BEST FRIEND

by Sally Hobart Alexander
photographs by George Ancona

The best thing about having a mom who's blind is getting a special dog like Marit, Mom's dog guide. At least that's what my brother, Joel, and I used to think. Then, four months ago, Marit died. And it became the worst thing.

Marit had been with us since before I was born. Her death left a big hole in our family. I kept thinking I heard her whimpering for a Frisbee game. Any time I left pizza on the counter, I would race back to the rescue. But there was no sneaky dog about to steal it.

For my birthday Joel gave me a rabbit that I named Methuselah. Although it helped to have a soft bunny, I still wanted Marit.

Mom missed her even more. She didn't lose just a sweet, furry pet. She lost her favorite way of traveling, too. She had to use her cane again, and crept along the sidewalk like a snail. Once, when she crossed the street, she missed the opposite curb and kept walking toward the traffic. I had to holler to get her onto the sidewalk.

After that, I worried about her running errands by herself. I asked her to "go sighted guide," holding Dad's, Joel's, or my arm. Sometimes she did. But mostly she used the cane. She didn't want to depend on us—or on anybody.

A lot of blind people do fine with a cane. It's like a real long arm to help them feel what's around: walkways, hedges, mailboxes.

With a dog guide, blind people use their hearing more than touch. Mom has trained her ears. It's amazing: she can tell when something, like a movie marquee, is above her head, and when she passes a lamppost. She knows from the change in the sound of her footsteps.

In spite of Mom's special hearing, I worried. I was relieved when she decided to go back to The Seeing Eye for a new dog guide.

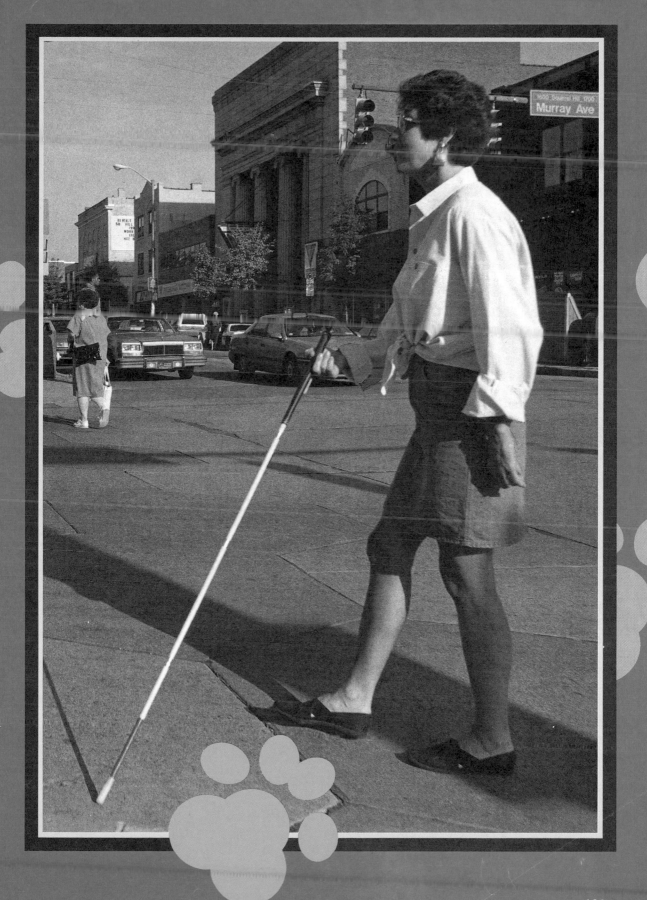

Before Mom left, I told her I wouldn't be able to love the new dog as much as Marit. Mom hugged me and said, "The night before you were born, I wondered how I could love a second child as much as your brother. Then you came, and like magic, I was just as crazy about you."

The Seeing Eye, in Morristown, New Jersey, was the first dog guide school in the United States. (Now there are nine others.) It trains German shepherds and Labrador and golden retrievers for three months. Then, for about a month, it teaches blind people to use the dogs.

When Mom arrived at The Seeing Eye, she was met by her instructor, Pete Jackson.

I missed Mom as much as I missed Marit, but at least Mom called every night. She also wrote letters and sent pictures.

Mom's first day was a cinch. She'd gone to Seeing Eye twelve years before to get Marit, and still remembered her way around. Usually when she's in a new place, she has to move from room to room with her cane, memorizing the layout.

In the morning Mom walked with Pete Jackson so that he could check her pace. He wanted to choose the dog that would suit her best. Then she was free to play the piano, exercise . . . and worry. Would she get along with the new dog? Would they work well together?

The next day she got Ursula. What a strange name! The staff at Seeing Eye's breeding station had named Ursula when she was born. (Ursula's brothers and sisters were also given names starting with *U*.) Dog guides need a name right away so that Seeing Eye can keep track of the four hundred or so pups born each year. At two months of age, the pups go to Seeing Eye puppy-raising families to learn how to live with people. At fifteen months, they are mature enough to return to Seeing Eye for the three-month training program.

Dad said that Ursula means "bear." But in the pictures Mom sent, Ursula looked too pip-squeaky to be called bear. Mom explained that Seeing Eye is now breeding some smaller dogs. They are easier to handle and fit better on buses and in cars.

My friends thought dog guides were little machines that zoomed blind people around. Until Mom went away, even I didn't understand all the things these dogs were taught.

But on Mom's first lesson in Morristown, Ursula seemed to forget her training. She veered on a street crossing and brushed Mom into a bush. Mom had to make her correct herself by backing up and walking around the bush. Then Mom praised her.

After ten practice runs with Pete, Mom and Ursula soloed. Ursula didn't stop at a curb, so Mom had to scold her and snap her leash, calling, "Pfui." Later Ursula crashed Mom into a low-hanging branch. "Ursula will have to start thinking tall," Mom said that night, "or I'll have to carry hedge clippers in my purse."

Even though Ursula had walked in Morristown a lot with Pete, she was nervous when Mom's hand was on the harness. Mom talked and walked differently. And Mom was nervous, too. Ursula moved so much faster than old Marit had, and Mom didn't trust her.

Every day Mom and Ursula made two trips. Every week they mastered new routes. Each route got longer and more complicated, and Mom had less time to learn it. Every night Mom gave Ursula obedience training: "Come. Sit. Down. Rest. Fetch." I thought she should try obedience training on Joel.

While Mom worked hard, Dad, Joel, and I went on with our normal lives—school, homework, soccer, piano, spending time with friends. We divided Mom's chores: Dad did the cooking, Joel, the vacuuming and laundry, and I did the dishes, dusting, weeding. The first two weeks were easy.

In a phone call Mom said that things were getting easier for her, too. "Remember how tough curb ramps have been for me?" she asked. "They feel like any other slope in the sidewalk, so I can't always tell that I've reached the street. Well, Ursula stopped perfectly at every ramp. And she guided me around, not under, a ladder and right past a huge parking lot without angling into it. But best of all, she actually saved my life. A jackhammer was making so much noise that I couldn't hear whether the light was green or red. When I told Ursula, 'Forward!' she refused to move and kept me from stepping in front of a car. (Of course, Pete would have saved me if Ursula hadn't.)"

Mom barely asked about us. It was all Ursula, Ursula, Ursula! She seemed to be forgetting Marit, too. When a letter came a few days later, I was sure she didn't miss anyone.

Dear Bob, Joel, and Leslie,

Today Ursula and I faced several disasters! She tried hard to ignore a boxer dog who wanted to play. A few minutes later, a great Dane lunged out from nowhere, jumped all over her, and loped off. Ursula's instinct is to chase dogs, but she didn't move a paw after that one. As if the dogs weren't enough trouble, fire engine sirens went off. Ursula just strolled down the sidewalk.

Mostly, life is smooth here. Seeing Eye is a vacation—no cooking, no cleaning, lots of time to talk to new friends, like Dr. Holle, the veterinarian. And since I don't have many blind friends, it's a treat to be with my roommate and the twenty other students. We laugh about the same things, like the great enemy of the blind—trash collection day! Every twenty feet, there's a garbage can reeking of pizza, hoagies, old cheese. Usually Ursula snakes me around these smelly obstacles. But sometimes the temptation to her nose wins out, and I have to correct her, all the while holding my own nose.

Some trainees really inspire me, like Julie Hensley, who became blind from diabetes at twenty-two. Even though she's been blind for twelve years, she still teaches horses to do stunts. She judges her location from a radio playing music in the center of the pen, and gallops around as fast as she ever did when she could see.

Bob Pacheco used to race motorcycles and hunt. Then, two years ago, when he was twenty-nine, he developed optic atrophy and became blind two months later. He took up fishing, swimming, even trapping. But something was missing. He couldn't get around quickly enough. After the first trip with his dog guide, he was overjoyed. "Sally!" He grabbed my hand. "I don't feel blind any more."

The dogs are wonderful, and the people here are very special. So are you.

Love,
Mom

Well, life at home wasn't very wonderful or special. Dad ran out of the casseroles Mom had frozen ahead of time, and although his meals were okay, I missed Mom's cooking. Worse, the dishes kept piling up. I never knew Joel ate so much.

Then things got really bad. While Dad was teaching his American literature night class, Joel and I faced a disaster Mom and Ursula couldn't have dreamed of: the toilet bowl overflowed! We wiped the floor with towels. As Joel took the towels down to the washing machine, he found water dripping through the ceiling—all over the dining room table, all over the carpet. He ran for more towels, and I ran for the furniture polish and rug shampoo. When Dad got home, everything looked perfect. But I wrote a braille letter.

Dear Mom,
    Come home soon. The house misses you.
    Love,
    Exhausted in Pittsburgh

Mom wrote back.

Dear Exhausted,
    Hang on. We'll be home to "hound" you Thursday. Be prepared. When you see me, I will have grown four more feet.
    Mom

I couldn't laugh. I was too tired and worried. What if I couldn't love Ursula? Marit was the best dog ever.

Soon they arrived. Ursula yanked at her leash and sprang up on me. She pawed my shoulders, stomach, and arms just the way Marit used to, nearly knocking me over. She leaped onto Joel, licking him all over. As she bounded up onto me again, I realized Mom was right. Like magic, I was crazy about this shrimpy new dog.

But by the end of the day, I had a new worry. Was *Ursula* going to love *me?* She seemed friendly enough, but keyed up, even lost in our house.

Mom explained that Ursula had already given her heart away three times: first to her mother, then to the Seeing Eye puppy-raising family, and finally to Pete. Mom said we had to be patient.

"Remember how Marit loved you, Leslie? When you were little, she let you stand on her back to see out the window. Ursula will be just as nuts about you. Love is the whole reason this dog guide business works."

So I tried to be patient and watched Mom work hard. First she showed one route in our neighborhood to Ursula and walked it over and over. Then she taught her a new route, repeated that, and reviewed the old one. Every day she took Ursula on two trips, walking two or three miles. She fed her, groomed her, gave her obedience training. Twice a week Mom cleaned Ursula's ears and brushed her teeth.

"I'm as busy as I was when you and Joel were little!" she said.

Mom and Ursula played for forty-five minutes each day. Joel, Dad, and I were only allowed to watch. Ursula needed to form her biggest attachment to Mom

Mom made Ursula her shadow. When she showered or slept, Ursula was right there.

Still, Ursula didn't eat well— only half the amount she'd been eating at Seeing Eye. And she tested Mom, pulling her into branches, stepping off curbs. Once she tried to take a shortcut home. Another time, because she was nervous, she crossed a new street diagonally.

Crossing streets is tricky. Ursula doesn't know when the light is green. Mom knows. If she hears the cars moving beside her in the direction in which she's walking, the light is green. If they're moving right and left in front of her, it's red.

I worried about Ursula's mistakes, but Mom said they were normal. She kept in touch with her classmates and knew that their dog guides were goofing, too. One kept eating grass, grazing like a cow. Another chased squirrels, pigeons, and cats. Still another always stopped in the middle of the street, ten feet from

the curb. Once in a while her friends got lost, just like Mom, and had to ask for help.

Mom said it takes four to six months for the dogs to settle down. But no matter how long she and Ursula are teamed up together, Ursula will need some correcting. For instance, Ursula might act so cute that a passerby will reach out to pet her. Then Mom will have to scold Ursula and ask the person not to pet a dog guide. If people give Ursula attention while she's working, she forgets to do her job.

After a month at home, Ursula emptied her food bowl every time. She knew all the routes, and Mom could zip around as easily as she had with Marit.

"Now it's time to start the loneliness training," Mom said. She left Ursula alone in the house, at first for a short time while she went jogging with Dad. Ursula will never be able to take Mom jogging because she can't guide at high speeds.

Each week Mom increased the amount of time Ursula was alone. I felt sorry for our pooch, but she did well: no barking, no chewing on furniture.

Then Mom said Joel and I could introduce Ursula to our friends, one at a time. They could pet her when she was out of harness.

Every morning Ursula woke Joel and me. Every night she sneaked into my bed for a snooze.

Finally Mom allowed Joel and me to play with Ursula, and I knew: shrimpy little Ursula had fallen for us, and we were even crazier about her.

But we haven't forgotten Marit. Joel says that Ursula is the best dog alive. And I always say she's the best dog in this world.

Meet
Sally Hobart Alexander

Sally Hobart Alexander loved stories as a child. She and her friends would often put on plays and write stories for their classmates.

Alexander's sight problems began as an adult, but she didn't let them keep her from writing. Instead, she published her first two books, *Mom Can't See Me* and *Sarah's Surprise*. Now, several books later, Sally Hobart Alexander's message is simple: "If I can do it, you can, too!"

Meet
George Ancona

Curiosity drives George Ancona's work. He says, "I love to find myself in strange places, meeting people, getting to know them and learning about them. This helps me to learn about myself."

He felt lucky to have spent time with Sally Hobart Alexander and her family. He describes them as "wonderful" and "warm."

Ancona says he often remains friends with the people he photographs. With nearly 80 books to his credit, that's a lot of friends!

GOOD INTENTIONS LEAD TO

"**C**uriosity killed the cat," some say. Tracy Phillips feels it "educates the cat." For Tracy, it inspired a "talking wallet" invention. From the time her younger brother developed a brain tumor, which led to blindness and ended his life, Tracy has wanted to help the blind.

"Money Talks" won Tracy Phillips second place in the 54th Westinghouse Science Talent Search.

54th Westinghouse Science Talent Search
ENTRY FORM

PHILLIPS   TRACY   CAROLINE
LAST NAME   FIRST NAME   MIDDLE NAME

MAIL EARLY — All entries for the 54th Westinghouse Science Talent Search (1994-95 school year) must be received by 11:59 p.m. on Thursday, December 1, 1994, at Science Service, 1719 N Street, N.W., Washington, DC 20036. If the judging process has not been completed, late entries will be accepted ONLY if (1) metered in a U.S. Post Office by November 24, 1994, or (2) sent by a carrier that guaranteed delivery in writing by the midnight deadline. Priority mail DOES NOT GUARANTEE IN WRITING two-day delivery.

"MONEY TALKS": A WALLET-SIZED CURRENCY VOCALIZER FOR THE BLIND
TITLE OF RESEARCH REPORT:

Scientific Field of Research:

___ Astronomy (A)
___ Biochemistry (B)
___ Biology (C)
___ Biophysics (D)
___ Computers (E)
_X_ Electronics (F)

Most Influential Person

What person has been most influential in the development of your scientific career? Please name someone with whom you have had personal contact.

FULL NAME (include titles such as Dr., Ms., Professor, etc.)

MR. PETER J. RUBINO (teacher)

Westinghouse STS Attachment | Tracy Phillips |

Q What do you hope to contribute to science or knowledge in general? What benefits do you think your research will bring to the world and its inhabitants?

A I hope that my research will help give blind people the independence to get along in a world that is designed for sighted people. In today's technological world, we have change machines giving us quarters for dollars to play video games. We have soda machines that exchange a one or five dollar bill for both the correct change and the drink. We even have computers that tell us the car door is ajar. I would like to utilize modern technology to help physically challenged people also.

As a scientist, I plan to use my skills to benefit society, humanity and the planet. Moreover, I hope to steer science in the direction of service to others and the environment.

GOOD INVENTIONS

Westinghouse Science Talent Search winners, from left, Irene Ann Chen, San Diego, Tracy Caroline Phillips, Long Beach, N.Y., and Martin Tibor Stiaszny, Overland Park, Kan., with their medals.

Here's How She Made Money Talk

"**M**oney Talks," the prize-winning science project built by Tracy Phillips of Long Beach, is a battery-operated sensing system that counts currency for the blind.

Designed to fit an ordinary billfold, the system identifies different denominations of paper currency, ranging from $1 to $20. This is done by six small infrared detectors that distinguish the varying light and dark patterns of different bills.

When the wallet-sized sensing device is folded around a bill, an electronic vocalizer announces the denomination — for example, "twenty dollars." The purpose is to let blind people know they have received correct change.

Tracy, who developed her project over a two-year period, now would like to find a company interested in mass-producing the device. She says the cost should be reasonable — perhaps less than the $80 spent on parts for the original model.

— Hildebrand

JUSTIN *and the* BEST BISCUITS *in the* WORLD

by Mildred Pitts Walter

Ten-year-old Justin lives with his mother and two sisters. Justin's family expects him to help with the household chores, but he thinks cooking and cleaning are women's work. He would rather play ball with his friend Anthony. When Justin's cowboy grandfather invites him to visit his ranch, Justin is delighted. Justin is certain that he and his grandfather will do real men's work together, like riding the range. But Justin's grandfather is full of surprises. Before his visit is over, Justin learns a lot more from his grandfather than he ever imagined.

Illustrated by Floyd Cooper

The smell of coffee and home-smoked ham woke Justin. His grandpa was already up and downstairs cooking breakfast. Justin jumped out of bed and quickly put on his clothes.

Grandpa had hot pancakes, apple jelly, and ham all ready for the table. Justin ate two stacks of pancakes with two helpings of everything else.

After breakfast, Grandpa cleared the table, preparing to wash the dishes. "Would you rather wash or dry?" he asked Justin.

"Neither," Justin replied, quickly thinking how little success he had with dishes.

Grandpa said nothing as he removed the dishes from the table. He took his time, carefully measuring liquid soap and letting hot water run in the sink. Then he washed each dish and rinsed it with care, too. No water splashed or spilled. Soapsuds were not all over. How easy it looked, the way Grandpa did it.

After washing the dishes, Grandpa swept the floor and then went upstairs.

Justin stood around downstairs. He had a strange feeling of guilt and wished he had helped with the dishes. He heard Grandpa moving about, above in his room. Justin thought of going outside, down into the meadow, but he decided to see what was going on upstairs.

When he saw his grandpa busy making his own big bed, Justin went into his room. His unmade bed and his pajamas on the floor bothered him. But he decided that the room didn't look too bad. He picked up his pajamas and placed them on the bed and sat beside them. He waited.

Finally Grandpa came in and said, "Are you riding fence with me today?"—

"Oh yes!"

"Fine. But why don't you make your bed? You'll probably feel pretty tired tonight. A well-made bed can be a warm welcome."

Justin moved slowly, reluctant to let Grandpa see him struggle with the bed. He started. What a surprise! Everything was tightly in place. He only had to smooth the covers. The bed was made. No lumps and bumps. Justin looked at Grandpa and grinned broadly. "That was easy!" he shouted.

"Don't you think you should unpack your clothes? They won't need ironing if you hang them up. You gotta look razor sharp for the festival." He gave Justin some clothes hangers.

"Are we *really* going to the festival every day?" Justin asked.

"You bet, starting with the judging early tomorrow and the dance tomorrow night." Grandpa winked at him.

Justin's excitement faded when he started
unpacking his rumpled shirts. "They sure are
wrinkled, Grandpa," he said.

"Maybe that's because they weren't folded."

"I can't ever get them folded right," Justin cried.

"Well, let's see. Turn it so the buttons face down."
Grandpa showed Justin how to bring the sleeves
to the back, turning in the sides so that the sleeves
were on top. Then he folded the tail of the shirt over
the cuffs, and made a second fold up to the collar.
"Now you try it."

Justin tried it. "Oh, I see. That was easy,
Grandpa." Justin smiled, pleased with himself.

"Everything's easy when you know how."

Justin, happy with his new-found skill, hurriedly
placed his clothes on the hangers. He hoped the
wrinkles would disappear in time for the festival.

"Now you'll look sharp," Grandpa said.

Justin felt a surge of love for his grandpa. He
would always remember how to make a bed snug as
a bug and fold clothes neatly. He grabbed Grandpa's
hand. They walked downstairs, still holding hands, to
get ready to ride fence.

Riding fence meant inspecting the fence all
around the ranch to see where it needed mending.
Riding fence took a great deal of a rancher's time.
Justin and Grandpa planned to spend most of the
day out on the plains. Grandpa said he'd pack a
lunch for them to eat on the far side of the ranch.

Justin was surprised when Grandpa packed only flour, raisins, shortening, and chunks of smoked pork. He also packed jugs of water and makings for coffee.

The horses stood in the meadow as if they knew a busy day awaited them. While Grandpa saddled Pal, he let Justin finish the saddling of Black Lightning. Justin tightened the cinches on Black, feeling the strong pull on his arm muscles. With their supplies in their saddlebags, they mounted Pal and Black, leaving Cropper behind to graze in the meadow.

The early sun shone fiery red on the hilltops while the foothills were cast in shades of purple. The dew still lingered heavily on the morning. They let their horses canter away past the house through the tall green grass. But on the outer edge of the ranch where the fence started, they walked the horses at a steady pace.

The fence had three rows of taut wire. "That's a pretty high fence," Justin said.

"We have to keep the cattle in. But deer sometimes leap that fence and eat hay with the cattle." When it got bitter cold and frosty, Grandpa rode around the ranch dropping bales of hay for the cattle. It took a lot of hay to feed the cattle during the winter months.

"I didn't think a cow could jump very high," Justin said.

"Aw, come on. Surely you know that a cow jumped over the moon." Grandpa had a serious look on his face.

"I guess that's a joke, eh?" Justin laughed.

Justin noticed that Grandpa had a map. When they came to a place in the fence that looked weak, Grandpa marked it on his map. Later, helpers who came to do the work would know exactly where to mend. That saved time.

Now the sun heated up the morning. The foothills were now varying shades of green. Shadows dotted the plains. Among the blackish green trees on the rolling hills, fog still lingered like lazy clouds. Insects buzzed. A small cloud of mosquitoes swarmed just behind their heads, and beautiful cardinals splashed their redness on the morning air. Justin felt a surge of happiness and hugged Black with his knees and heels.

Suddenly he saw a doe standing close to the fence. "Look, Grandpa!" he said. She seemed alarmed but did not run away. Doe eyes usually look peaceful and sad, Justin remembered. Hers widened with fear. Then Justin saw a fawn caught in the wire of the fence.

Quickly they got off their horses. They hitched them to a post and moved cautiously toward the fawn.

The mother rushed to the fence but stopped just short of the sharp wire. "Stay back and still," Grandpa said to Justin. "She doesn't know we will help her baby. She thinks we might hurt it. She wants to protect it."

The mother pranced restlessly. She pawed the ground, moving as close to the fence as she could. Near the post the fence had been broken. The wire curled there dangerously. The fawn's head, caught in the wire, bled close to an ear. Whenever it pulled its head the wire cut deeper.

Grandpa quickly untangled the fawn's head.

Blood flowed from the cut.

"Oh, Grandpa, it will die," Justin said sadly.

"No, no," Grandpa assured Justin. "Lucky we got here when we did. It hasn't been caught long."

The fawn moved toward the doe. The mother, as if giving her baby a signal, bounded off. The baby trotted behind.

As they mounted their horses, Justin suddenly felt weak in the stomach. Remembering the blood, he trembled. Black, too, seemed uneasy. He moved his nostrils nervously and strained against the bit. He arched his neck and sidestepped quickly. Justin pulled the reins. "Whoa, boy!"

"Let him run," Grandpa said.

Justin kicked Black's sides and off they raced across the plain. They ran and ran, Justin pretending he was rounding up cattle. Then Black turned and raced back toward Grandpa and Pal.

"Whoa, boy," Justin commanded. Justin felt better and Black seemed calm, ready now to go on riding fence.

The sun beamed down and sweat rolled off Justin as he rode on with Grandpa, looking for broken wires in the fence. They were well away from the house, on the far side of the ranch. Flies buzzed around the horses and now gnats swarmed in clouds just above their heads. The prairie resounded with songs of the bluebirds, the bobwhite quails, and the mockingbirds mimicking them all. The cardinal's song, as lovely as any, included a whistle.

Justin thought of Anthony and how Anthony whistled for Pepper, his dog.

It was well past noon and Justin was hungry. Soon they came upon a small, well-built shed, securely locked. Nearby was a small stream. Grandpa reined in his horse. When he and Justin dismounted, they hitched the horses, and unsaddled them.

"We'll have our lunch here," Grandpa said. Justin was surprised when Grandpa took black iron pots, other cooking utensils, and a table from the shed. Justin helped him remove some iron rods that Grandpa carefully placed over a shallow pit. These would hold the pots. Now Justin understood why Grandpa had brought uncooked food. They were going to cook outside.

First they collected twigs and cow dung. Grandpa called it cowchips. "These," Grandpa said, holding up a dried brown pad, "make the best fuel. Gather them up."

There were plenty of chips left from the cattle that had fed there in winter. Soon they had a hot fire.

Justin watched as Grandpa carefully washed his hands and then began to cook their lunch.

"When I was a boy about your age, I used to go with my father on short runs with cattle. We'd bring them down from the high country onto the plains."

"Did you stay out all night?"

"Sometimes. And that was the time I liked most. The cook often made for supper what I am going to make for lunch."

Grandpa put raisins into a pot with a little water and placed them over the fire. Justin was surprised when Grandpa put flour in a separate pan. He used his fist to make a hole right in the middle of the flour. In that hole he placed some shortening. Then he added water. With his long delicate fingers he mixed the flour, water, and shortening until he had a nice round mound of dough.

Soon smooth circles of biscuits sat in an iron skillet with a lid on top. Grandpa put the skillet on the fire with some of the red-hot chips scattered over the lid.

Justin was amazed. How could only those ingredients make good bread? But he said nothing as Grandpa put the chunks of smoked pork in a skillet and started them cooking. Soon the smell was so delicious, Justin could hardly wait.

Finally Grandpa suggested that Justin take the horses to drink at the stream. "Keep your eyes open and don't step on any snakes."

Justin knew that diamondback rattlers sometimes lurked around. They were dangerous. He must be careful. He watered Black first.

While watering Pal, he heard rustling in the grass. His heart pounded. He heard the noise again. He wanted to run, but was too afraid. He looked around carefully. There were two black eyes staring at him. He tried to pull Pal away from the water, but Pal refused to stop drinking. Then Justin saw the animal. It had a long tail like a rat's. But it was as big as a cat. Then he saw something crawling on its back. They were little babies, hanging on as the animal ran.

A mama opossum and her babies, he thought, and was no longer afraid.

By the time the horses were watered, lunch was ready. *"M-mm-m,"* Justin said as he reached for a plate. The biscuits were golden brown, yet fluffy inside. And the sizzling pork was now crisp. Never had he eaten stewed raisins before.

"Grandpa, I didn't know you could cook like this," Justin said when he had tasted the food. "I didn't know men could cook so good."

"Why, Justin, some of the best cooks in the world are men."

Justin remembered the egg on the floor and his rice burning. The look he gave Grandpa revealed his doubts.

"It's true," Grandpa said. "All the cooks on the cattle trail were men. In hotels and restaurants they call them chefs."

"How did you make these biscuits?"

"That's a secret. One day I'll let you make some."

"Were you a cowboy, Grandpa?"

"I'm still a cowboy."

"No, you're not."

"Yes, I am. I work with cattle, so I'm a cowboy."

"You know what I mean. The kind who rides bulls, broncobusters. That kind of cowboy."

"No, I'm not that kind. But I know some."

"Are they famous?"

"No, but I did meet a real famous Black cowboy once. When I was eight years old, my grandpa took me to meet his friend Bill Pickett. Bill Pickett was an old man then. He had a ranch in Oklahoma."

"Were there lots of Black cowboys?"

"Yes. Lots of them. They were hard workers, too. They busted broncos, branded calves, and drove cattle. My grandpa tamed wild mustangs."

"Bet they were famous."

"Oh, no. Some were. Bill Pickett created the sport of bulldogging. You'll see that at the rodeo. One cowboy named Williams taught Rough Rider Teddy Roosevelt how to break horses; and another one named Clay taught Will Rogers, the comedian, the art of roping." Grandpa offered Justin the last biscuit.

When they had finished their lunch they led the horses away from the shed to graze. As they watched the horses, Grandpa went on, "Now, there were some more very famous Black cowboys. Jessie Stahl. They say he was the best rider of wild horses in the West."

"How could he be? Nobody ever heard about him. I didn't."

"Oh, there're lots of famous Blacks you never hear or read about. You ever hear about Deadwood Dick?"

Justin laughed. "No."

"There's another one. His real name was Nate Love. He could outride, outshoot anyone. In Deadwood City in the Dakota Territory, he roped, tied, saddled, mounted, and rode a wild horse faster than anyone. Then in the shooting match, he hit the bull's-eye every time. The people named him Deadwood Dick right on the spot. Enough about cowboys, now. While the horses graze, let's clean up here and get back to our men's work."

Justin felt that Grandpa was still teasing him, the way he had in Justin's room when he had placed his hand on Justin's shoulder. There was still the sense of shame whenever the outburst about women's work and the tears were remembered.

As they cleaned the utensils and dishes, Justin asked, "Grandpa, you think housework is women's work?"

"Do you?" Grandpa asked quickly.

"I asked you first, Grandpa."

"I guess asking you that before I answer is unfair. No, I don't. Do you?"

"Well, it seems easier for them," Justin said as he splashed water all over, glad he was outside.

"Easier than for me?"

"Well, not for you, I guess, but for me, yeah."

"Could it be because you don't know how?"

"You mean like making the bed and folding the clothes."

"Yes." Grandpa stopped and looked at Justin. "Making the bed is easy now, isn't it? All work is that way. It doesn't matter who does the work, man or woman, when it needs to be done. What matters is that we try to learn how to do it the best we can in the most enjoyable way."

"I don't think I'll ever like housework," Justin said, drying a big iron pot.

"It's like any other kind of work. The better you do it, the easier it becomes, and we seem not to mind doing things that are easy."

With the cooking rods and all the utensils put away, they locked the shed and went for their horses.

"Now, I'm going to let you do the cinches again. You'll like that."

There's that teasing again, Justin thought. "Yeah. That's a man's work," he said, and mounted Black.

"There are some good horsewomen. You'll see them at the rodeo." Grandpa mounted Pal. They went on their way, riding along silently, scanning the fence.

Finally Justin said, "I was just kidding, Grandpa." Then without planning to, he said, "I bet you don't like boys who cry like babies."

"Do I know any boys who cry like babies?"

"Aw, Grandpa, you saw me crying."

"Oh, I didn't think you were crying like a baby. In your room, you mean? We all cry sometime."

"You? Cry, Grandpa?"

"Sure."

They rode on, with Grandpa marking his map. Justin remained quiet, wondering what could make a man like Grandpa cry.

As if knowing Justin's thoughts, Grandpa said, "I remember crying when you were born."

"Why? Didn't you want me?"

"Oh, yes. You were the most beautiful baby. But, you see, your grandma, Beth, had just died. When I held you I was flooded with joy. Then I thought, *Grandma will never see this beautiful boy.* I cried."

The horses wading through the grass made the only sound in the silence. Then Grandpa said, "There's an old saying, son. 'The brave hide their fears, but share their tears.' Tears bathe the soul."

Justin looked at his grandpa. Their eyes caught. A warmth spread over Justin and he lowered his eyes. He wished he could tell his grandpa all he felt, how much he loved him.

meet MILDRED PITTS WALTER

Mildred Pitts Walter wrote her first book, *Lillie of Watts,* when she was a teacher in Los Angeles. Since then she has written a number of award-winning books about African-American children, including *Justin and the Best Biscuits in the World,* which won the Coretta Scott King Award.

African-American traditions are often a part of Walter's stories. In *Have a Happy . . . ,* for example, Chris, a boy whose birthday falls on December 25 and whose father is looking for work, fears his birthday won't seem very important to anyone. But as the family prepares for Kwanzaa, the seven-day celebration of African-American heritage, Chris begins to feel that his birthday may not be so disappointing after all.

Speaking about her stories, Walter says, "I like to think that the images I create will make all young people thoughtful and African Americans aware of themselves as well."

▲ **EARLY SPANISH *VAQUERO*.**
Wide-brimmed, low-crowned sombrero. Leggings. Short pants and jacket. Big spurs.

▲ **MEXICAN *VAQUERO*.**
Very large, ornamented sombrero. Tight, buttoned leather chaps. Large heel spurs.

▲ **SOUTHWEST-TYPE COWBOY.**
Plain wing chaps. Four-pronged rowels on spurs. Wide-brimmed sombrero.

Nothing says "cowboy" louder than a tall, wide-brimmed hat. Wranglers used hats to signal each other, keep their heads dry, carry water, and distract a charging bull.

In Spanish, *LA RIATA* (la ree AH ta) means "the rope." Say it fast. Faster. Soon, you'll say it cowboy-style: lariat. A lariat, or lasso, is a long rope with a loop for catching cattle and horses.

If you rode "drag," behind a herd of cattle, you ate dust. A bandanna helped keep the grit from getting in your teeth. Bandannas made good bandages and slings, and they kept cold winds from whistling down your collar.

Cowboy shirts didn't have pockets. Cowboys put tobacco, matches, and good-luck charms in their vest pockets. Modern western shirts sport fringe, fancy stitching, and even beads and rhinestones.

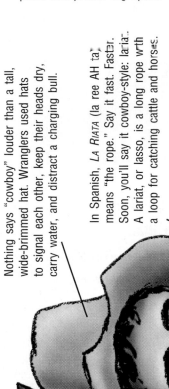

The Well-Fitted Cowboy

I see by your outfit that you are a cowboy...
"The Cowboy's Lament"

The wrangler's outfit is unique. From high hat to silver spurs, it can't help but stand out in a crowd (unless it's a crowd of cowboys, of course!). Yet just about every stitch has a purpose. The western outfit was designed for the rugged job of handling large, four-legged animals. In the late 1800's, here's how the West was worn.

▲ **COWBOY OF THE PLAINS.**
Closed-leg, fringed chaps. Wide-brimmed hat with leather-laced rim. Flannel shirt, shield front.

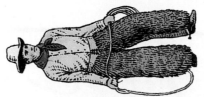

▲ **TYPICAL WEST COAST BUCKAROO**
a Few Years Back. Closed-leg angora chaps. Medium hat.

▲ **NORTHWEST-TYPE COWBOY.**
Closed-leg chaps of goat, wolf, or dog hair. Medium-brimmed hat.

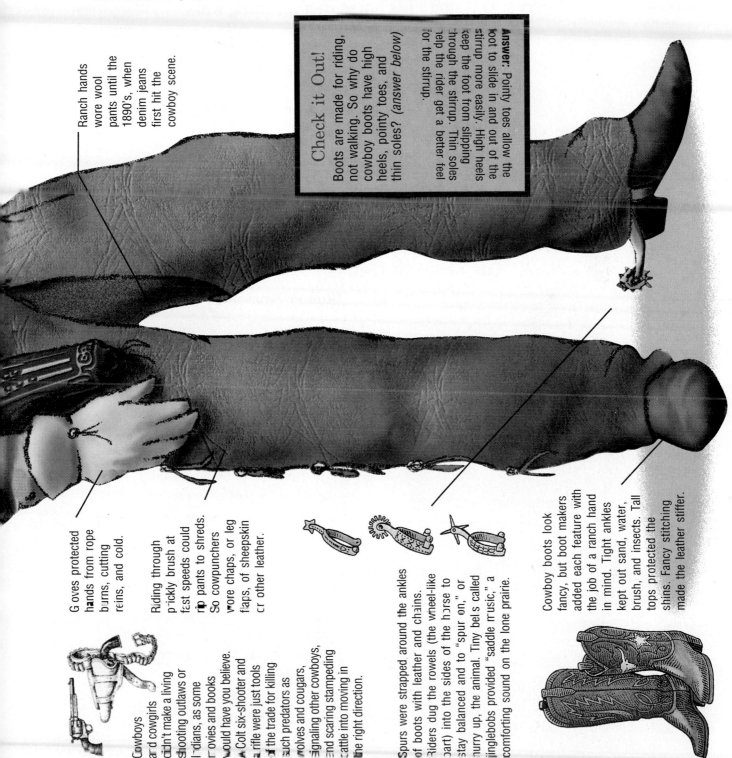

Check it Out!

Boots are made for riding, not walking. So why do cowboy boots have high heels, pointy toes, and thin soles? *(answer below)*

Answer: Pointy toes allow the boot to slide in and out of the stirrup more easily. High heels keep the foot from slipping through the stirrup. Thin soles help the rider get a better feel for the stirrup.

Ranch hands wore wool pants until the 1890's, when denim jeans first hit the cowboy scene.

Gloves protected hands from rope burns, cutting reins, and cold.

Riding through prickly brush at fast speeds could rip pants to shreds. So cowpunchers wore chaps, or leg flaps, of sheepskin or other leather.

Cowboys and cowgirls didn't make a living shooting outlaws or Indians, as some movies and books would have you believe. A Colt six-shooter and a rifle were just tools of the trade for killing such predators as wolves and cougars, signaling other cowboys, and scaring stampeding cattle into moving in the right direction.

Spurs were strapped around the ankles of boots with leather and chains. Riders dug the rowels (the wheel-like part) into the sides of the horse to "spur on," or hurry up, the animal. Tiny bells called jinglebobs provided "saddle music," a comforting sound on the lone prairie.

Cowboy boots look fancy, but boot makers added each feature with the job of a ranch hand in mind. Tight ankles kept out sand, water, brush, and insects. Tall tops protected the shins. Fancy stitching made the leather stiffer.

233

A Time to Talk

When a friend calls to me from the road
And slows his horse to a meaning walk,
I don't stand still and look around
On all the hills I haven't hoed,
And shout from where I am, "What is it?"
No, not as there is a time to talk.
I thrust my hoe in the mellow ground,
Blade-end up and five feet tall,
And plod: I go up to the stone wall
For a friendly visit.

Robert Frost

Young Corn, a painting by Grant Wood, 1931.
Courtesy of the Cedar Rapids, Iowa, Community School District.

Nicholasa Mohr

Nicholasa Mohr studied to be an artist, not a writer. "Writing," she says, "just happened."

Maybe writing seems natural to Mohr because she creates stories out of her own experiences. Like the girl in *Felita*, Nicholasa Mohr grew up in New York City's El Barrio. Like Felita, too, she moved away from a neighborhood and then moved back to it. Mohr also based parts of *Felita* on other memories she had of growing up, such as problems she had with her best friend.

Not all of Mohr's characters are based on real people, however. Some come entirely from her imagination. One of these is Abuelita, the grandmother in *Felita*.

Nicholasa Mohr didn't know her grandmother, but she did grow up respecting older people. "It is part of my culture," she says. "I would love someday to be a grandmother like Abuelita—to have that kind of wisdom."

Felita

by
Nicholasa Mohr

*W*hen Felita and her family move back to their old neighborhood, she is thrilled to be reunited with her best friend, Gigi. Although there have not been many changes in the neighborhood itself, Felita soon learns that people, even best friends, can change. With her grandmother Abuelita's help, Felita works to make her friendship with Gigi survive these changes.

ILLUSTRATED BY RUDY GUTIERREZ

A wonderful thing happened this new school year. Gigi, Consuela, Paquito, and I were all going into the fourth grade, and we were put in the same class. It had never happened before. Once I was in the same class with Consuela, and last year Gigi and Paquito were together. But this—it was too good to be true! Of course knowing Gigi and I were in the same class made me the happiest.

Our teacher, Miss Lovett, was friendly and laughed easily. In early October, after we had all settled into our class and gotten used to the routine of school once more, Miss Lovett told us that this year our class was going to put on a play for Thanksgiving. The play we were going to perform was based on a poem by Henry Wadsworth Longfellow, called "The Courtship of Miles Standish." It was about the Pilgrims and how they lived when they first landed in America.

We were all so excited about the play. Miss Lovett called for volunteers to help with the sets and costumes. Paquito and I agreed to help with the sets. Consuela was going to work on makeup. Gigi had not volunteered for anything. When we asked her what she was going to do, she shrugged and didn't answer.

Miss Lovett said we could all audition for the different parts in the play. I was really interested in being Priscilla. She is the heroine. Both

Captain Miles Standish and the handsome, young John Alden are in love with her. She is the most beautiful maiden in Plymouth, Massachusetts. That's where the Pilgrims used to live. I told my friends how much I would like to play that part. Everyone said I would be perfect . . . except Gigi. She said that it was a hard part to do, and maybe I wouldn't be able to play it. I really got annoyed and asked her what she meant.

"I just don't think you are right to play Priscilla. That's all," she said.

"What do you mean by right?" I asked. But Gigi only shrugged and didn't say another word. She was beginning to get on my nerves.

Auditions for the parts were going to start Tuesday. Lots of kids had volunteered to audition. Paquito said he would try out for the brave Captain Miles Standish. Consuela said she was too afraid to get up in front of everybody and make a fool of herself. Gigi didn't show any interest in the play and refused to even talk to us about it. Finally the day came for the girls to read for the part of Priscilla. I was so excited I could hardly wait. Miss Lovett had given us some lines to study. I had practiced real hard. She called out all the names of those who were going to read. I was surprised when I heard her call out "Georgina Mercado." I didn't even know Gigi wanted to try out for Priscilla. I looked at Gigi, but she ignored me. We began reading. It was my turn. I was very nervous and kept forgetting my lines. I had to look down at the script a whole lot. Several other girls were almost as nervous as I was. Then it was Gigi's turn. She recited the part almost by

heart. She hardly looked at the script. I noticed that she was wearing one of her best dresses. She had never looked that good in school before. When she finished, everybody clapped. It was obvious that she was the best one. Miss Lovett made a fuss.

"You were just wonderful, Georgina," she said, "made for the part!" Boy, would I have liked another chance. I bet I could have done better than Gigi.

Why hadn't she told me she wanted the part? It's a free country, after all. She could read for the same part as me. I wasn't going to stop her! I was really angry at Gigi.

"I have to meet my brothers down by the next street," I said. "I'm splitting. See you." They hardly noticed. Only Consuela said goodbye. The rest just kept on hanging all over Gigi. Big deal, I thought.

Of course walking by myself and watching out for the tough kids was not something I looked forward to. Just last Friday Hilda Gonzales had gotten beat up and had her entire allowance stolen. And at the beginning of the term Paquito had been walking home by himself and gotten mugged. A bunch of big bullies had taken his new schoolbag complete with pencil and pen case, then left him with a swollen lip. No, sir, none of us ever

After school everyone was still making a fuss over her. Even Paquito had to open his stupid mouth.

"Oh, man, Gigi!" he said. "You were really good. I liked the part when John Alden asked you to marry Captain Miles Standish and you said, 'Why don't you speak for yourself, John?' You turned your head like this." Paquito imitated Gigi and closed his eyes. "That was really neat!" Consuela and the others laughed and agreed.

I decided I wasn't walking home with them.

walked home from school alone if we could help it. We knew it wasn't a safe thing to do. Those mean kids never bothered us as long as we stuck together. Carefully I looked around to make sure none of the bullies were in sight. Then I put some speed under my feet, took my chances, and headed for home.

Just before all the casting was completed, Miss Lovett offered me a part as one of the Pilgrim women. All I had to do was stand in the background like a zombie. It wasn't even a speaking part.

"I don't get to say one word," I protested.

"Felicidad Maldonado, you are designing the stage sets and you're assistant stage manager. I think that's quite a bit. Besides, all the speaking parts are taken."

"I'm not interested, thank you," I answered.

"You know"—Miss Lovett shook her head—"you can't be the best in everything."

I turned and left. I didn't need to play any part at all. Who cared?

Gigi came over to me the next day with a great big smile all over her face. I just turned away and made believe she wasn't there.

"Felita, are you taking the part of the Pilgrim woman?" she asked me in her sweetest voice, just like nothing had happened.

"No," I said, still not looking at her. If she thought I was going to fall all over her like those dummies, she was wasting her time.

"Oh," was all she said, and walked away. Good, I thought. I don't need her one bit!

At home Mami noticed something was wrong.

"Felita, what's the matter? You aren't going out at all. And I haven't seen Gigi for quite a while. In fact I haven't seen any of your friends."

"Nothing is the matter, Mami. I just got lots of things to do."

"You're not upset because we couldn't give you a birthday party this year, are you?" Mami asked. "You know how hard the money situation has been for us."

My birthday had been at the beginning of November. We had celebrated with a small cake after dinner, but there had been no party.

"No. It's not that," I said and meant it. Even though I had been a little disappointed, I also knew Mami and Papi had done the best they could.

"We'll make it up to you next year, Felita, you'll see."

"I don't care, Mami. It's not important now."

"You didn't go having a fight with Gigi or something? Did you?"

"Now why would I have a fight with anybody!"

"Don't raise your voice, miss," Mami said. "Sorry I asked. But you just calm down."

The play was going to be performed on the day before Thanksgiving. I made the drawings for most of the scenery. I made a barn, a church, trees and grass, cows, and a horse. I helped the others make a real scarecrow. We used a broom and old clothes. Paquito didn't get the part of Captain Miles Standish, but he made a wonderful fence out of cardboard. It looked just like a real wooden fence. Consuela brought in her mother's old leftover makeup. She did a good job of making up everybody.

By the time we set up the stage, everything looked beautiful. Gigi had tried to talk to me a few times. But I just couldn't be nice back to her. She acted like nothing had happened, like I was supposed to forget she hadn't told me she was going to read for the part! I wasn't going to forget that just because she was now Miss Popularity. She could go and stay with all her newfound friends for all I cared!

The morning of the play, at breakfast, everybody noticed how excited I was.

"Felita," Papi exclaimed, "stop jumping around like a monkey and eat your breakfast."

"She's all excited about the school play today," Mami said.

"That's right. Are you playing a part in the play?" Papi asked.

"No," I replied.

"But she's done most of the sets. Drawing and designing. Isn't that right, Felita?"

"Mami, it was no big deal."

"That's nice," said Papi. "Tell us about it."

"What kind of sets did you do?" Johnny asked.

"I don't know. Look, I don't want to talk about it."

"Boy, are you touchy today," Tito said with a laugh.

"Leave me alone!" I snapped.

"Okay." Mami stood up. "Enough. Felita, are you finished?" I nodded. "Good. Go to school. When you come back, bring home a better mood. Whatever is bothering you, no need to take it out on us." Quickly I left the table.

"Rosa," I heard Papi say, "sometimes you are too hard on her."

"And sometimes you spoil her, Alberto!" Mami snapped. "I'm not raising fresh kids."

I was glad to get out of there. Who needs them, I thought.

The play was a tremendous hit. Everybody looked wonderful and played their parts really well. The stage was brilliant with the color I had used on my drawings. The background of the countryside, the barn, and just about everything stood out clearly. Ernesto Bratter, the stage manager, said I was a good assistant. I was glad to hear that, because a couple of times I'd had to control my temper on account of his ordering me around. But it had all worked out great.

No doubt about it. Gigi was perfect as Priscilla. Even though the kids clapped and cheered for the entire cast, Gigi got more applause than anybody else. She just kept on taking a whole lot of bows.

Afterward Miss Lovett had a party for our class. We had lots of treats. There was even a record player and we all danced. We had a really good time.

Of course Priscilla, alias Gigi, was the big star. She just couldn't get enough attention. But not from me, that was for sure. After the party Gigi spoke to me.

"Your sets were really great. Everybody said the stage looked wonderful."

"Thanks." I looked away.

"Felita, are you mad at me?"

"Why should I be mad at you?"

"Well, I did get the leading part, but . . ."

"Big deal," I said. "I really don't care."

"You don't? But . . . I . . ."

"Look," I said, interrupting her, "I gotta go. I promised my mother I'd get home early. We have to go someplace."

I rushed all the way home. I didn't know why, but I was still furious at Gigi. What was worse was that I was unhappy about having those feelings. Gigi and I had been real close for as far back as I could remember. Not being able to share things with her really bothered me.

We had a great Thanksgiving. The dinner was just delicious. Abuelita brought her flan. Tío Jorge brought lots of ice cream. He always brings us kids a treat when he visits. Sometimes he even brings each one of us a small gift—a nature book or crayons for me and puzzles or sports magazines for my brothers. He's really very nice to us. One thing about him is that he's sort of quiet and doesn't talk much. Papi says that Tío Jorge has been like that as far back as he can remember.

Abuelita asked me if I wanted to go home with her that evening. Boy, was I happy to get away from Mami. I just couldn't face another day of her asking me questions about Gigi, my friends, and my whole life. It was getting to be too much!

It felt good to be with Abuelita in her apartment. Abuelita never questioned me about anything really personal unless I wanted to talk about it.

She just waited, and when she sensed that I was worried or something, then she would ask me. Not like Mami. I love Mami, but she's always trying to find out every little thing that happens to me. With my abuelita sometimes we just sit and stay quiet, not talk at all. That was nice too. We fixed the daybed for me. And then Tío Jorge, Abuelita, and I had more flan as usual.

"Would you like to go to the park with me this Sunday?" Tío Jorge asked me.

"Yes."

"We can go to the zoo and later we can visit the ducks and swans by the lake."

"Great!" I said.

Whenever Tío Jorge took me to the zoo, he would tell me stories about how he, Abuelita, and their brothers and sisters had lived and worked as youngsters taking care of farm animals. These were the only times I ever heard him talk a whole lot.

"It's not just playing, you know," he would say. "Taking care of animals is hard work. Back on our farm in Puerto Rico we worked hard, but we had fun too. Every one of us children had our very own favorite pets. I had a pet goat by the name of Pepe. He used to follow me everywhere." No matter how many times he told me the same stories, I always enjoyed hearing them again.

"Well." Tío Jorge got up. "It's a date then on Sunday, yes?"

"Yes, thank you, Tío Jorge."

"Good night," he said and went off to bed.

Abuelita and I sat quietly for a while, then Abuelita spoke.

"You are getting to be a big girl now, Felita. You just turned nine years old. My goodness! But I still hope you will come to bed with your abuelita for a little while, eh?"

I got into bed and snuggled close to Abuelita. I loved her the best, more than anybody. I hadn't been to stay with her since the summer, and somehow this time things felt different. I noticed

how tired Abuelita looked. She wasn't moving as fast as she used to. Also I didn't feel so little next to her anymore.

"Tell me, Felita, how have you been? It seems like a long time since we were together like this." She smiled her wonderful smile at me. Her dark, bright eyes looked deeply into mine. I felt her warmth and happiness.

"I'm okay, Abuelita."

"Tell me about your play at school. Rosa tells me you worked on the stage sets. Was the play a success?"

"It was. It was great. The stage looked beautiful. My drawings stood out really well. I never made such big drawings in my life. There was a farm in the country, a barn, and animals. I made it the way it used to be in the olden days of the Pilgrims. You know, how it was when they first came to America."

"I'm so proud of you. Tell me about the play. Did you act in it?"

"No." I paused. "I didn't want to."

"I see. Tell me a little about the story."

I told Abuelita all about it.

"Who played the parts? Any of your friends?"

"Some."

"Who?"

"Well, this boy Charlie Martinez played John Alden. Louie Collins played Captain Miles Standish. You don't know them. Mary Jackson played the part of the narrator. That's the person who tells the story. You really don't know any of them."

I was hoping she wouldn't ask, but she did.

"Who played the part of the girl both men love?"

"Oh, her? Gigi."

"Gigi Mercado, your best friend?" I nodded. "Was she good?"

"Yes, she was. Very good."

"You don't sound too happy about that."

"I don't care." I shrugged.

"But if she is your best friend, I should think you would care."

"I . . . I don't know if she is my friend anymore, Abuelita."

"Why do you say that?"

I couldn't answer. I just felt awful.

"Did she do something? Did you two argue?" I nodded. "Can I ask what happened?"

"Well, it's hard to explain. But what she did wasn't fair."

"Fair about what, Felita?"

I hadn't spoken about it before. Now with Abuelita it was easy to talk about it.

"Well, we all tried out for the different parts. Everybody knew what everybody was trying out

for. But Gigi never told anybody she was going to try out for Priscilla. She kept it a great big secret. Even after I told her that I wanted to try for the part, she kept quiet about it. Do you know what she did say? She said I wasn't right for it . . . it was a hard part and all that bunch of baloney. She just wanted the part for herself, so she was mysterious about the whole thing. Like . . . it was . . . I don't know." I stopped for a moment, trying to figure this whole thing out. "After all, I am supposed to be her best

252

friend . . . her very best friend. Why shouldn't she let me know that she wanted to be Priscilla? I wouldn't care. I let her know my plans. I didn't go sneaking around."

"Are you angry because Gigi got the part?"

It was hard for me to answer. I thought about it for a little while. "Abuelita, I don't think so. She was really good in the part."

"Were you as good when you tried out for Priscilla?"

"No." I looked at Abuelita. "I stunk." We both laughed.

"Then maybe you are not angry at Gigi at all."

"What do you mean?"

"Well, maybe you are a little bit . . . hurt?"

"Hurt?" I felt confused.

"Do you know what I think? I think you are hurt because your best friend didn't trust you. From what you tell me, you trusted her, but she didn't have faith in you. What do you think?"

"Yes." I nodded. "Abuelita, yes, I don't know why. Gigi and I always tell each other everything. Why did she act like that to me?"

"Have you asked her?"

"No."

"Why not? Aren't you two speaking to each other?"

"We're speaking. Gigi tried to be friendly a few times."

"Don't you want to stay her friend?"

"I do. Only she came over to me acting like . . . like nothing ever happened. And something did happen! What does she think? That she can go around being sneaky and I'm going to fall all over her? Just because she got the best part, she thinks she's special."

"And you think that's why she came over. Because she wants to be special?"

"I don't know."

"You should give her a chance. Perhaps Gigi acted in a strange way for a reason."

"She wasn't nice to me, Abuelita. She wasn't."

"I'm not saying she was. Or even that she was right. Mira, Felita, friendship is one of the best things in this whole world. It's one of the few things you can't go out and buy. It's like love. You can buy clothes, food, even luxuries, but there's no place I know of where you can buy a real friend. Do you?"

I shook my head. Abuelita smiled at me and waited. We were both silent for a long moment. I wondered if maybe I shouldn't have a talk with Gigi. After all, she had tried to talk to me first.

"Abuelita, do you think it's a good idea for me to . . . maybe talk to Gigi?"

"You know, that's a very good idea." Abuelita nodded.

"Well, she did try to talk to me a few times. Only there's just one thing. I won't know what to say to her. I mean, after what's happened and all."

"After so many years of being close, I am sure you could say 'Hello, Gigi. How are you?' That should be easy enough."

"I feel better already, Abuelita."

"Good," Abuelita said. "Now let's you and I get to sleep. Abuelita is tired."

"You don't have to tuck me in. I'll tuck you in instead." I got out of bed and folded the covers carefully over my side. Then I leaned over her and gave her a kiss. Abuelita hugged me real tight.

"My Felita has become a young lady," she whispered.

I kept thinking of what Abuelita had said, and on Monday I waited for Gigi after school. It was as if she knew I wanted to talk. She came over to me.

"Hello, Gigi," I said. "How are you?"

"Fine." Gigi smiled. "Wanna walk home together?"

"Let's take the long way so we can be by ourselves," I said.

We walked without saying anything for a couple of blocks. Finally I spoke.

"I wanted to tell you, Gigi, you were really great as Priscilla."

"Did you really like me? Oh, Felita, I'm so glad. I wanted you to like me, more than anybody else. Of course it was nothing compared to the sets you did. They were something special. Everybody liked them so much."

"You were right too," I said. "I wasn't very good for the part of Priscilla."

"Look." Gigi stopped walking and looked at me. "I'm sorry about . . . about the way I acted. Like, I didn't say anything to you or the others. But, well, I was scared you all would think I was silly or something. I mean, you wanted the part too. So, I figured, better not say nothing."

"I wouldn't have cared, Gigi. Honest."

"Felita . . . it's just that you are so good at a lot of things. Like, you draw just fantastic. You beat everybody at hopscotch and kick-the-can. You know about nature and animals, much more than the rest of us. Everything you do is always better than . . . what I do! I just wanted this part for me. I wanted to be better than you this time. For once I didn't wanna worry about you. Felita, I'm sorry."

I was shocked. I didn't know Gigi felt that way. I didn't feel better than anybody about anything I did. She looked so upset, like she was about to cry any minute. I could see she was miserable and I wanted to comfort her. I had never had this kind of feeling before in my whole life.

"Well, you didn't have to worry. 'Cause I stunk!" We both laughed with relief. "I think I was the worst one!"

"Oh, no, you weren't." Gigi laughed. "Jenny Fuentes was the most awful."

"Worse than me?"

"Much worse. Do you know what she sounded like? She sounded like this. 'Wha . . . wha . . . why don't you . . . speeek for your . . . yourself *Johnnnn?*" Gigi and I burst into laughter.

"And how about that dummy, Louie Collins? I didn't think he read better than Paquito."

"Right," Gigi agreed. "I don't know how he got through the play. He was shaking so much that I was scared the sets would fall right on his head."

It was so much fun, Gigi and I talking about the play and how we felt about everybody and everything. It was just like before, only better.

A Lot of Kids

There are a lot of kids
Living in my apartment building
And a lot of apartment buildings on my street
And a lot of streets in this city
And cities in this country
And a lot of countries in the world.
So I wonder if somewhere there's a kid I've never met
Living in some building on some street
In some city and country I'll never know—
And I wonder if that kid and I might be best friends
If we ever met.

JEFF MOSS

TEAM

by Peter Golenbock

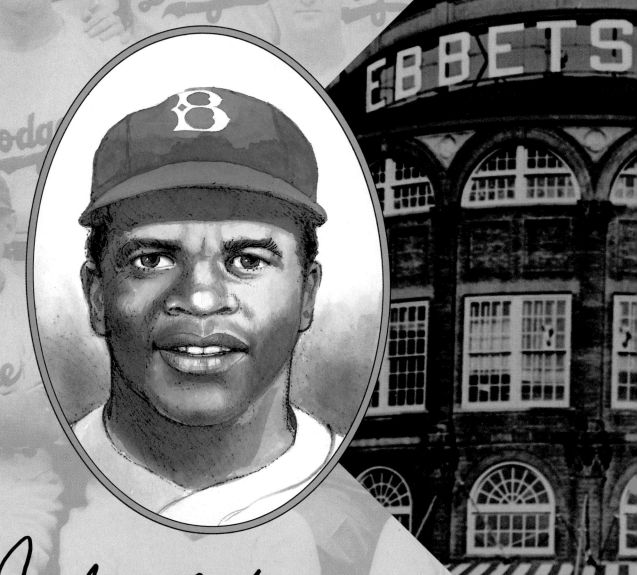

Jackie Robinson

MATES

illustrated by Paul Bacon

"Pee Wee" Reese

Jackie Robinson was more than just my teammate. He had a tremendous amount of talent, ability, and dedication. Jackie set a standard for future generations of ball players. He was a winner.

Jackie Robinson was also a man.

PEE WEE REESE
October 31, 1989

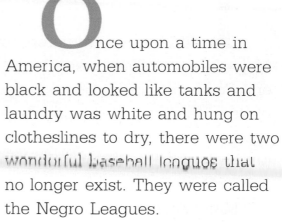

Once upon a time in America, when automobiles were black and looked like tanks and laundry was white and hung on clotheslines to dry, there were two wonderful baseball leagues that no longer exist. They were called the Negro Leagues.

The Negro Leagues had extraordinary players, and adoring fans came to see them wherever they played. They were heroes, but players in the Negro Leagues didn't make much money and their lives on the road were hard.

Laws against segregation didn't exist in the 1940s. In many places in this country, black people were not allowed to go to the same schools and churches as white people. They couldn't sit in the front of a bus or trolley car. They couldn't drink from the same drinking fountains that white people drank from.

Back then, many hotels didn't rent rooms to black people, so the Negro League players slept in their cars. Many towns had no restaurants that would serve them, so they often had to eat meals that they could buy and carry with them.

263

Life was very different for the players in the Major Leagues. They were the leagues for white players. Compared to the Negro League players, white players were very well paid. They stayed in good hotels and ate in fine restaurants. Their pictures were put on baseball cards and the best players became famous all over the world.

Many Americans knew that racial prejudice was wrong, but few dared to challenge openly the way things were. And many people were apathetic about racial problems. Some feared that it could be dangerous to object. Vigilante groups, like the Ku Klux Klan, reacted violently against those who tried to change the way blacks were treated.

The general manager of the Brooklyn Dodgers baseball team was a man by the name of Branch Rickey. He was not afraid of change. He wanted to treat the Dodger fans to the best players he could find, regardless of the color of their skin. He thought segregation was unfair and wanted to give everyone, regardless of race or creed, an opportunity to compete equally on ballfields across America.

To do this, the Dodgers needed one special man.

Branch Rickey launched a search for him. He was looking for a star player in the Negro Leagues who would be able to compete successfully despite threats on his life or attempts to injure him. He would have to possess the self-control not to fight back when opposing players tried to intimidate or hurt him. If this man disgraced himself on the field, Rickey knew, his opponents would use it as an excuse to keep blacks out of Major League baseball for many more years.

Rickey thought Jackie Robinson might be just the man.

BRANCH RICKEY

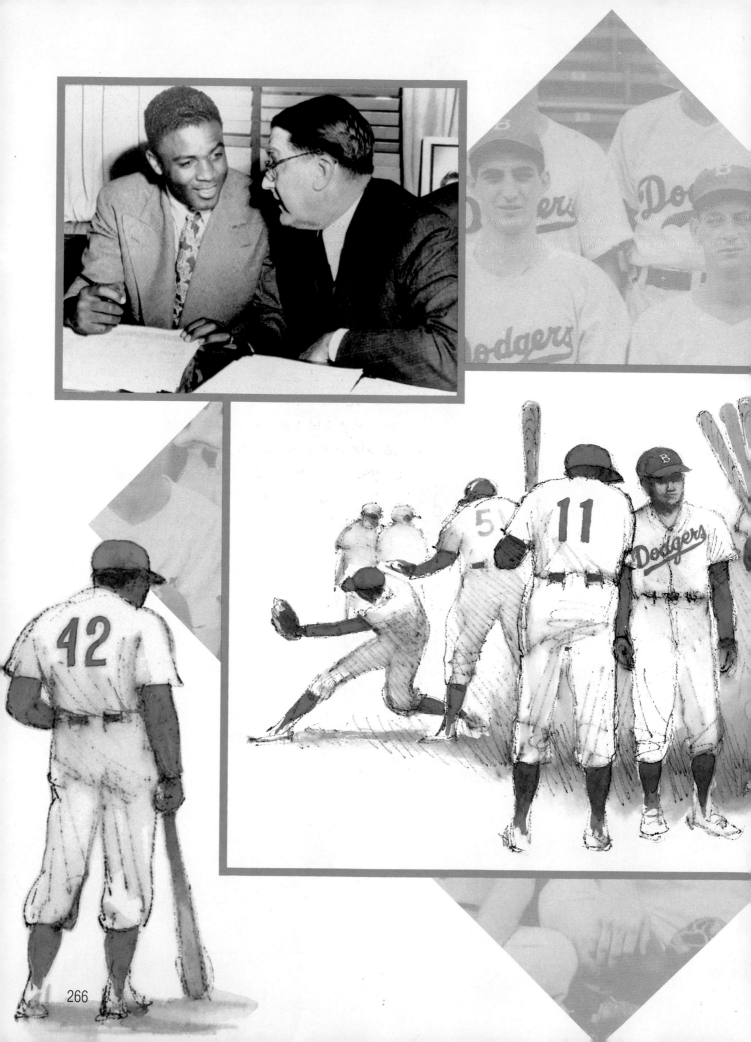

J ackie rode the train to Brooklyn to meet Mr. Rickey. When Mr. Rickey told him, "I want a man with the courage not to fight back," Jackie Robinson replied, "If you take this gamble, I will do my best to perform." They shook hands. Branch Rickey and Jackie Robinson were starting on what would be known in history as "the great experiment."

At spring training with the Dodgers, Jackie was mobbed by blacks, young and old, as if he were a savior. He was the first black player to try out for a Major League team. If he succeeded, they knew, others would follow.

Initially, life with the Dodgers was for Jackie a series of humiliations. The players on his team who came from the South, men who had been taught to avoid black people since childhood, moved to another table whenever he sat down next to them. Many opposing players were cruel to him, calling him nasty names from their dugouts. A few tried to hurt him with their spiked shoes. Pitchers aimed at his head. And he received threats on his life, both from individuals and from organizations like the Ku Klux Klan.

Despite all the difficulties, Jackie Robinson didn't give up. He made the Brooklyn Dodgers team.

Making the Dodgers was only the beginning. Jackie had to face abuse and hostility throughout the season, from April through September. His worst pain was inside. Often he felt very alone. On the road he had to live by himself, because only the white players were allowed in the hotels in towns where the team played.

The whole time Pee Wee Reese, the Dodger shortstop, was growing up in Louisville, Kentucky, he had rarely even seen a black person, unless it was in the back of a bus. Most of his friends and relatives hated the idea of his playing on the same field as a black man. In addition, Pee Wee Reese had more to lose than the other players when Jackie joined the team.

Jackie had been a shortstop, and everyone thought that Jackie would take Pee Wee's job. Lesser men might have felt anger toward Jackie, but Pee Wee was different. He told himself, "If he's good enough to take my job, he deserves it."

When his Southern teammates circulated a petition to throw Jackie off the team and asked him to sign it, Pee Wee responded, "I don't care if this man is black, blue, or striped"—and refused to sign. "He can play and he can help us win," he told the others. "That's what counts."

Very early in the season, the Dodgers traveled west to Ohio to play the Cincinnati Reds. Cincinnati is near Pee Wee's hometown of Louisville.

The Reds played in a small ballpark where the fans sat close to the field. The players could almost feel the breath of the fans on the backs of their necks. Many who came that day screamed terrible, hateful things at Jackie when the Dodgers were on the field.

More than anything else, Pee Wee Reese believed in doing what was right. When he heard the fans yelling at Jackie, Pee Wee decided to take a stand.

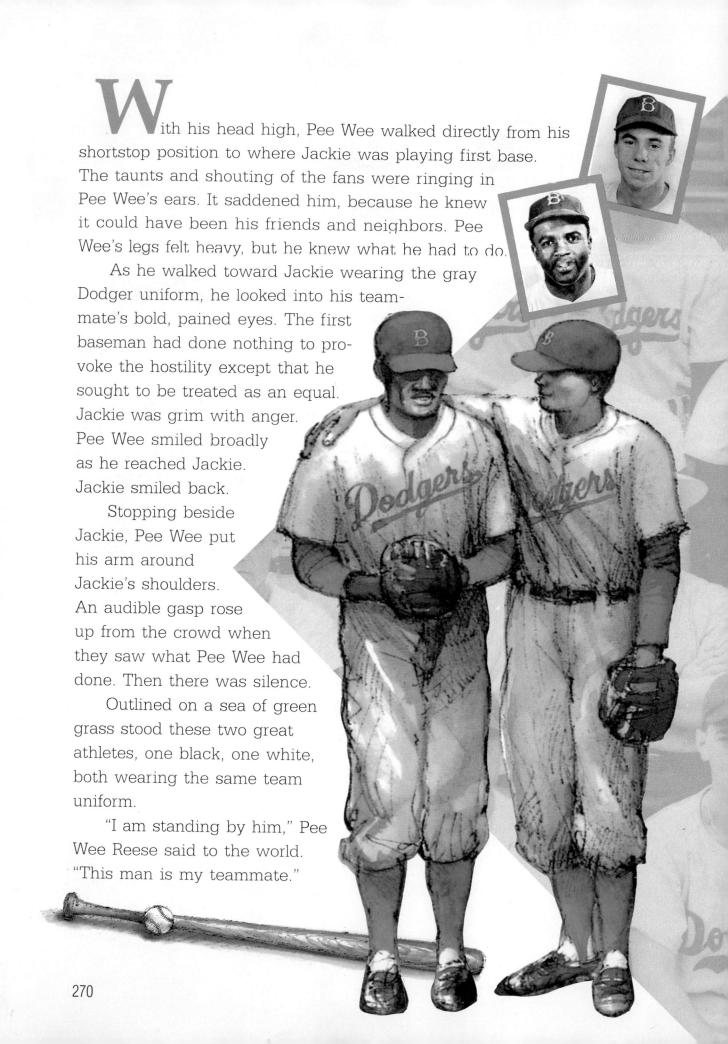

With his head high, Pee Wee walked directly from his shortstop position to where Jackie was playing first base. The taunts and shouting of the fans were ringing in Pee Wee's ears. It saddened him, because he knew it could have been his friends and neighbors. Pee Wee's legs felt heavy, but he knew what he had to do.

As he walked toward Jackie wearing the gray Dodger uniform, he looked into his teammate's bold, pained eyes. The first baseman had done nothing to provoke the hostility except that he sought to be treated as an equal. Jackie was grim with anger. Pee Wee smiled broadly as he reached Jackie. Jackie smiled back.

Stopping beside Jackie, Pee Wee put his arm around Jackie's shoulders. An audible gasp rose up from the crowd when they saw what Pee Wee had done. Then there was silence.

Outlined on a sea of green grass stood these two great athletes, one black, one white, both wearing the same team uniform.

"I am standing by him," Pee Wee Reese said to the world. "This man is my teammate."

MEET *Peter Golenbock*

When Peter Golenbock was thirteen, he met one of his heroes. After a World Series game between the Dodgers and the Yankees, he was introduced to Jackie Robinson. Meeting the great baseball player was quite an experience. "I was in awe of him," Golenbock remembers. "Robinson was huge. When I shook his hand, mine disappeared in his."

Years later, Golenbock became a sportswriter and learned more about Robinson. Rex Barney, who had pitched for the Dodgers when Robinson was a player, told the writer a true story about two teammates—Jackie Robinson and Pee Wee Reese, the Dodgers' shortstop. Peter Golenbock never forgot that story.

When he was asked to write about baseball for young people, he thought about Jackie Robinson. He remembered Robinson's courage—as an athlete and as the first African-American player in the major leagues. He also remembered the story that Rex Barney had told him. In Teammates, Peter Golenbock wrote about baseball and how Robinson changed it. It is a story you, like the author, may never forget.

Oath of Friendship

This papercut was created by the Chinese artist Wang, Mei. Papercuts have been used as decorations in Chinese homes for centuries.

Shang ya!
I want to be your friend
For ever and ever without break or decay.
When the hills are all flat
And the rivers are all dry,
When it lightens and thunders in winter,
When it rains and snows in summer,
When Heaven and Earth mingle—
Not till then will I part from you.

Anonymous,
China, 1st century B.C.

Unit 4

Meet DyAnne DiSalvo-Ryan

As a child, DyAnne DiSalvo-Ryan drew all the time. She recalls, "I always loved a sharp pencil and a new piece of paper." People would ask if she wanted to be an artist someday. She'd say, "I'm an artist already."

DiSalvo-Ryan hopes her drawings will feel familiar to children. She wants them "to be able to see themselves or their neighbors" in her art.

DiSalvo-Ryan's stories often grow out of her own experiences. *Uncle Willie and the Soup Kitchen* is based on her volunteer work at a soup kitchen. The garden lot she always passed on the way there inspired *City Green*.

CITY GREEN

by DyAnne DiSalvo-Ryan

There used to be a building right here on this lot. It was three floors up and down, an empty building nailed up shut for as long as I could remember. My friend Miss Rosa told me Old Man Hammer used to live there—some other neighbors too. But when I asked him about that, he only hollered, "Scram."

Old Man Hammer, hard as nails.

Last year two people from the city came by, dressed in suits and holding papers. They said, "This building is unsafe. It will have to be torn down."

By winter a crane with a wrecking ball was parked outside. Mama gathered everyone to watch from our front window. In three slow blows that building was knocked into a heap of pieces. Then workers took the rubble away in a truck and filled the hole with dirt.

Now this block looks like a big smile with one tooth missing. Old Man Hammer sits on his stoop and shakes his head. "Look at that piece of junk land on a city block," Old Man Hammer says. "Once that building could've been saved. But nobody even tried."

And every day when I pass this lot it makes me sad to see it. Every single day.

Then spring comes, and right on schedule Miss Rosa starts cleaning her coffee cans. Miss Rosa and I keep coffee cans outside our windowsills. Every year we buy two packets of seeds at the hardware store—sometimes marigolds, sometimes zinnias, and one time we tried tomatoes. We go to the park, scoop some dirt, and fill up the cans halfway.

This time Old Man Hammer stops us on the way to the park. "This good for nothin' lot has plenty of dirt right here," he says.

Then all at once I look at Miss Rosa. And she is smiling back at me. "A *lot* of dirt," Miss Rosa says.

"Like one big coffee can," I say.

That's when we decide to do something about this lot.

Quick as a wink I'm digging away, already thinking of gardens and flowers. But Old Man Hammer shakes his finger. "You can't dig more dirt than that. This lot is city property."

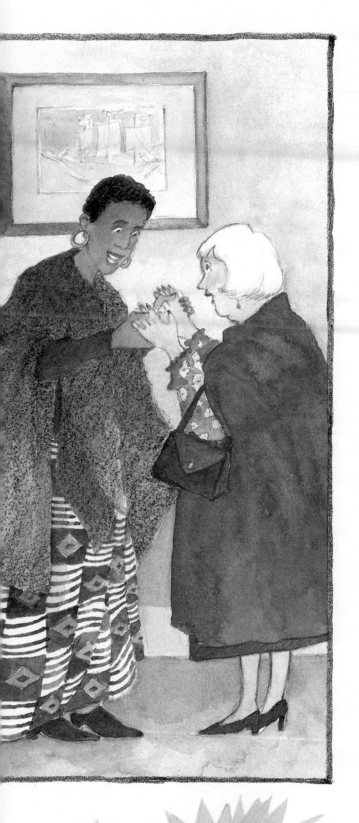

Miss Rosa and I go to see Mr. Bennett. He used to work for the city. "I seem to remember a program," he says, "that lets people rent empty lots."

That's how Miss Rosa and I form a group of people from our block. We pass around a petition that says: WE WANT TO LEASE THIS LOT. In less than a week we have plenty of names.

"Sign with us?" I ask Old Man Hammer.

"I'm not signin' nothin'," he says. "And nothin' is what's gonna happen."

But something did.

The next week, a bunch of us take a bus to city hall. We walk up the steps to the proper office and hand the woman our list. She checks her files and types some notes and makes some copies. "That will be one dollar, please."

We rent the lot from the city that day. It was just as simple as that.

Saturday morning I'm up with the sun and looking at this lot. My mama looks out too. "Marcy," she says, and hugs me close. "Today I'm helping you and Rosa."

After shopping, Mama empties her grocery bags and folds them flat to carry under her arm. "Come on, Mrs. B.," Mama tells her friend. "We're going to clear this lot."

Then what do you know but my brother comes along. My brother is tall and strong. At first, he scratches his neck and shakes his head just like Old Man Hammer. But Mama smiles and says, "None of that here!" So all day long he piles junk in those bags and carries them to the curb.

Now, this time of day is early. Neighbors pass by and see what we're doing. Most say, "We want to help too." They have a little time to spare. Then this one calls that one and that one calls another.

"Come on and help," I call to Old Man Hammer.

"I'm not helpin' nobody," he hollers. "You're all wastin' your time."

Sour grapes my mama'd say, and sour grapes is right.

Just before supper, when we are good and hungry, my mama looks around this lot. "Marcy," she says, "you're making something happen here."

Next day the city drops off tools like rakes and brooms, and a Dumpster for trash. Now there's even more neighbors to help. Miss Rosa, my brother, and I say "Good morning" to Old Man Hammer, but Old Man Hammer just waves like he's swatting a fly.

"Why is Old Man Hammer so mean and cranky these days?" my brother asks.

"Maybe he's really sad," I tell him. "Maybe he misses his building."

"That rotten old building?" My brother shrugs. "He should be happy the city tore down that mess."

"Give him time," Miss Rosa says. "Good things take time."

Mr. Bennett brings wood—old slats he's saved—and nails in a cup. "I knew all along I saved them for something," he says. "This wood's good wood."

Then Mr. Rocco from two houses down comes, carrying two cans of paint. "I'll never use these," he says. "The color's too bright. But here, this lot could use some brightening up."

Well, anyone can tell with all the excitement that something is going on. And everyone has an idea about what to plant—strawberries, carrots, lettuce, and more. Tulips and daisies, petunias, and more! Sonny turns the dirt over with a snow shovel. Even Leslie's baby tries to dig with a spoon.

For lunch, Miss Rosa brings milk and jelly and bread and spreads a beach towel where the junk is cleared. By the end of the day a fence is built and painted as bright as the sun.

Later, Mama kisses my cheek and closes my bedroom door. By the streetlights I see Old Man Hammer come down his steps to open the gate and walk to the back of this lot. He bends down quick, sprinkling something from his pocket and covering it over with dirt.

In the morning I tell my brother. "Oh, Marcy," he says. "You're dreaming. You're wishing too hard."

But I know what I saw, and I tell my mama, "Old Man Hammer's planted some seeds."

Right after breakfast, I walk to the back of this lot. And there it is—a tiny raised bed of soil. It is neat and tidy, just like the rows we've planted. Now I know for sure that Old Man Hammer planted something. So I pat the soil for good luck and make a little fence to keep the seeds safe.

Every day I go for a look inside our garden lot. Other neighbors stop in too. One day Mrs. Wells comes by. "This is right where my grandmother's bedroom used to be," she says. "That's why I planted my flowers there."

I feel sad when I hear that. With all the digging and planting and weeding and watering, I'd forgotten about the building that had been on this lot. Old Man Hammer had lived there too. I go to the back, where he planted his seeds. I wonder if this was the place where his room used to be.

I look down. Beside my feet, some tiny stems are sprouting. Old Man Hammer's seeds have grown! I run to his stoop. "Come with me!" I beg, tugging at his hand. "You'll want to see."

I walk him past the hollyhocks, the daisies, the peppers, the rows of lettuce. I show him the strawberries that I planted. When Old Man Hammer sees his little garden bed, his sour grapes turn sweet. "Marcy, child." He shakes his head. "This lot was good for nothin'. Now it's nothin' but good," he says.

Soon summertime comes, and this lot really grows. It fills with vegetables, herbs, and flowers. And way in the back, taller than anything else, is a beautiful patch of yellow sunflowers. Old Man Hammer comes every day. He sits in the sun, eats his lunch, and sometimes comes back with supper.

Nobody knows how the sunflowers came—not Leslie, my brother, or Miss Rosa. Not Mr. Bennett, or Sonny, or anyone else. But Old Man Hammer just sits there smiling at me. We know whose flowers they are.

Starting a Community Garden

All across America people have joined together to turn ugly lots into beautiful gardens. You may not imagine that you can do it—but you *can*. If there is already a community garden in your neighborhood, ask your neighbors how they got started. But if you are the first on your block to "make something happen," this is what you can do:

1. Find an interested grown-up who wants to help you: a parent or guardian, a teacher, a librarian, or a neighbor.

2. Find out the address of the lot. This is very important. You may have to talk to neighbors or look at the address of the buildings next door. Example: The lot I am interested in is on Main Street. It is between 75 Main Street and 81 Main Street.

3. While you are finding out the address of the lot, get in touch with the local gardening program in your area (see end of this note). Say that you are interested in starting a garden. Since every city is different, your local program will be able to steer you in the right direction.

4. Find out who the owner is. The Department of Records at your local city hall can help. Look in the telephone book for the address of city hall in your area.

5. If the lot is owned by the city, the people at city hall can help you get permission to use the lot. Usually there is a small fee. If the lot is owned by an individual person or group, you will need to get permission from that person or group to use the lot.

6. Once you get permission to use the lot, it's yours to name!

There are hundreds of gardening programs that are ready to help community gardeners with information, soil, seeds, fencing, and more.

To find out the community gardening program that is nearest you, write to:

American Community Gardening Association
325 Walnut Street
Philadelphia, PA 19106

Community gardens bring people together. Join the work and join the fun!

LANDSCAPE

What will you find at the edge of the world?
A footprint,
a feather,
desert sand swirled?
A tree of ice,
a rain of stars,
or a junkyard of cars?

What will there be at the rim of the earth?
A mollusc,
a mammal,
a new creature's birth?
Eternal sunrise,
immortal sleep,
or cars piled up in a rusty heap?

Eve Merriam

WHA

By Seymour Simon

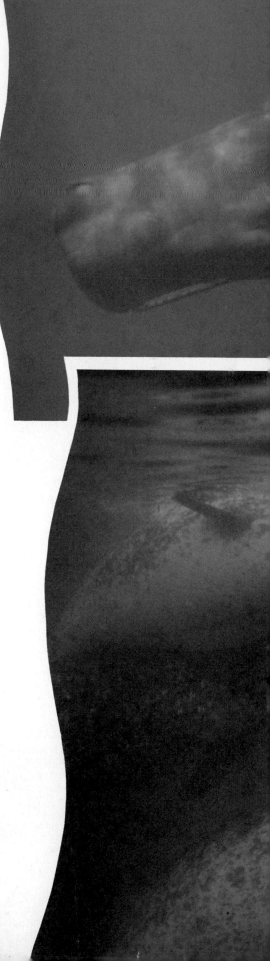

There are about ninety kinds of whales in the world. Scientists divide them into two main groups: toothed whales and baleen whales.

Toothed whales have teeth and feed mostly on fish and squid. They have only one blowhole and are closely related to dolphins and porpoises.

The **sperm whale** is the only giant among the toothed whales. It is the animal that comes to mind when most people think of a whale. A sperm whale has a huge, squarish head, small eyes, and a thin lower jaw. All the fist-sized teeth, about fifty of them, are in the lower jaw. The male grows to sixty feet long and weighs as much as fifty tons. The female is smaller, reaching only forty feet and weighing less than twenty tons.

A sperm whale's main food is squid, which it catches and swallows whole. A sperm whale is not a very fast swimmer, but it is a champion diver. It dives to depths of a mile in search of giant squid and can stay underwater for more than an hour.

There are smaller and less familiar kinds of toothed whales. The **narwhal** is a leopard-spotted whale about fifteen feet long. It is sometimes called the unicorn whale, because the male narwhal has a single tusk. The tusk is actually a ten-foot-long front left tooth that grows through the upper lip and sticks straight out. No one knows for sure how the narwhal uses its tusk. Narwhals live along the edge of the sea ice in the Arctic.

Narwhals

Perhaps the best known of the toothed whales is the killer whale, or **orca**. That's because there are killer whales that perform in marine parks around the country. A killer whale is actually the largest member of the dolphin family. A male can grow to over thirty feet and weigh nine tons.

rcas are found in all of the world's oceans, from the poles to the tropics. They hunt for food in herds called pods. Orcas eat fish, squid, and penguins, as well as seals, sea lions, and other sea mammals, including even the largest whales. Yet they are usually gentle in captivity, and there is no record that an orca has ever caused a human death.

Orcas

307

Baleen whales differ from toothed whales. They have a two-part nostril or blowhole; and, instead of teeth, they have food-gathering baleen plates. Each whale has several hundred baleen plates, which hang down from the whale's upper jaw. The plates can be two to seven feet long and hang about one quarter of an inch apart. The inside edge of each plate is frayed and acts like a filter.

Baleen whales are the biggest whales of all, yet they feed on small fish and other very small sea animals, such as the shrimplike animals called krill. Krill, which are only as big as your little finger, occur in huge amounts in the Antarctic Ocean. In northern waters, baleen whales eat different kinds of small shrimplike animals.

Some baleen whales, such as the right whale, skim open-mouthed through the water. The frayed inner edges of the baleen trap the food animals while the water pours out through the gaps. In this way a right whale can filter thousands of gallons of seawater and swallow two tons of food each day.

The **right whale** was once very common in the North Atlantic Ocean. It was given its name by early whalers who regarded it as the "right whale" to catch, because it swam slowly, had lots of baleen and blubber, and floated when dead. So many right whales were killed that they are now quite rare.

Right whales may reach more than fifty feet and weigh more than seventy tons. They have large flippers and a long lower lip that covers and protects their baleen plates. Each right whale has its own pattern of strange bumps along its head called callosities. Scientists sometimes identify individual whales by the patterns of their callosities.

Gray Whales

The **gray whale** feeds differently from the way any other whale does. It swims on its side on the ocean bottom and pushes water out of its mouth between its baleen plates, stirring up sediment from the ocean floor. Then the whale draws back its tongue and sucks the sediment, and any living things around, into its mouth. As the whale rises to the surface, it rinses its mouth with fresh seawater and swallows the catch. This method of bottom feeding is sometimes called "grubbing."

Gray whales once swam, in both the North Atlantic and North Pacific oceans, in the shallow waters along the coasts. Now, because of whaling in the Atlantic, they live only in the North Pacific and Arctic seas.

In the summer, the gray whales feed in the cold waters of the Arctic. In the winter, they travel about ten thousand miles to Mexican waters. There, the females give birth in the warm, protected lagoons along the Baja California peninsula The journey of the gray whales is the longest known yearly migration for any mammal.

With its long, streamlined body, its pointed head, and its thin flukes, the **fin whale** has the right shape to be a fast and nimble swimmer—and it is. The long grooves on its throat allow the throat to expand while the whale is feeding. Whales that have these grooves, such as the fin, minke, humpback, and blue, are called rorquals, from the Norwegian word for groove or furrow.

Fin whales often work in pairs to round up and eat schools of fish. Fin whales are second only to blue whales in size. They can reach seventy to nearly ninety feet in length and weigh eighty tons.

The **blue whale** is bigger than the largest dinosaur that ever lived. The largest known dinosaur may have been 100 feet long and weighed 100 tons. But the biggest blue whales are over 110 feet long and weigh more than 150 tons. That's the weight of twenty-five full-grown elephants. The heart of a blue whale is the size of a small car.

A blue whale swims along the surface of the ocean up to a cloud of krill, opens its mouth wide, and sucks in fifty or more tons of water in one gulp. Then it opens its lips and strains out the krill through its baleen plates. In one day a blue whale eats more than four tons of krill, about forty *million* of these animals.

Blue whales have been hunted for many years. Even though they are now protected, only small numbers of blue whales are found in the Antarctic or anywhere else in the world.

Blue Whale

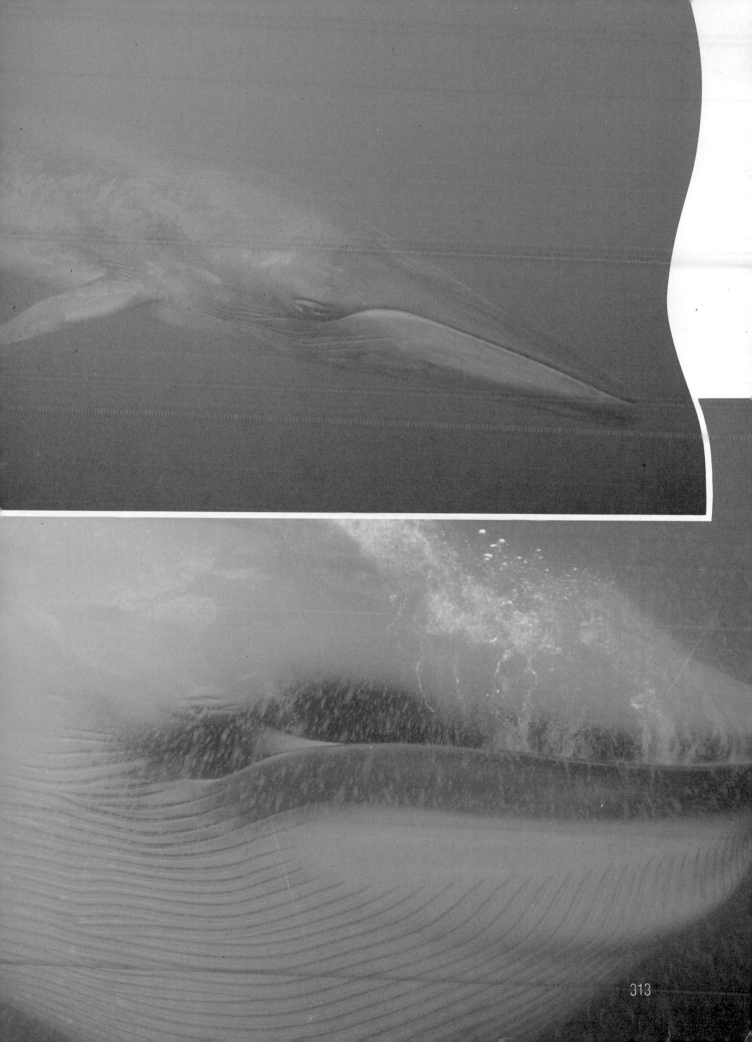

Humpback whales appear to be curious and seem to be accustomed to whale-watching boats. The whales show no hostility to the boats and are careful to avoid collisions.

Many whales make sounds, but the most famous are the songs of the humpbacks. They are sung only by the males. Some scientists think the songs may help to attract females or to keep other males from coming too close.

Whatever the reasons the whales have for singing them, the songs are strange and beautiful. Each one lasts as long as twenty or thirty minutes and is sung over and over again. The songs have patterns that repeat, but are different from one whale to another and from one year to the next. The song of a humpback can be heard from miles away.

Humpbacks feed in different ways. One way is called "bubble netting." A humpback sends out clouds of bubbles in a circle beneath a school of small fish or other food animals. When the fish are trapped by the bubbles, the whale lunges up inside the circle with its mouth open, swallowing huge amounts of water and food. A humpback's throat expands to make lots of room for the food and water. Sometimes several humpbacks feed together in the circle of bubbles.

In 1946, the International Whaling Commission (IWC) was set up to establish rules to limit whaling. Despite the rules, the numbers of whales steadily shrank. Some kinds of whales may be about to become extinct. Because of a worldwide movement to save the whales, the IWC banned all commercial whaling, beginning in 1985. But the governments of a few countries still allow their citizens to hunt whales.

Whales are one of the few wild animals that are commonly friendly to humans they encounter. Many people feel that we have an obligation to preserve these intelligent and special animals.

Will whales be allowed to remain to share the world with us? The choice is ours.

Meet Seymour Simon

From a very young age, Seymour Simon has been fascinated by whales. Simon's interest in the giant creatures has led him on whale watching expeditions from New York to Hawaii, and even to Alaska. "Whales are the greatest things going," he says.

The author of more than one hundred books, Simon has had more than forty of his books named as Outstanding Science Trade Books for Children. To Simon, a former teacher, science is a way of finding out about the world. Many of his books contain projects and questions that help readers find things out for themselves.

Simon enjoys receiving letters from readers who have answered a question using one of his books. For him, sharing a reader's experience is "as much fun as the first time I found out something myself."

THE SONG OF THE WORLD'S LAST

I heard the song of the world's last whale,
As I rocked in the moonlight and reefed the sail:
It'll happen to you also without fail,
If it happens to me, sang the world's last whale.

It was down off Bermuda early last spring,
Near an underwater mountain where the humpbacks sing.
I lowered the microphone a quarter mile down,
Switched on the recorder and let the tape spin round.

I didn't just hear grunting; I didn't just hear squeaks.
I didn't just hear bellows; I didn't just hear shrieks.
It was the musical singing and the passionate wail,
That came from the heart of the world's last whale.

Down in the Antarctic the harpoons wait,
But it's upon the land they decide my fate.
In London Town they'll be telling the tale,
If it's life or death for the world's last whale.

So here's a little test to see how you feel,
Here's a little test for this age of the automobile.
If we can save our singers in the sea,
Perhaps there's a chance to save you and me.

I heard the song of the world's last whale,
As I rocked in the moonlight and reefed the sail:
It'll happen to you also without fail,
If it happens to me, sang the world's last whale.

PETE SEEGER

WHALE

319

A California gray whale surfaces for air. These animals were nearly wiped out by whaling in the 19th century.

Endangered Species Make Comebacks

The bald eagle named Hope sat calmly in the woman's arms. Suddenly, the woman thrust Hope away from her, up into the air. As Hope rose high into the sky, her wingbeats grew stronger and steadier. In seconds, Hope disappeared.

Hope was discovered in Maryland with a broken wing last winter. Zoo workers helped Hope get better and regain her strength. When Hope was released this summer, she became a symbol for bald eagles and other endangered species that are slowly making a comeback after years of being threatened with extinction.

Bald Eagles Soar Again

In the fall of 1994, the American bald eagle was taken off the endangered species list for most areas of the United States. Instead, eagles are listed as threatened, which means that eagles are no longer in serious danger. Bald eagles are still given the same protection as they were before, however. Their nesting areas are still preserved, and they are still protected from hunters by federal law.

Bald eagles came a long way in 30 years. In 1963, only 800 eagles survived in the continental United States. Hunting, habitat destruction, and pesticide use had nearly wiped out our national symbol.

A veterinarian makes sure an eaglet, born in the wilds of New Jersey, is healthy.

But laws were passed banning the pesticide that was harming the eagles. Other laws imposed fines and jail sentences on hunters who killed bald eagles. Captive breeding programs also helped the birds' population grow.

Other Species Rebound

The bald eagle is not the only animal to creep back from the edge of extinction. This summer, wildlife officials took the California gray whale off the endangered species list. Some experts estimate that there are as many gray whales today as there were before whalers nearly caused the species to become extinct.

Other animals that have made recent comebacks include the American alligator, the Aleutian Canada goose, and the peregrine falcon. Still more species, including the red wolf, the grizzly bear, and the black-footed ferret, are slowly recovering.

Why are those comebacks good news? The comebacks could mean that people are taking better care of the environment. Says Mollie Beattie, director of the U.S. Fish and Wildlife Service, "People need to understand that when species become endangered, it is a signal that our environment and our own health are at risk."

'Extinct' Butterfly Surprises Scientists

Researchers recently got a surprise when they noticed a group of Palos Verdes blue butterflies fluttering in the tall grass in southern California. In the early 1980s, the small blue butterfly was declared extinct. But researchers now estimate that about 200 of the butterflies are still alive. Scientists hope to breed hundreds more of the butterflies in captivity and then release them into their natural habitat.

Eagles
Are on the Rise

The graph shows the rise in the number of bald eagle pairs. Figures do not include Alaska.

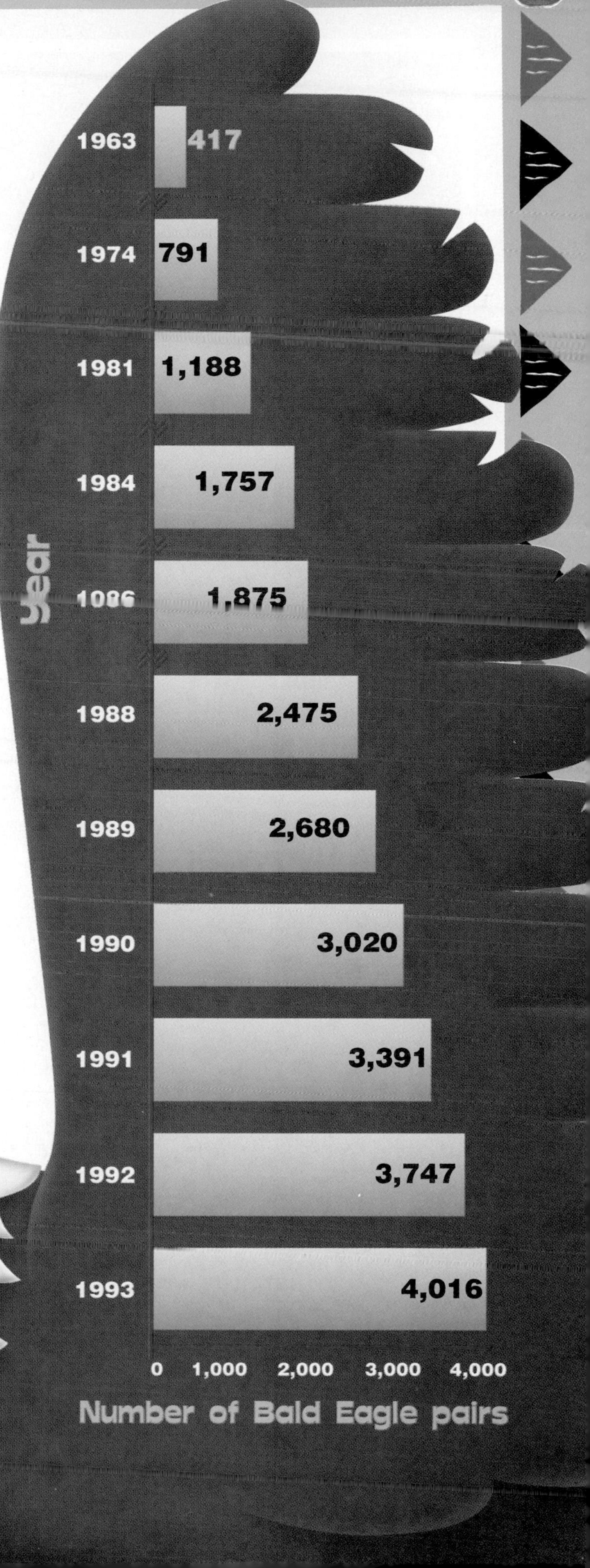

Year	Number of Bald Eagle pairs
1963	417
1974	791
1981	1,188
1984	1,757
1986	1,875
1988	2,475
1989	2,680
1990	3,020
1991	3,391
1992	3,747
1993	4,016

0   1,000   2,000   3,000   4,000

Number of Bald Eagle pairs

As usual, Walter stopped at the bakery on his way home from school. He bought one large jelly-filled dough-nut. He took the pastry from its bag, eating quickly as he walked along. He licked the red jelly from his fingers. Then he crumpled up the empty bag and threw it at a fire hydrant.

Just a Dream

Written and Illustrated by
Chris Van Allsburg

At home Walter saw Rose, the little girl next door, watering a tree that had just been planted. "It's my birthday present," she said proudly. Walter couldn't understand why·anyone would want a tree for a present. His own birthday was just a few days away, "And I'm not getting some dumb plant," he told Rose.

After dinner Walter took out the trash. Three cans stood next to the garage. One was for bottles, one for cans, and one for everything else. As usual, Walter dumped everything into one can. He was too busy to sort through garbage, especially when there was something good on television.

The show that Walter was so eager to watch was about a boy who lived in the future. The boy flew around in a tiny airplane that he parked on the roof of his house.

He had a robot and a small machine that could make any kind of food with the push of a button.

Walter went to bed wishing he lived in the future. He couldn't wait to have his own tiny plane, a robot to take out the trash, and a machine that could make jelly doughnuts by the thousands. When he fell asleep, his wish came true. That night Walter's bed traveled to . . .

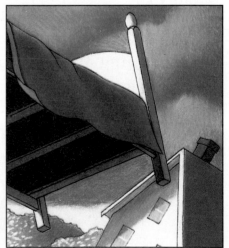

the future.

Walter woke up in the middle of a huge dump. A bulldozer was pushing a heap of bulging trash bags toward him. "Stop!" he yelled.

The man driving the bulldozer put his machine in neutral. "Oh, sorry," he said. "Didn't see you."

Walter looked at the distant mountains of trash and saw half-buried houses. "Do people live here?" he asked.

"Not anymore," answered the man.

A few feet from the bed was a rusty old street sign that read

FLORAL AVENUE. "Oh no," gasped Walter. He lived on Floral Avenue.

The driver revved up his bulldozer. "Well," he shouted, "back to work!"

Walter pulled the covers over his head. This can't be the future, he thought. I'm sure it's just a dream. He went back to sleep.

But not for long . . .

Walter peered over the edge of his bed, which was caught in the branches of a tall tree. Down below, he could see two men carrying a large saw. "Hello!" Walter yelled out.

"Hello to you!" they shouted back.

"You aren't going to cut down this tree, are you?" Walter asked.

But the woodcutters didn't answer. They took off their jackets, rolled up their sleeves, and got to work. Back and forth they pushed the saw, slicing through the trunk of Walter's tree. "You must need

this tree for something important," Walter called down.

"Oh yes," they said, "very important." Then Walter noticed lettering on the wood-cutters' jackets. He could just make out the words: QUALITY TOOTHPICK COMPANY. Walter sighed and slid back under the blankets.

Until . . .

Walter couldn't stop coughing. His bed was balanced on the rim of a giant smokestack. The air was filled with smoke that burned his throat and made his eyes itch. All around him, dozens of smokestacks belched thick clouds of hot, foul smoke. A workman climbed one of the stacks.

"What is this place?" Walter called out.

"This is the Maximum Strength Medicine Factory," the man answered.

"Gosh," said Walter, looking at all the smoke, "what kind of medicine do they make here?"

"Wonderful medicine," the

workman replied, "for burning throats and itchy eyes."

Walter started coughing again.

"I can get you some," the man offered.

"No thanks," said Walter. He buried his head in his pillow and, when his coughing stopped, fell asleep.

But then . . .

$\mathcal{S}$nowflakes fell on Walter. He was high in the mountains. A group of people wearing snow-shoes and long fur coats hiked past his bed.

"Where are you going?" Walter asked.

"To the hotel," one of them replied.

Walter turned around and saw an enormous building. A sign on it read HOTEL EVEREST. "Is that hotel," asked Walter, "on the top of Mount Everest?"

"Yes," said one of the hikers. "Isn't it beautiful?"

"Well," Walter began. But the group didn't wait for his answer. They waved goodbye and marched away. Walter stared at the flashing yellow sign, then crawled back beneath his sheets.

But there was more to see . . .

Walter's hand was wet and cold. When he opened his eyes, he found himself floating on the open sea, drifting toward a fishing boat. The men on the boat were laughing and dancing.

"Ship ahoy!" Walter shouted.

The fishermen waved to him.

"What's the celebration for?" he asked.

"We've just caught a fish," one of them yelled back. "Our second one this week!" They held up their small fish for Walter to see.

"Aren't you supposed to throw the little ones back?" Walter asked.

336

But the fishermen didn't hear him.
They were busy singing and dancing.
Walter turned away. Soon the rocking
of the bed put him to sleep.

But only for a moment . . .

𝒜 loud, shrieking horn nearly lifted Walter off his mattress. He jumped up. There were cars and trucks all around him, horns honking loudly, creeping along inch by inch. Every driver had a car phone in one hand and a big cup of coffee in the other.

When the traffic stopped completely, the honking grew even louder. Walter could not get back to sleep.

Hours passed, and he wondered if he'd be stuck on this highway forever. He pulled his pillow tightly around his head.

This can't be the future, he thought. Where are the tiny airplanes, the robots? The honking continued into the night, until finally, one by one, the cars became quiet as their drivers, and Walter, went to sleep.

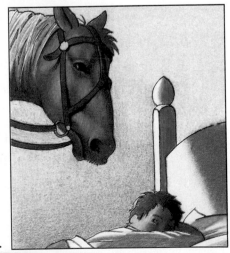

But his bed traveled on . . .

Walter looked up. A horse stood right over his bed, staring directly at him. In the saddle was a woman wearing cowboy clothes. "My horse likes you," she said.

"Good," replied Walter, who wondered where he'd ended up this time. All he could see was a dull yellow haze.

"Son," the woman told him, spreading her arms in front of her, "this is the mighty Grand Canyon."

Walter gazed into the foggy distance.

"Of course," she went on, "with all this smog, nobody's gotten a good look at it for years." The woman offered to sell Walter some

postcards that showed the canyon in the
old days. "They're real pretty," she said.

    But he couldn't look. It's just a dream,
he told himself. I know I'll wake up soon,
back in my room.

But he didn't . . .

Walter looked out from under his sheets. His bed was flying through the night sky. A flock of ducks passed overhead. One of them landed on the bed, and to Walter's surprise, he began to speak. "I hope you don't mind," the bird said, "if I take a short rest here." The ducks had been flying for days, looking for the pond where they had always stopped to eat.

"I'm sure it's down there somewhere," Walter said, though he suspected something awful might have happened. After a

while the duck waddled to the edge of
the bed, took a deep breath, and flew off.
"Good luck," Walter called to him. Then he
pulled the blanket over his head. "It's just
a dream," he whispered, and wondered if
it would ever end.

Then finally . . .

Walter's bed returned to the present. He was safe in his room again, but he felt terrible. The future he'd seen was not what he'd expected. Robots and little airplanes didn't seem very important now. He looked out his window at the trees and lawns in the early morning light, then jumped out of bed.

He ran outside and down the block, still in his pajamas. He found the empty jelly doughnut bag he'd thrown at the fire hydrant the day before. Then Walter went back home and, before the sun came up, sorted all the trash by the garage.

A few days later, on Walter's birthday, all his friends came over for cake and ice cream. They loved his new toys: the laser gun set, electric yo-yo, and inflatable dinosaurs. "My best present,"

Walter told them, "is outside." Then he showed them the gift that he'd picked out that morning—a tree.

After the party, Walter and his dad planted the birthday present. When he went to bed, Walter looked out his window. He could see his tree and the tree Rose had planted on her birthday. He liked the way they looked, side by side. Then he went to sleep, but not for long, because that night Walter's bed took him away again.

When Walter woke up, his bed was standing in the shade of two tall trees. The sky was blue. Laundry hanging from a clothesline flapped in the breeze. A man pushed an old motorless lawn mower. This isn't the future, Walter thought. It's the past.

"Good morning," the man said. "You've found a nice place to sleep."

"Yes, I have," Walter agreed. There was something very peaceful about the huge trees next to his bed.

The man looked up at the rustling leaves. "My great-grandmother planted one of these trees," he said, "when she was a little girl."

Walter looked up at the leaves too, and realized where his bed had taken him. This was the future, after all, a different kind of future. There were still no robots or tiny airplanes. There weren't even any clothes dryers or gas-powered lawn mowers. Walter lay back and smiled. "I like it here," he told the man, then drifted off to sleep in the shade of the two giant trees—the trees he and Rose had planted so many years ago.

MEET
Chris Van Allsburg

Chris Van Allsburg is often asked where he gets the ideas for his books. Sometimes he says they are sent through the mail or beamed in from outer space. The truth, admits Van Allsburg, is that he isn't sure where he gets them. They just seem to arrive.

For Van Allsburg, who is both an artist and a writer, a story often begins with an image. He had just such an image in mind when he began *The Polar Express*, a book that won the Caldecott Medal. Van Allsburg pictured a boy looking at a train in front of his house and then taking trips on the train. Eventually, the train rolled all the way to the North Pole.

For *Just a Dream*, Van Allsburg pictured a polluted environment. How could he make this real problem into a good story? He decided to have a boy named Walter travel in his bed to various places. "Bed, with the covers up, is supposed to be a safe place," says the author. "But it's not safe to be in bed in a garbage dump."

Van Allsburg writes before he draws pictures for his stories. He can usually see the pictures in his mind as he writes, though. Creating a story, he says, is a little like making a film. He has to decide which parts to show in his drawings.

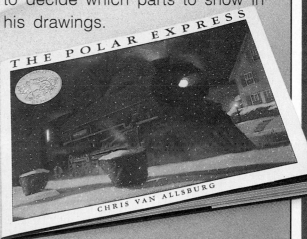

A full-grown tree is about 50 years old — that's when it's cut down. It takes about 2 - 3 days to cut down a tree and truck it to the lumber mill. After

The Lifeline of a Tree

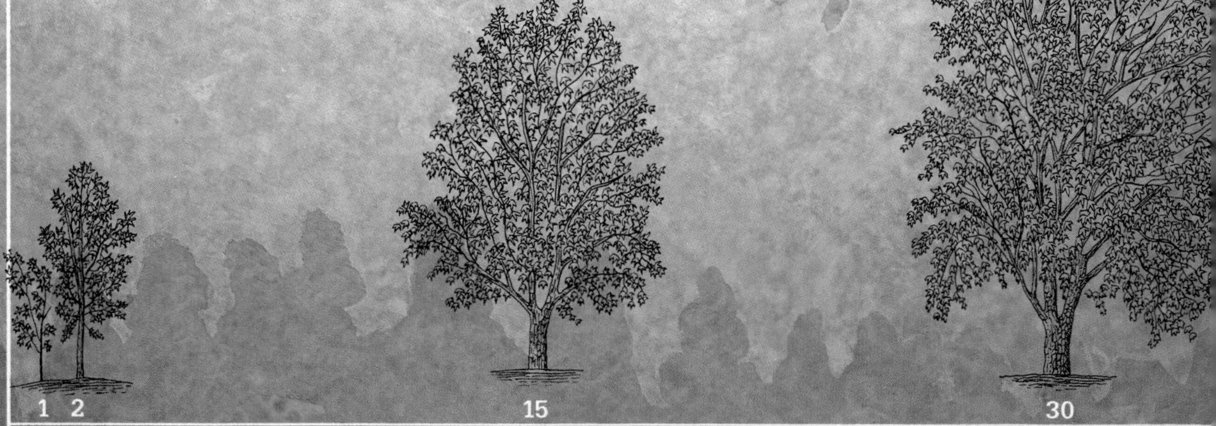

YEARS
1
2
15
30
seedling
sapling
young tree

One edition of a Sunday newspaper can use 140 acres of pulpwood timber.

the tree is cut into lumber, the branches, bark, and wood chips are

made into a wood pulp. Paper is made from the wood pulp. The paper-making process

WHO CARES ABOUT TREES?

Who cares about trees
except beetles and bees,
fruit eaters, book readers,
and garden lovers galore,
bat shakers, box makers,
boat builders, woodcarvers,
and carpenters by the score?

Who cares?

What's special 'bout trees
except that they take
years to grow through rain
and through snow
and only a day to cut down.

And does anyone care
that trees clean the air, give shelter
and shade, and . . . what else?

And who'd want a tree
to plant in the yard, to
hold down the soil, hold up
a swing, bear sweet fruit, and
make your heart sing,
"Oh thank you, Tree!"

Who cares about trees?
You! Me!

40   50

cut down/
made into paper/
used/paper trash

takes about 12 hours. It takes 4 pounds of wood pulp to make 1 pound of paper.

SHUMATE

Hail, Polluters

Motor exhaust
Chimney smoke
Oil refiners
Chemical plants
Burning garbage
Tobacco fumes—

You give

The air

An edge

That hurts

Whenever

I try

To breathe it.

Robert Froman

meet
Virginia Evarts Wadsworth

Virginia Evarts Wadsworth grew up loving books. But she didn't spend all her time reading. The author has always enjoyed being outdoors, too.

Because of her love for books and nature, it's not surprising that Wadsworth became a writer—or that she decided to write about Rachel Carson. Carson, the writer and scientist who loved nature and fought to protect the environment, seems the perfect subject for Virginia Evarts Wadsworth. "I found her to be a fascinating person," Wadsworth says. "She accomplished things in her time that were unheard of for a woman. I wanted to share her extraordinary accomplishments with others."

Rachel Carson

Protector of Planet Earth

by
Virginia
Evarts
Wadsworth

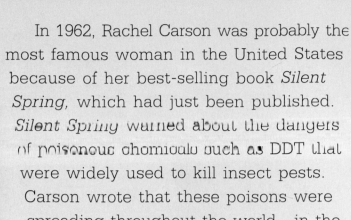

In 1962, Rachel Carson was probably the most famous woman in the United States because of her best-selling book *Silent Spring,* which had just been published. *Silent Spring* warned about the dangers of poisonous chemicals such as DDT that were widely used to kill insect pests. Carson wrote that these poisons were spreading throughout the world—in the air, water, and soil. She wanted everyone to be aware of the long-term consequences of spraying crops and orchards with chemicals.

How did Rachel Carson come to write about pesticides and pollution, little known subjects more than twenty-five years ago? From an early age, Carson loved nature. Born in 1907, she grew up on a farm in Pennsylvania. At the age of ten, she had a story published in *St. Nicholas,* a children's magazine. She planned to become a writer when she grew up.

When she graduated from college in 1928, however, her degree was in zoology, the study of animals. She felt that work in the world of nature was more important to her than writing fiction. That summer, Carson saw the ocean for the first time when she did research at the U.S. Biological Laboratory on Cape Cod, Massachusetts. For the rest of her life, Carson was rarely far away from the ocean.

Carson continued her education in marine biology, the study of the sea and its animal life. She landed a job with the Bureau of Fisheries and wrote factual articles about the ocean that were adapted for radio broadcasts. Carson later collected her articles into one manuscript and sold it to the *Atlantic Monthly.* This article grew into Carson's first book, *Under the Sea Wind,* which describes the sea's living creatures in relation to their surroundings and each other. Reviewers loved

Carson's writing, but *Under the Sea Wind* came out just as World War II began, and the book got lost in the shuffle.

After World War II, Carson wrote *The Sea Around Us*, which describes the sea's size, depths, currents, animal life, and underwater land formations. Writing about science with a poet's hand, Carson taught the American public to look at nature in a new way. *The Sea Around Us* stayed on the best-seller list for a year and a half, making Carson famous. Fan mail poured in, as readers wanted to meet her and read more of her writing. Although she made public appearances, she wrote a friend, "I'm much more at home barefoot in the sand . . . than on hardwood floors in high heels."

Carson won the National Book Award for *The Sea Around Us*. Newspaper editors named her Woman of the Year in Literature. She quit her government job and bought a house on the coast of Maine, where she wrote full-time. Her next book, *The Edge of the Sea*, which is about animal life along the seashore, also became a best seller.

A few years later, one of Carson's friends told her that a plane had sprayed her property with DDT to kill mosquitoes. Ten songbirds had died, she said, noting that she had "emptied and scrubbed the birdbath after the spraying, but you can never kill DDT."

Carson knew she must write about the dangers of pesticides and told fellow scientists and friends that "knowing what I do, I have no choice but to set it down to be read." Years of research, writing, and rewriting went into this book. Carson wanted to be sure that she had scientific proof of her allegations. She expected to be challenged by the powerful chemical companies and even the U.S. Department of Agriculture, which recommended the use of pesticides.

During those years, Carson battled cancer. She continued her project while undergoing tests and treatments because she so strongly believed in the subject. In a letter, she wrote, "Now my body falters and I know there is little time left."

The fruit of her labor, *Silent Spring,* opens in a beautiful fictitious town. When a white powder is sprayed from the sky, the "shadow of death" falls upon the town, and "only silence lay over the fields and wood and marsh." Carson's message—that the destruction of any part of the web of life threatens the human race—was a far cry from her gentle books about the sea.

Millions of copies of *Silent Spring* were sold. The book was discussed in newspapers and magazines across the country. Some people demanded that the government do something about the evils Carson had exposed. Others did not believe her, and still others labeled her a Communist. Critics accused her of being a sentimental bird watcher who would rather see people starve because their crops were destroyed by insects than kill a few birds. The chemical industry attacked her and advertised the importance of chemicals.

Because of the uproar over *Silent Spring*, John F. Kennedy formed the President's Science Advisory Committee to investigate the situation. A year after her book came out, the government issued a report that confirmed Carson's findings about pesticides.

As a result of her work, Carson received many honors. She became the first woman to receive the National Audubon Society Medal and was one of only a handful of women elected to the American Academy of Arts and Letters. Modest about her accomplishments, she reportedly said, "I could never again listen happily to a thrush song if I had not done all I could."

Carson died on April 14, 1964, at the age of fifty-seven. Eight years later, the U.S. government banned the use of DDT and some other chemical pesticides in the United States. In 1980, President Jimmy Carter posthumously awarded Carson the Presidential Medal of Freedom, the government's highest civilian award.

Rachel Carson was ahead of her time when she wrote that the songbirds would no longer sing in the spring unless people stopped polluting the environment. A gifted writer and scientist, she changed the way the world looks at planet Earth.

Rachel Carson
USA 17c

We sang songs that carried in their melodies
all the sounds of nature—
the running of waters, the sighing of winds,
and the calls of the animals.
Teach these to your children,
that they may come to love nature as we love it.

Native Americans Representing Many Nations

Unit 5

Memories
to Keep

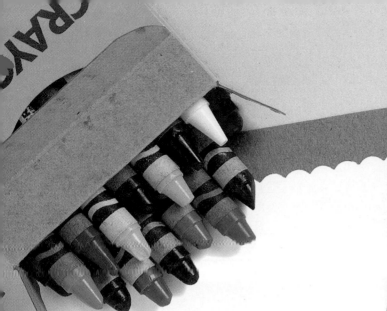

PAT CUMMINGS:
MY STORY

by Pat Cummings

Birthday: November 9, 1950

I've been drawing ever since I can remember. The first thing I ever drew was . . . a scribble. I would scribble all over a piece of paper and then I would go and get my box of Crayolas. I had made my mother get me the really huge, fifty-million-color size. I needed all those colors. And then I'd spend all afternoon coloring my scribbles.

I would take my drawing to my mother, and she would look at it thoughtfully and say, "What a nice *duck*!" And I would tell her, "It's not a duck, Mommy." So, she might turn the paper around and think about it and say, "Oh, I see, it's a *dinosaur*." And I would have to tell her, "It's a picture of Daddy."

yellow

It didn't take long to realize that nobody really knew what the pictures were supposed to be. But my mother would put them up on the refrigerator door, and that always made me feel good.

The first thing I remember drawing that people could recognize was the result of an adventure I had when I was about five years old.

My father was in the army and so my family moved every three years or so. At that time we lived in Kaiserslautern, Germany. My older sister, Linda, and I had decided to play outside and had taken lots of our toys and spread them out on the grass. After a while, she told me to watch all the toys while she went inside for a minute. She didn't come back.

I was getting very bored all by myself when a little bus came along and stopped at the corner. I got up, ran straight across the grass, and hopped on! I didn't know who the girls on the bus were or where they were headed and I certainly didn't speak any German, but the doors closed and we were off. After a while, we stopped at a small building and everyone got off the bus. So I got off the bus. They all ran into the building. So I ran in right behind them. Then they all got into tutus and toeshoes—it was a ballet school!

The girls were dancing around and doing stretches, so I just danced around and tried to do whatever they did. The teacher looked at me like I had just landed from Mars. All the girls were older than I was. When class ended, the teacher pinned a note on my blouse that said, "Please don't send her back until she's at least eight."

I was put back on the bus and got off when I saw my house. When I got home after a fun afternoon, I found I had worried my mother so much that I was in *huge* trouble. She had been up and down the street looking for me, knocking on neighbors' doors. She had even called the army police. I had to stay in the house for a good, long time after that and I got plenty of time to practice my drawing. And what I started drawing was . . . ballerinas, of course.

Even when I started school, I kept drawing ballerinas. I found my friends would give me a nickel for the drawings or a dime if I had really worked hard on one. Sometimes I got paid with M & M's or Twinkies. That was as good as money. Or sometimes I would trade drawings with someone else in my class who specialized in something else, maybe dinosaurs or horses. I loved to draw, and I had discovered that it could be good business, too!

Since we moved so often, my sisters and brother and I were always the "new kids" at school. I found if I joined the art club or helped make posters for other clubs, it was a way to make new friends.

Basically, I've just kept drawing because I love it, and it's never occurred to me to do anything else. I didn't know when I was growing up that there were so many types of art jobs possible. But I always felt lucky to know just what I wanted to do when I got older. I still feel incredibly lucky to be doing something I enjoy so much.

And it even pays better than the ballerinas!

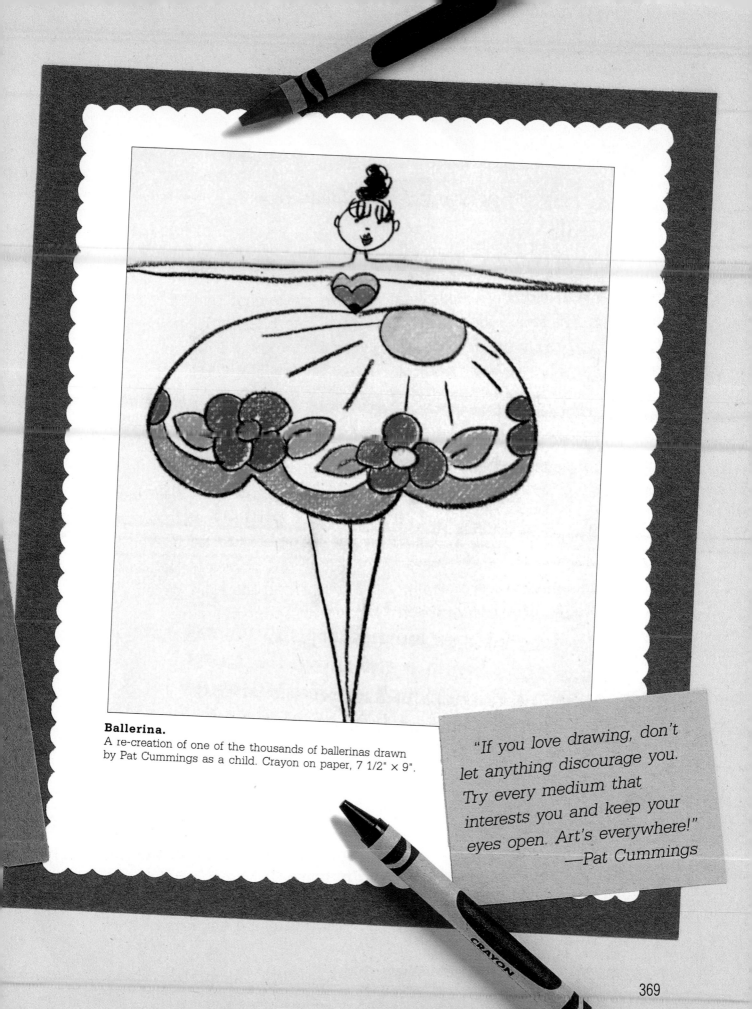

Ballerina.
A re-creation of one of the thousands of ballerinas drawn by Pat Cummings as a child. Crayon on paper, 7 1/2" × 9".

"If you love drawing, don't let anything discourage you. Try every medium that interests you and keep your eyes open. Art's everywhere!"
—Pat Cummings

Where do you get your ideas from?

Sometimes I get ideas from things I see around me, cloud formations or clothes people wear or things I've seen when I travel. One thing I really like about traveling to places where you don't speak or understand the language is that you usually look harder at things and see more. Your senses seem a little sharper.

I also get ideas from my dreams, which are usually pretty entertaining. I have great flying dreams sometimes, and that is why I usually put aerial views in my books. I'm always so disap-pointed to wake up and find I can't really fly, but drawing a scene from that perspective gives me back a bit of the feel-ing I have in the dreams.

Sometimes, ideas hit me smack in the head when I'm doing something like swimming or reading, or when I'm halfway through a drawing. Then, if I'm smart, I'll stop and write them down or sketch what I saw in my imagination. I have even jumped out of bed to paint at three in the morning because an idea won't let me sleep.

What is a normal day like for you?

I don't have any normal days because every job is different. Some days I meet with my edi-tor, some days I get up early and work all day. Sometimes I work all night. Some days I teach a class at a local college. And sometimes I'm traveling to schools and libraries around the country. I work just about every day, and I work most of the time I'm home. If I have a deadline I am trying to meet, I might not leave the house for days at a time. I'll work until I'm sleepy, sleep until I wake up, and start again. Usually, I do try to go to the gym, and I might go to the movies to reward myself for finishing a page. There are usually thirty-two pages in a book. That can get to be a lot of movies.

3 Where do you work?

I live and work in a big loft in beautiful downtown Brooklyn, New York. If I look out of my back windows, I see the Statue of Liberty. Looking out of the window near my desk, I see the Brooklyn Bridge. It's great on the Fourth of July! There are fifteen windows and five skylights, so there's plenty of sunlight and, sometimes, moonlight.

My drawing table, desk, shelves, and filing cabinets are on one side of the loft, and my husband's work area is right across from mine. The whole place is one big, open space that we are always working on.

4 Do you have any children? Any pets?

We don't have any children, but we have talked about trying to find a twelve-year-old who likes to do dishes.

We have a cat named Cash who is very smart. She is on the cover of *Storm in the Night.* She comes when she's called, sits if you tell her to, and fetches if you throw her toy. I think she might be a dog.

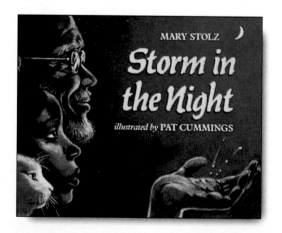

MARY STOLZ

Storm in the Night

illustrated by PAT CUMMINGS

C.L.O.U.D.S. 1986.
Airbrush, watercolor, and pencil, 15 1/2" × 10".
Published by Lothrop, Lee & Shepard Books.

5 What do you enjoy drawing the most?

People I know and faces in general. There is so much going on in a person's face. I like fantasy, too . . . drawing things that only exist in the imagination.

6 Do you ever put people you know in your pictures?

Definitely. Sometimes I do it to surprise the person. I might use old family photos or take new ones to use as reference. I draw my husband, Chuku, a lot. He's just about the only one who will pose for me at two-thirty in the morning. I've drawn neighbors, neighbors' pets, and friends who might even ask me to change their hairstyles or make them look thinner. I will also find models to draw who fit the image I have in my mind of the characters in the book.

I used my sister Linda and my niece Keija on the cover of *Just Us Women*. Keija told me once that her picture was the only reason people read the book! That book is filled with family; my mother, Chuku, my brother-in-law Hassan, my grandfather, my sister Barbara, and a friend or two. It makes the book more personal for me.

7 What do you use to make your pictures?

Everything. I like to use different materials. Sometimes it's big fun, but sometimes it's disastrous. I use watercolors and colored pencils most often; gouache, acrylics, pastels, airbrush, and pen and ink sometimes. I've experimented with collage and even rubber stamps, but I don't think I've tried half of the stuff I see in the art supply stores.

I also maintain a big picture file for reference. If I have to draw an armadillo, it helps a lot to have a picture to look at while I work.

8 How did you get to do your first book?

I put some illustrations from art school into a portfolio and went to see editors at publishing houses. They gave me good advice but no work. Then an editor saw my artwork in a newsletter and offered me a book to illustrate. I was so excited that when she asked if I knew what to do, I said, "Sure, no problem." I didn't have a clue how to start, but I didn't want to let her know.

I knew somebody, who knew somebody, who knew someone who used to know Tom Feelings, a children's book illustrator whose work I admired. So I looked in the phone book, called Tom up, and asked him if he would help me. He was wonderful. He gave me advice on how to pick which parts of the story to illustrate and how to decide where the pages should turn. He reminded me always to leave lots of room for the words to fit, to be sure that the character looks like the same person all the way through the book, and to try and keep important details away from the middle of the book, where the pages are sewn together. You don't want your reader pulling the book apart to see something important that's been hidden in the seam!

Tom taught me a lot that afternoon. He and many other illustrators still inspire me. I still learn from looking at their work. The most important thing I learned from Tom that day was that we have to help each other. He helped me get started, and I never forget that when someone who wants to illustrate calls me.

Draw!

by Kim Solga

3-D Doodles

Simple drawings like stick figures look flat because they're *two-dimensional:* They don't show *depth.* Being able to show depth means drawing not just the front of objects but also the sides. Drawing in 3-D is magic—you're still drawing simple lines on a flat page, but suddenly your drawings don't look flat. They look like they're jumping off the paper at you!

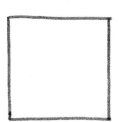

1 Draw a square.

2 Make a line like this for the back edge of the box.

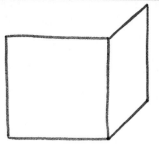

3 Draw two slanted lines to finish the side.

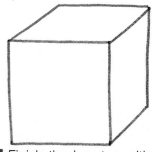

4 Finish the box top with these two lines.

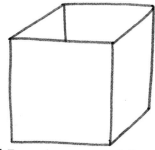

5 For a box open at the top, draw a line like this.

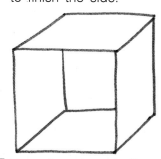

6 For a box open in the front, draw these lines.

Box doodle

Box open at the top

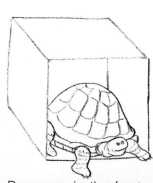

Box open in the front

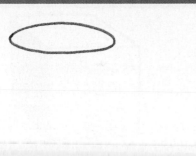 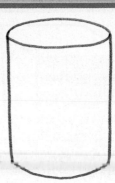 

1 To make a cylinder, start with an oval shape.

2 Drop two sides straight down.

3 Draw a rounded edge for the bottom.

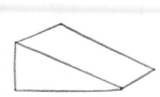 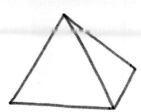 

A wedge is like a thick triangle.

A pyramid is a 3-D triangle that comes to a point on top.

A cone is a triangle with a rounded bottom (or top).

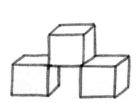 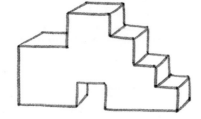 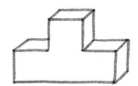

Add depth to any shape by adding lines to show the back edges and sides.

 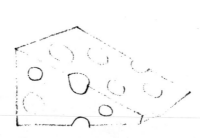 

Cylinder doodle

Wedge doodle

Building doodle

Shading Doodles

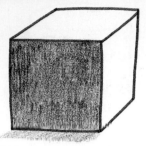

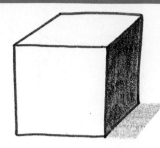

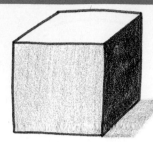

1 You can show depth by adding shading and shadows.

2 Pick a side to be in the shade and make that side dark.

3 Add even more depth by shading another side lighter.

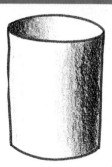

1 Shading wraps around a curved surface in a *blended tone*.

2 Make the shade dark in the back and lighter in the front.

3 To make the cylinder look open, shade part of the top oval.

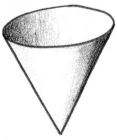

Use these rules to shade any shape.

Pick a *light source* and always shade the opposite side.

Use the same shading for all the sides that face the same way.

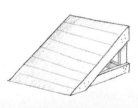

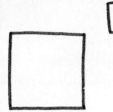 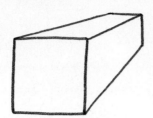 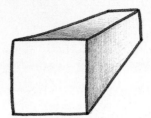

1 To make a long box, draw a big square and a tiny square.

2 Draw three long lines and erase the inside edges.

3 Add shading for a long 3-D box.

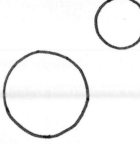 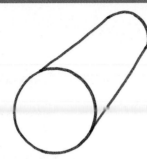 

1 For a cylinder, make a big front circle and a tiny back circle.

2 Draw two long lines and erase the bottom of the back circle.

3 Shade it dark on the bottom and lighter in the middle.

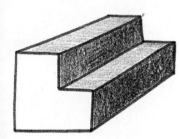 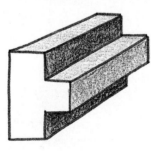 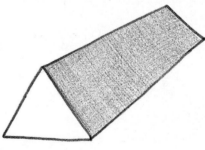

You can make any shape look long.

Remember that things look smaller the farther away they are.

So make the back end much smaller than the front end.

379

Memory

Memory is a tape recorder
And there's one in every head
Storing everything we've ever seen,
Or felt, or heard, or said.
The word, remember, simply means
We're playing back a part
Of all that's been recorded there
And lives close to our heart.
Sad thing, sweet thing,
Whatever it be,
The calling it back is a
Memory.

Mary O'Neill

MEET
Lucille Clifton

It's not hard to get ideas for stories when you have six children, as Lucille Clifton does. But sometimes her children aren't the ones to give her ideas. Their friends are. Clifton based Jacob, in *My Friend Jacob*, on the boy next door. *Everett Anderson's Friend* is another book that the author wrote by paying attention to children around her. She also gets ideas for stories from another source. "I have such a good memory of my own childhood, my own time," she says.

Lucille Clifton's own memories and her experiences with young people make her characters seem very real. That's exactly what she wants. "I wish to have children see people like themselves in books," she explains. Clifton also wants readers to find joy in her stories. She writes books, she says, "that tend to celebrate life. I'm about that."

382

The LUCKY STONE

by Lucille Clifton

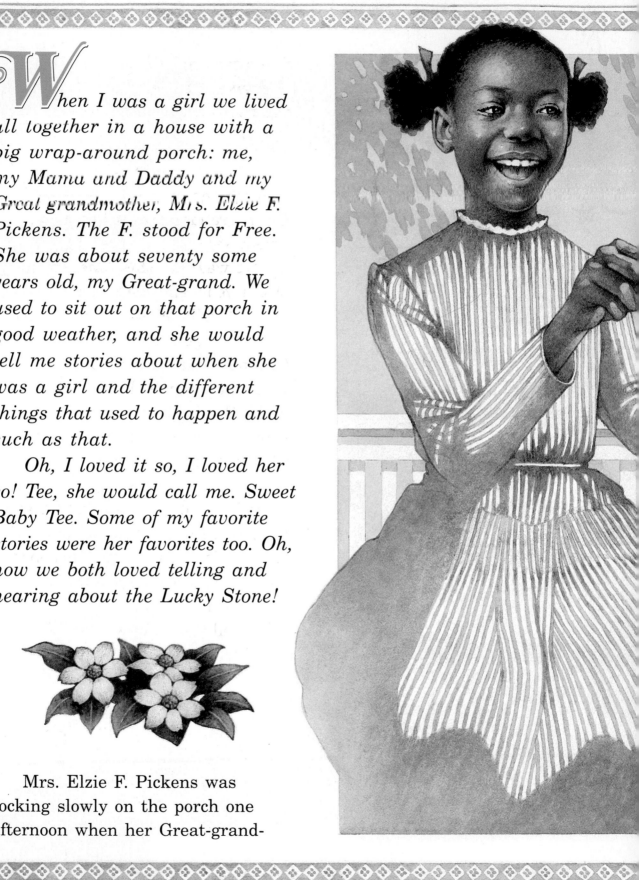

When I was a girl we lived all together in a house with a big wrap-around porch: me, my Mama and Daddy and my Great-grandmother, Mrs. Elzie F. Pickens. The F. stood for Free. She was about seventy some years old, my Great-grand. We used to sit out on that porch in good weather, and she would tell me stories about when she was a girl and the different things that used to happen and such as that.

Oh, I loved it so, I loved her so! Tee, she would call me. Sweet Baby Tee. Some of my favorite stories were her favorites too. Oh, how we both loved telling and hearing about the Lucky Stone!

Mrs. Elzie F. Pickens was rocking slowly on the porch one afternoon when her Great-grand-

daughter brought her a big bunch of dogwood blooms, and that was the beginning of that story.

"Ahhh, now that dogwood reminds me of the day I met your Great-granddaddy, Mr. Pickens, Sweet Tee.

"It was just this time, spring of the year, and me and my best friend Ovella Wilson, who is now gone, was goin to join the Silas Greene. Usta be a kinda show went all through the South, called it the Silas Greene show. Somethin like the circus. Me and Ovella wanted to join that thing and see the world. Nothin wrong at home or nothin, we just wanted to travel and see new things and have high times. Didn't say nothin to nobody but one another. Just up and decided to do it.

"Well, this day we plaited our hair and put a dress and some things in a crokasack and started out to the show. Spring day like this.

"We got there after a good little walk and it was the world, Baby, such music and wonders as we never had seen! They had everything there, or seemed like it.

"Me and Ovella thought we'd walk around for a while and see the show before goin to the office to sign up and join.

"While we was viewin it all we come up on this dancin dog. Cutest one thing in the world next to you, Sweet Tee, dippin and movin and head bowin to that music. Had a little ruffly skirt on itself and up on two back legs twistin and movin to the music. Dancin dancin dancin till people started throwin pennies out of they pockets.

"Me and Ovella was caught up too and laughin so. She took a penny out of her pocket and threw it to the ground where that dog was dancin, and I took two pennies and threw 'em both.

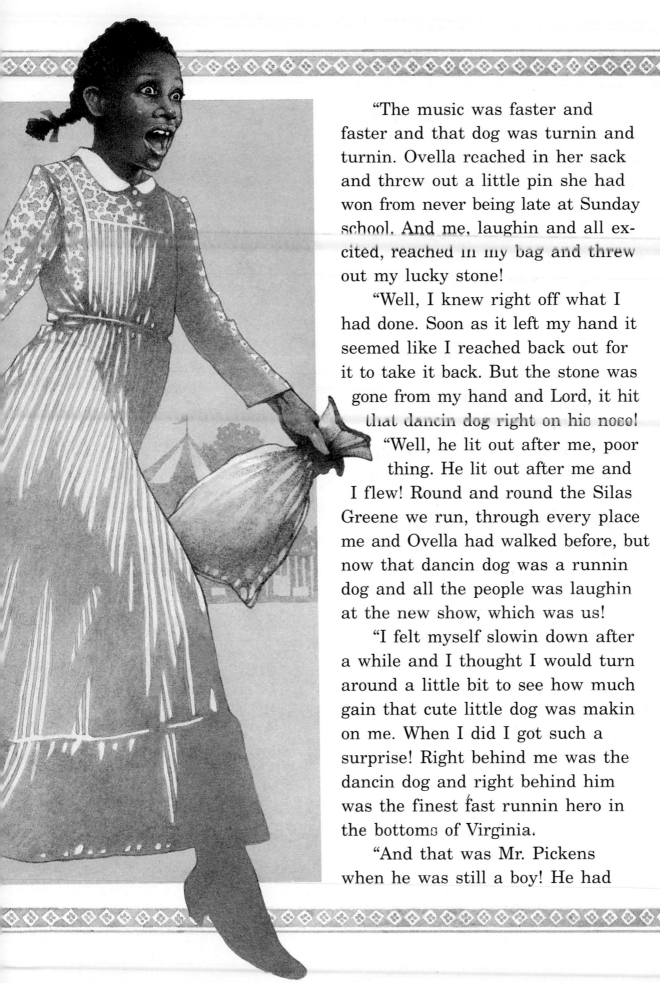

"The music was faster and faster and that dog was turnin and turnin. Ovella reached in her sack and threw out a little pin she had won from never being late at Sunday school. And me, laughin and all excited, reached in my bag and threw out my lucky stone!

"Well, I knew right off what I had done. Soon as it left my hand it seemed like I reached back out for it to take it back. But the stone was gone from my hand and Lord, it hit that dancin dog right on his nose!

"Well, he lit out after me, poor thing. He lit out after me and I flew! Round and round the Silas Greene we run, through every place me and Ovella had walked before, but now that dancin dog was a runnin dog and all the people was laughin at the new show, which was us!

"I felt myself slowin down after a while and I thought I would turn around a little bit to see how much gain that cute little dog was makin on me. When I did I got such a surprise! Right behind me was the dancin dog and right behind him was the finest fast runnin hero in the bottoms of Virginia.

"And that was Mr. Pickens when he was still a boy! He had

a length of twine in his hand and he was twirlin it around in the air just like the cowboy at the Silas Greene and grinnin fit to bust.

"While I was watchin how the sun shined on him and made him look like an angel come to help a poor sinner girl, why, he twirled that twine one extra fancy twirl and looped it right around one hind leg of that dancin dog and brought him low.

"I stopped then and walked slow and shy to where he had picked up that poor dog to see if he was hurt, cradlin him and talkin to him soft and sweet. That showed me how kind and gentle he was, and when we walked back to the dancin dog's place in the show he let the dog loose and helped me to find my stone. I told him how shiny black it was and how it had the letter *A* scratched on one side. We searched and searched and at last he spied it!

"Ovella and me lost heart for shows then and we walked on home. And a good little way, the one who was gonna be your Great-granddaddy was walkin on behind. Seein us safe. Us walkin kind of slow. Him seein us safe. Yes." Mrs. Pickens' voice trailed off softly and

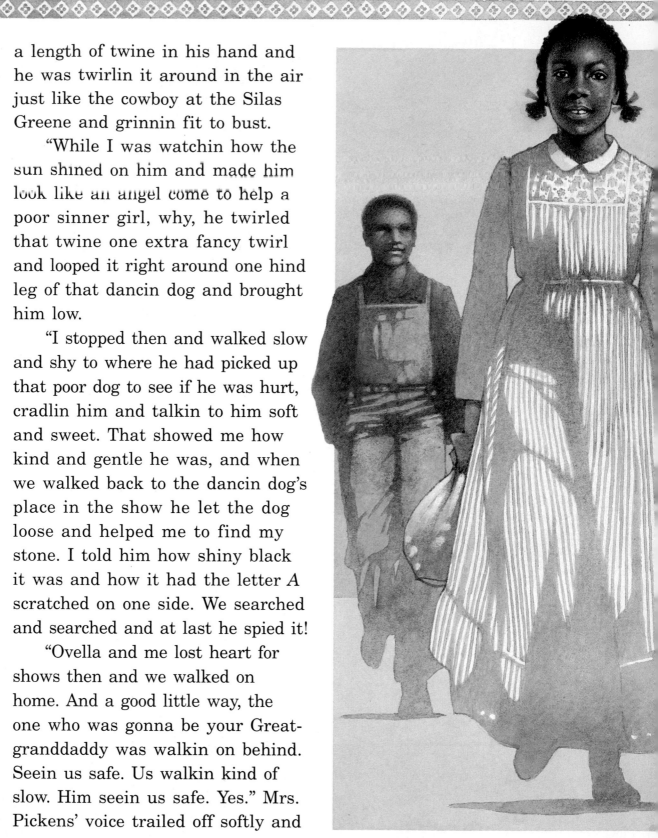

Tee noticed she had a little smile on her face.

"Grandmama, that stone almost got you bit by a dog that time. It wasn't so lucky that time, was it?"

Tee's Great-grandmother shook her head and laughed out loud.

"That was the luckiest time of all, Tee Baby. It got me acquainted with Mr. Amos Pickens, and if that ain't luck, what could it be! Yes, it was luckier for me than for anybody, I think. Least mostly I think it."

Tee laughed with her Great-grandmother though she didn't exactly know why.

"I hope I have that kind of good stone luck one day," she said.

"Maybe you will someday," her Great-grandmother said.

And they rocked a little longer and smiled together.

Children by a Brook, by the 19th Century painter, Francis Danby.

Grandmother's Brook

Grandmother tells me about a brook
  She used to pass on her way to school;
A quick, brown brook with a rushing sound,
  And moss-green edges, thick and cool.
When she was the age that I am now
  She would cross over it, stone by stone.
I like to think how she must have looked
  Under the greenery, all alone.
Sometimes I ask her: "Is it there,
  That brook you played by—the same, today?"
And she says she hasn't a doubt it is—
  It's children who change and go away.

RACHEL FIELD

Creation of a California Tribe

Grandfather's Maidu Indian Tales

Travis could see his grandfather from
a distance, as the older man leaned against a
giant oak tree in the front yard. Looking younger than
his sixty years, Grandfather was a wiry man
of average height. His black hair was still untouched
by gray. Grandfather was a Maidu Indian who was
greatly respected by the Maidu people. As a
tribal historian, Grandfather was the
keeper of their traditions. He was also a teacher of
the tribe's past here in California. He knew all
of the Maidu stories, and he often shared them
with his children and grandchildren.

BY LEE ANN SMITH-TRAFZER & CLIFFORD E. TRAFZER
ILLUSTRATED BY CLIFFORD BECK

The sky above Grandfather's head was deep blue,
except for billowy white clouds forming around the Sierra
Nevada Mountains. It was a beautiful fall day, but the
wind had a touch of winter in it. Deep in thought, Travis
pulled his jacket closer as he walked down the road to
Grandfather's house. By the time he reached his grandfather, Travis knew exactly what he wanted to say.

"Hello, Grandfather!" the boy called out as he
approached the gate. Grandfather raised his hand to
wave in reply.

"Hello, Travis," he responded with his slight accent.
"How was school today?"

Grandfather was always interested in his grandchildren's schoolwork, so his question was not a surprise to Travis. But today the boy was delighted to hear this familiar question. He explained to Grandfather that Ms. Smith, his fourth grade teacher at Newcastle Elementary School, had given the class a history assignment. The children had to write a paper on the history of California, and Travis really wanted Grandfather's help on this project.

"You know, Grandfather," Travis said, "most of the kids think that history began with the coming of the Spanish people and the missions." Grandfather nodded his head to show he understood. "But that's just not true! You are always telling us about our history, the history of the Maidu people. I want my paper to be different. I want to write about the time when no one lived in California except the Indians and the animal people."

Grandfather smiled his wide, toothy smile. "How can I help you, Travis?" he asked.

"I want to use what you have told me about the Maidu people to write my paper," Travis explained. "I've written a first draft of my paper. I used a story you told me about the creation of the land the Maidu lived on here in California. Can I read you this story?"

Grandfather nodded his head in agreement. The boy excitedly pulled out his white lined paper and began to read out loud.

People all over the earth have stories to explain the creation of the world. Maidu Indians have creation stories, too, and these stories are handed down by parents and grandparents to their children. To this very day the Maidu Indians remember these stories and share them with others.

The Maidu say that long ago the earth was filled with water. The blue water and sky blended together into a magnificent scene, melting together so that it was impossible to say where the water ended and the sky began. Earth Maker and Coyote floated about seeing nothing but sky and water. Earth Maker grew tired of floating and wanted to find a place to call his own. This idea impressed Coyote.

As Earth Maker and Coyote traveled in the water, they took turns singing a powerful song:

"Little world, where are you?
Little world, where are you?"

Over and over they sang this song. Eventually, it occurred to them that this song was not working. So Earth Maker and Coyote changed their song. Now they took turns singing:

"My world of great mountains, where are you?
My foggy mountains, where are you?"

Coyote grew tired and stopped singing these songs. "You can sing those power songs," he said to Earth Maker, "but I'm not going to sing any more."

Nevertheless, Earth Maker was convinced that one day they would find a country to call their own. When they did, they would arrange the land in a fine way! Meanwhile, they continued to float in the vast water.

Then one day, the travelers came upon another floating object. It looked like a bird's nest. Although it was very small, Earth Maker was convinced that he could transform it into a place for his country. The nest would have to be stretched and expanded if it were to become a country. Earth Maker thought about this for a long time. Then an idea struck him.

"I will take this strong rope," Earth Maker said to Coyote, "and extend it to the west, the north, and the northwest." Then Earth Maker went to work.

He extended the ropes to the west, the north, and the northwest, just as he had told Coyote he would. Then Earth Maker called upon the Robin to pack mud all around the nest. The Robin happily complied, singing a beautiful song of creation as she worked. It took many days for the Robin to complete her job, but she continued to sing until the land was finally made. If you listen today, the Robin still sings that wonderful creation song.

Earth Maker now asked Coyote to sing his creation song. Coyote sang a powerful song about the land he wanted created. Coyote sang in a loud voice:

"My world, where one will travel by the valley's edge, by great foggy mountains, by the zigzag paths through range after range. I sing of the country I shall travel in. In this world I shall wander."

This song was so beautiful that Earth Maker joined Coyote in chorus after chorus. Slowly, the Maidu world took shape. The only problem was that this world was very small.

Earth Maker decided to make the world larger, so he used his mighty foot to stretch the earth far to the east, the west, the north, and the south. In every direction the earth became larger. The movement and force of the stretching caused the mountains and the valleys to form. Although the Maidu world was becoming larger, it was not stable, because the earth rested on the various ropes.

"Now and then," Earth Maker warned, "when the ropes move back and forth, this earth will shake and tremble." Earth Maker was warning that earthquakes would shake the earth now and then.

Earth Maker was pleased with his country, but it was a lonely land because it was devoid of life. For this reason, he and Coyote created living things. Animals, plants, and human beings were formed and placed on the land. Coyote decided to paint the earth red, since blood was the life-giving source of humans and animals. Even today the rocks and soil of Maidu country are a little bit red in color.

Earth Maker and Coyote gave to human beings their separate lands, languages, and physical traits. Earth Maker traveled in every direction of the world, placing white people in one location, black people in another, Asians in still another, and so on. Earth Maker finally returned to his home at the center of the earth. This is where he placed the Maidu people.

When Earth Maker created human beings, he gave them intelligence, wisdom, and the means of survival. But most importantly to the Maidu Indians, he instructed them to be kind to one another and to be hospitable to strangers.

People all over the world have their own stories about the beginnings of this planet, as does each of the Indian tribes in America. This Maidu creation story is just one example of the rich variety of such stories. There are actually many other parts to the Maidu story of creation, but this is the main story about the origins of one California Indian tribe—the Maidu.

When Travis finished reading Grandfather his report, he waited for the older man to speak. The Maidu people teach their children to respect their elders and to have patience. Grandfather gazed off toward the Sierras, and his mind seemed to be miles away. Finally he turned his attention to Travis.

"Grandson," he said, "you have done well."

Travis smiled, feeling both pleased and relieved. He was happy that he had remembered the creation story accurately.

"You have captured on paper much of what we have taught through the spoken word for generations." Grandfather's face seemed to brighten with his smile. "Travis,

you have remembered the creation story well," he continued, placing his arm around the boy's shoulders. "I hope you will be able to share it with the other children in your class."

Although Grandfather said nothing more, Travis knew what he meant. He was pleased with the way his grandson had written the story. But Grandfather believed that it was especially important to tell the Maidu stories. Telling the stories, discussing them, and having the stories repeated time and again was the traditional way of passing on tribal history.

Grandfather and Travis walked together up the path by the large oak tree and into the older man's house. Grandfather's approval of the paper made Travis feel warm inside. He was looking forward to the next school day. Perhaps it would even be possible to tell the Maidu creation story to the rest of the class. Normally Travis would be scared to talk in front of the class, but Grandfather's pride in being a Maidu Indian made Travis proud, too. How nice it would be to share some of the Maidu tribal heritage with his friends at school!

Travis had not thought much about his paper on the Maidu creation story since he placed it on the teacher's desk. Then, nearly a week after he handed in the story, Ms. Smith announced that she had finished reading all of the papers.

"Overall I am very pleased," she said with a smile. "A few of the essays are really outstanding. I'm going to read a few of them to you now."

Travis's early interest in this project came rushing back to him as he listened to Ms. Smith. Despite Grandfather's urging, Travis had not asked Ms. Smith if he could read his story to the class. Travis was ashamed that he had not followed through with Grandfather's suggestion. Now the boy sat tensely in his seat, hoping that his would be one of the papers read by Ms. Smith. More than anything else, he wanted to be able to tell Grandfather that the children in his class had heard the Maidu creation story.

First, Ms. Smith read Emily Martinez's paper about the Gold Rush. Then she read Steve Foley's work about

modern day mountain men in California. Both of the papers were interesting, full of historical facts and funny little stories. As Travis listened to Ms. Smith read these papers, he sank sadly into his chair. Perhaps he had missed the point of the assignment! His paper wasn't about this kind of history at all. Travis was suddenly sure that he would receive a failing grade on this project.

Suddenly, Ms. Smith was talking about Travis. "Travis Molma has written a different type of history paper," she said. "He chose to share a part of his history and that of the Maidu Indians. It is an excellent report."

Travis felt as though every pair of eyes in the classroom were staring right at him. Since he was really only an average student, Travis wasn't used to this kind of attention in school.

"The Maidu Indians lived here long before anyone else," Ms. Smith continued. "Travis has written down what is called an oral history. Indians did not write down their stories, but kept them alive by passing them on from parents and grandparents to children."

A hand shot up in the front row. "But what if the kids forgot what their parents told them? Then the stories would be lost forever!"

"Well, the grown-ups didn't just tell them a story once. They would tell it over and over again, over a long period of time. Then, as the children got older, they would tell the stories back to the grown-ups. If a child made a mistake, he or she was corrected. Then they would tell the story again later. Isn't that right, Travis?"

Travis felt himself nod his head weakly in agreement.

"It is a very good way to teach. We do the same thing here at school. We talk about assignments in class so that you will think about and remember them."

Ms. Smith must have noticed that many of the students were losing interest, because she immediately began reading the Maidu creation story that Travis had written.

Grandfather would be pleased, Travis thought. The students were really listening to the story and seemed to be enjoying it. Most of the children had never before heard a story created by Indians to explain their past. When Ms. Smith finished reading Travis's paper, many of the students raised their hands to ask questions.

"Why did the Maidu Indians have this story?" Melissa asked.

Ms. Smith thought for a moment before answering. "That's not an easy question to answer," she began slowly. "I suppose everyone, including Indians, looks for ways to explain how the earth came to exist. This creation story is the Maidu Indian explanation." Ms. Smith hesitated, then looked at Travis. "What would you say, Travis?"

Holding onto the back of his chair for support, Travis stood up and faced the class. "My Grandfather has told my brothers, sisters, cousins, and me many Maidu stories," he said. "Grandfather says that these stories are the history of the Maidu people. The stories are literature, too. They tell us about ourselves, and they teach us how to think and live."

Travis was surprised to find that it was easy to talk to his class about Maidu Indian traditions. He explained that Grandfather had told him that the stories of the Maidu taught the difference between right and wrong, and between good and bad. In many of the stories the Earth Maker teaches the Maidu people what is good, but Coyote goes the other way. He is often bad, and the people are taught not to act like Coyote.

At this point Caitlin Riley said, "But I thought history had to come from something written down. Who wrote down the Maidu stories?"

"Many people believe that Indians had no history until things were written down," Travis responded. "But like Ms. Smith said, our way of passing down our stories is reliable, too."

This time Travis's friend Michael had a question. "I'm not sure I know how the Maidu Indians lived. I mean, what did they eat and what kind of houses did they live in? Could you tell us, Travis?"

Grandfather had told Travis all about how the Maidu Indians had lived. "The Maidu ate fruits, vegetables, and meat just like we do today," he said. "Women gathered wild strawberries, blackberries, and currants. The Maidu ate these fruits fresh, but they also dried them in the sun so they could eat them in winter, too. All they had to do was add some water and they could be eaten.

"The Maidu also ate wild lettuce and carrots. They gathered roots of the tule and camas. These looked and tasted something like potatoes, and had lots of vitamin C."

"Didn't they do any hunting?" one of the boys asked.

"Sure," Travis said. "They hunted deer, bear, quail, rabbits, raccoons, squirrels, geese, and porcupine. The Indians didn't just use the meat from the animal, though. For example, they used animal skins for blankets and clothing. Porcupine spines were used for needles and to make jewelry."

One of the students asked if the Maidu lived in tipis like Indians they had seen on television.

"No," Travis said, shaking his head. "They lived in different kinds of houses. When the Maidu moved around hunting and gathering food, they built temporary homes made out of logs and brush mats. When they made their winter homes, they used the same materials but made their houses larger and warmer. Grandfather told me that the people spent a lot of the winter months inside, where they told stories.

"In fact, it was during the cold, rainy winter months that Grandfather's parents and grandparents had told him the Maidu Indian stories. After hearing the stories repeated over and over, Grandfather was able to learn his lessons very well."

Ms. Smith stood up at her desk. "You know, Travis," she said, "I think you have learned your lessons well, too. Thank you for teaching us so much about the Maidu Indians."

To Travis's surprise, Ms. Smith began to clap her hands, and the rest of the class joined in, too! Travis couldn't wait to tell his grandfather that the other children had enjoyed hearing the Maidu creation story.

As the bell rang to signal the end of the school day, Ms. Smith came over to Travis's desk to speak to him. "Please give this note to your grandfather," she said, handing him a folded piece of paper. "I just want him to know how much we enjoyed learning about Maidu history. Perhaps he would visit our class one day and share more of his stories."

Later Grandfather said he was proud of his grandson for speaking in class. But everything Travis told his classmates came from his grandfather. One day, Travis thought, he would tell these same things to his own children.

Meet
Lee Ann Smith-Trafzer
and Clifford E. Trafzer

Clifford Trafzer's advice to young people who want to write is, "Write what you know. And write." Trafzer has followed his own advice. Part Wyandot Indian, he studies and teaches about Native Americans. Along with his wife, Lee Ann Smith-Trafzer, he also writes about them.

In books like *Grandmother's Christmas Story: A True Quechan Indian Story*, Clifford Trafzer, under the pen name Richard Red Hawk, retells Native American stories. Many of them have been handed down for generations.

"We want to share stories told to us by elders. We want to preserve them for our children and all children," says Lee Ann Smith-Trafzer, who worked with her husband on *Creation of a California Tribe: Grandfather's Maidu Indian Tales*. "We want to capture the rich traditions of America's first people." Smith-Trafzer grew up listening to the oral traditions of her own family. She wove these stories into a book, *Making Tracks: A Photo-Cultural History of an Arkansas Farm Family*.

Native American stories may be funny, sad, or exciting, but they often have deep meaning as well. By reading and listening to the stories, we can learn to appreciate the heritage of Native Americans.

Some readers may be surprised by how much they have in common with the characters in these stories. In *Creation of a California Tribe: Grandfather's Maidu Indian Tales*, Clifford Trafzer says, Travis is like "every young person who wants to know about his or her own history."

BOOK REVIEWS

Title: Creation of a California Tribe: Grandfather's Maidu Indian Tales

Author: Lee Ann Smith-Trafzer and Clifford E. Trafzer

Illustrator: Clifford Beck

Reviewed by:
Diana Elizabeth Segovia

I was deeply touched by the way the authors wrote this interesting literature. It made me feel like I was in Ms. Smith's class and I just could ask Travis to tell me more about it or to continue with another Maidu story.

Travis wrote a very interesting essay explaining how Maidu Indians think the earth was created. Travis wrote this story because he wanted to share with his classmates what he learned from his grandfather and because Maidu people are proud of their history.

I read this beautiful story several times because I loved it, and I liked to sing along with Earth Maker and Coyote the creation songs.

Diana E. Segovia

In this story, Travis has to write a report on California history. Travis writes about an old Maidu Indian tale which was one of many retold to him by his grandfather, who is a greatly respected tribal historian. It is about how Earth Maker and Coyote, two travelers in a world of water and sky, created the Earth.

Earth Maker and Coyote found a bird's nest, packed it with mud, and stretched it to make all the land. Then they created people and animals to live on the land. They warned that there would be earthquakes.

Travis's teacher picked three reports to read to the class. She read his report last, but it was everyone's favorite. Travis then answered the class's questions about his heritage and customs.

This is a wonderful story, I think, because it shows how people keep their culture and their past alive. This is done by telling tales and legends over and over again. It makes me think of how I try to keep my heritage alive by talking to my Tai-Tai (great-grandmother), who was born in China. The illustrations by Clifford Beck are gorgeous. They make this story even more beautiful.

I recommend this story to any young person because we all have a history that should not be forgotten.

Travis went to his grandfather for help on his school project about the history of California. He had written the whole paper by himself. His grandfather was very pleased with what Travis had written about the Maidu Indians.

In his paper, Travis told a very interesting story his grandfather had told him. It was about the time when only Native Americans and animals lived in California. The teacher was so pleased with his story that she asked if his grandfather would one day come to class and share stories and tales about the Maidu Indians.

It was interesting to read about the Maidu Indians in California. I have also studied about the Iroquoian and Algonquian Indians in Pennsylvania. I enjoy reading Native American tales.

I would recommend this story to anyone. I really like the picture on the first page of the story—the Native Americans, mountains, animals, the fish in the water and how the colors blend everything together.

Patrick O'Brien

Reviewed by:

Luciana Perelli

The best part of the story is when Travis tells his classmates more information about Maidu Indian traditions. He gets to share many of the interesting things that his grandfather has told him. This makes him feel proud of himself and his heritage. This story reminds me of the stories my grandmother tells me about my traditions. Her stories explain why we eat certain foods and follow certain customs.

The most surprising thing in the story is that the Native American traditions are passed down orally and they are not written. The traditions are passed down by the grandparents telling the stories to the children and grandchildren. It is amazing that these traditions are still being passed down today in the same way.

Luciana Perelli

THE AGES FLOW

The old brown photo album.
Grandfather's pictures tell of
Meiji, Taishō, Shōwa—
all the ages slowly
flowing by.
Smelling a little moldy,
the black-and-white photos
tell sturdily a tale of history.

Ikenaga Eri, fifth grade

The IRA Children's Book Award is presented annually to two new authors who show the most promise in writing for children. *No Star Nights* was the 1990 winner in the younger readers category.

By Anna Egan Smucker
Paintings by Steve Johnson

NO STAR NIGHTS

When I was little, we couldn't see the stars in the
nighttime sky because the furnaces of the mill turned the
darkness into a red glow. But we would lie on the hill and
look up at the sky anyway and wait for a bright orange
light that seemed to breathe in and out to spread across
it. And we would know that the golden spark-spitting steel
was being poured out of giant buckets into molds to cool.

Then we would look down on a train pulling cars
mounted with giant thimbles rocking back and forth.
They were filled with fiery hot molten slag that in the
night glowed orange. And when they were dumped,
the sky lit up again.

A loud steam whistle that echoed off the hills
announced the change of shifts, and hundreds of men

streamed out of the mill's gates. Everyone's dad worked in the mill, and carried a tin lunchbox and a big metal thermos bottle.

Work at the mill went on night and day. When Dad worked night shift, we children had to whisper and play quietly during the day so that we didn't wake him up. His job was too dangerous for him to go without sleep. He operated a crane that lifted heavy ingots of steel into a pit that was thousands of degrees hot.

When Dad worked the three-to-eleven shift, Mom made dinner early so we could all eat together. She made the best stuffed cabbage of anyone in the neighborhood. We sometimes tried to help fold the cabbage leaves around the meat and rice like she did, but our cabbage leaves always came unrolled.

During the school year days went by when we didn't see Dad at all because he was either at work or sleeping. When he changed shifts from daylight to night and back again it took him a while to get used to the different waking and sleeping times. We called these his grumpy times. We liked it best when he had daylight hours to spend with us. We played baseball until it was too dark to see the ball.

On a few very special summer afternoons he would load us all into the car for a hot, sweaty trip to Pittsburgh and a doubleheader Pirates game at Forbes Field. We sat in the bleachers way out in left field, eating popcorn and drinking lemonade that we brought from home, yelling our heads off for the Pirates. Our brother always wore his baseball glove, hoping to catch a foul ball that might come into the stands. Dad helped us mark our scorecards and bought us hot dogs during the seventh-inning stretch.

On our way home we passed the black silhouettes of Pittsburgh's steel mills, with their great heavy clouds of smoke billowing from endless rows of smokestacks. The road wound along as the river wound, and between us and the river were the mills, and on the other side of the road were the hills—the river, the mills, and the hills. And we sang as we rode home, "She'll be comin' round the mountain when she comes . . ."

July was just about the best month of the year. Everyone who worked in the mill got their vacation pay

then. We called it Christmas in July. All the stores had big sales. Even though it wasn't really Christmas, we each got a present.

And the Fourth of July parade was something everyone looked forward to. We were busy for weeks making flowers out of Kleenex to cover our Girl Scout float.

Some of our friends took baton lessons and were part of a marching unit called the Steel Town Strutters. They wore shiny black-and-gold-spangled leotards and threw their batons high up into the air and caught them! Something we sure couldn't do. But our favorites were the baby strutters. Some of them were only two years old. They did a good job just carrying their batons.

With all the bands and fire engines and floats, the parade
went on and on. There were convertibles with beauty queens
sitting on the back. Members of the Kennel Club marched
their dogs in circles and figure eights. Kids rode bikes
decorated with colored crepe paper, flags, and balloons.
The mayor drove an old-fashioned car, and his children
threw bubblegum and candies into the crowds.

We went to school across from the mill. The smokestacks towered above us and the smoke billowed out in great puffy clouds of red, orange, and yellow, but mostly the color of rust. Everything—houses, hedges, old cars—was a rusty red color.  Everything but the little bits of graphite, and they glinted like silver in the dust. At recess when the wind whirled these sharp, shiny metal pieces around, we girls would crouch so that our skirts touched the ground and kept our bare legs from being stung.

We would squint our eyes when the wind blew to keep the graphite out. Once a piece got caught in my eye, and no matter how much I blinked or how much my eye watered it wouldn't come out. When the eye doctor finally took it out and showed it to me, I was amazed that a speck that small could feel so big.

We played on the steep street that ran up the hill beside our school. Our favorite game was dodge ball. The kids on the bottom row knew they had to catch the ball. If they didn't, it would roll down onto the busy county road that ran in front of the school. Too often a truck carrying a heavy roll of steel would run over it and with a loud *bang* the ball would be flattened.

The windows in our school were kept closed to try to keep the graphite and smoke out. On really windy

days we could hear the dry, dusty sound of grit hitting against the glass. Dusting the room was a daily job. The best duster got to dust the teacher's desk with a soft white cloth and a spray that made the whole room smell like lemons. It was always a mystery to us how the nuns who were our teachers could keep the white parts of their habits so clean.

Some days it seemed as though there was a giant lid covering the valley, keeping the smoke in. It was so thick you couldn't see anything clearly. On days like that I felt as if we were living in a whirling world of smoke.

The road we took home from school went right through part of the mill. Tall cement walls with strands of barbed wire

at the top kept us on the sidewalk and out of the mill. But when we got to the bridge that spanned the railroad tracks, there was just a steel mesh fence. From there we could look straight down into the mill! There was always something wonderful to watch. Through a huge open doorway we could see the mammoth open-hearth furnace. A giant ladle would tilt to give the fiery furnace a "drink" of orange, molten iron. Sometimes we would see the golden, liquid steel pouring out the bottom of the open hearth into enormous bucketlike ladles. The workers were just small dark figures made even smaller by the great size of the ladles and the furnace. The hot glow of the liquid steel made the dark mill light up as if the sun itself was being poured out. And standing on the bridge we could feel its awful heat.

Warning sirens and the toots of steam whistles, the screeching sounds of train wheels and the wham-wham of cars being coupled and uncoupled—all these sounds surrounded us as we stood on the bridge. From the other side we could look into another part of the mill. Rows of lights hung from girders across the ceiling. White-hot steel bars glided smoothly over rollers on long tables. Men were using torches on the big slabs of steel. The torches gave off streaks of

burning, white light and showers of sparks that looked like our Fourth of July sparklers.

Behind the mill rose huge piles of black shiny coal and rich red iron ore, and a hill of rusting scrap metal. A crane that, to us looked like a dinosaur with huge jaws was constantly at work picking up twisted, jagged pieces of metal and dropping them into railroad cars to be taken into the mill. Sometimes we would imagine that the mill itself was a huge beast, glowing hot, breathing heavily, always hungry, always needing to be fed. And we would run home, not stopping once to look back over our shoulders.

Not too far from our house was a hill made of boulders of slag from the mill. Our grandfather told us that long ago it had been a deep ravine. Over the years truckload after truckload of slag from the mill had been dumped into it until the hole had become a hill. Now it towered over the old houses that were near it.

For an adventure, my best friend and I once decided to climb the slag hill. We slipped and slid and sent the pitted rocks rolling down as we scrambled up. Our younger sisters spied us, by now near the top, and started climbing too. It was then that my friend and I saw the dump truck with a heavy load of slag from the mill slowly winding its way up the hill.

"Don't dump! Don't dump!" we screamed. But the deep engine sounds of the truck straining under its great load drowned out our cries. Chunks of slag fell onto the roadway. The truck backed onto the flat place to dump its load. Stumbling toward it, we waved our arms and screamed

again, "Don't dump! Please don't dump! Our sisters are down there!" The driver finally heard us, and leaning out the window of the cab he saw the little girls. He nodded and waved his hand, then the truck lurched forward back onto the road and disappeared around the curve.

We sank exhausted to the ground, our hearts pounding
in our ears. The roar of the truck's engine became fainter
and fainter. The sky around us was turning red and orange
and gold. We looked down on the mill that seemed to go

on forever into the valley. From its long straight row of
stacks, clouds of orange smoke swirled into the colors of the
sunset. In the distance a whistle blew.

Many years have passed since then, and now the slag hill is covered with grasses and blackberry bushes and sumac trees. The night sky is clear and star filled because the mill is shut down. The big buckets no longer pour the hot, yellow steel. The furnaces whose fires lit up everything are rusting and cold.

Not many children live in the town now. Most of the younger people have moved away to other places to find work. The valley's steelworking way of life is gone forever. But whenever the grandchildren come back to visit, they love more than anything else to listen to stories about the days when all night long the sky glowed red.

MEET ANNA EGAN SMUCKER

Ever since she was a child, Anna Egan Smucker has been enchanted by books and writing. "I love words and how they strike you," she says. Today she works with words, teaching writing to West Virginia schoolchildren. Writing, Smucker believes, comes "from within," and our experiences allow us to write about anything.

No Star Nights came from her memories of growing up in Weirton, West Virginia, a steel mill town along the Ohio River. "I wrote the story when mills were closing all around the Pittsburgh area to try to preserve what I remembered about growing up in a steel mill town," she explains.

MEET STEVE JOHNSON

Steve Johnson never lets readers forget the steel mill's importance in *No Star Nights*. He never saw Weirton's steel mills, but he was able to imagine the reddish smoky skies. Here's what helped him: While he was preparing the paintings for the book, forest fires raged in Yellowstone. The smoke was carried to Minnesota, where he lives, and colored the air.

No Star Nights is Johnson's first picture book for children.

That Was Summer

Have you ever smelled summer?
Sure you have.
Remember that time
When you were tired of running
Or doing nothing much
And you were hot
And you flopped right down on the ground?
Remember how the warm soil smelled—
And the grass?
That was summer.

Remember that time
When the storm blew up quick
And you stood under a ledge
And watched the rain till it stopped
And when it stopped
You walked out again to the sidewalk,
The quiet sidewalk?
Remember how the pavement smelled—
All steamy warm and wet?
That was summer.

Remember that time
When you were trying to climb
Higher in the tree
And you didn't know how
And your foot was hurting in the fork
But you were holding tight
To the branch?
Remember how the bark smelled then—
All dusty dry, but nice?
That was summer.

If you try very hard,
Can you remember that time
When you played outside all day
And you came home for dinner
And had to take a bath right away,
Right away?
It took you a long time to pull
Your shirt over your head.
Do you remember smelling the sunshine?
That was summer.

Marci Ridlon

443

Unit 6

Twice-Told Tales

Yeh-Shen

A Cinderella Story from China

This story is older
than the Cinderella story as most
people know it. It predates
all European versions of the story by
at least 800 years.

retold by Ai-Ling Louie
illustrated by
Ed Young

447

In the dim past, even before the Ch'in and the Han dynasties, there lived a cave chief of southern China by the name of Wu. As was the custom in those days, Chief Wu had taken two wives. Each wife in her turn had presented Wu with a baby daughter. But one of the wives sickened and died, and not too many days after that Chief Wu took to his bed and died too.

Yeh-Shen, the little orphan, grew to girlhood in her stepmother's home. She was a bright child and lovely too, with skin as smooth as ivory and dark pools for eyes. Her stepmother was jealous of all this beauty and goodness, for her own daughter was not pretty at all. So in her displeasure, she gave poor Yeh-Shen the heaviest and most unpleasant chores.

The only friend that Yeh-Shen had to her name was a fish she had caught and raised. It was a beautiful fish with golden eyes, and every day it would come out of the water and rest its head on the bank of the pond, waiting for Yeh-Shen to feed it. Stepmother gave Yeh-Shen little enough food for

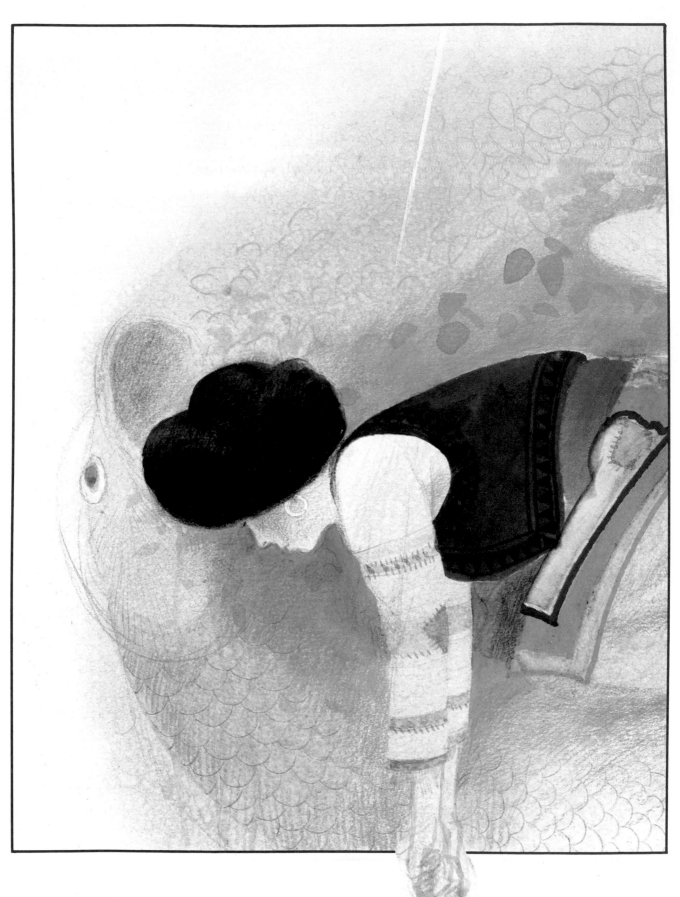

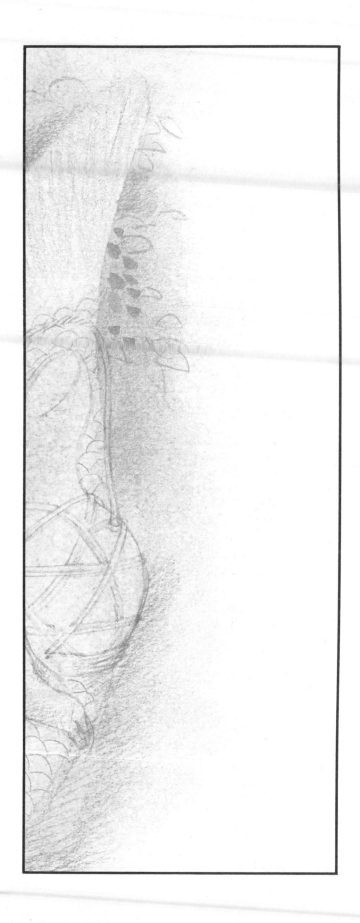

herself, but the orphan child always found something to share with her fish, which grew to enormous size.

Somehow the stepmother heard of this. She was terribly angry to discover that Yeh-Shen had kept a secret from her. She hurried down to the pond, but she was unable to see the fish, for Yeh-Shen's pet wisely hid itself. The stepmother, however, was a crafty woman, and she soon thought of a plan. She walked home and called out, "Yeh-Shen, go and collect some firewood. But wait! The neighbors might see you. Leave your filthy coat here!" The minute the girl was out of sight, her stepmother slipped on the coat herself and went down again to the pond. This time the big fish saw Yeh-Shen's familiar jacket and heaved itself onto the bank, expecting to be fed. But the stepmother, having hidden a dagger in her sleeve, stabbed the fish, wrapped it in her garments, and took it home to cook for dinner.

When Yeh-Shen came to the
pond that evening, she found her
pet had disappeared. Overcome
with grief, the girl collapsed
on the ground and dropped her
tears into the still waters of
the pond.

"Ah, poor child!" a voice said.

Yeh-Shen sat up to find a
very old man looking down at
her. He wore the coarsest of
clothes, and his hair flowed
down over his shoulders.

"Kind uncle, who may you
be?" Yeh-Shen asked.

"That is not important, my
child. All you must know is
that I have been sent to tell you
of the wondrous powers of
your fish."

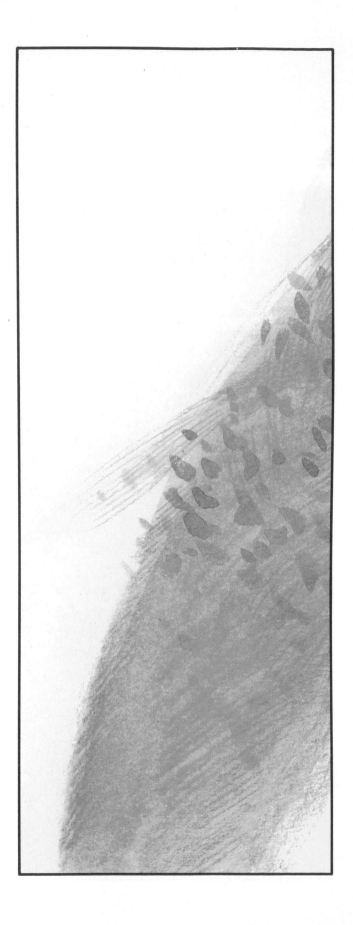

"My fish, but sir . . ." The girl's eyes filled with tears, and she could not go on.

The old man sighed and said, "Yes, my child, your fish is no longer alive, and I must tell you that your stepmother is once more the cause of your sorrow." Yeh-Shen gasped in horror, but the old man went on. "Let us not dwell on things that are past," he said, "for I have come bringing you a gift. Now you must listen carefully to this: The bones of your fish are filled with a powerful spirit. Whenever you are in serious need, you must kneel before them and let them know your heart's desire. But do not waste their gifts."

Yeh-Shen wanted to ask the old sage many more questions, but he rose to the sky before she could utter another word. With heavy heart, Yeh-Shen made her way to the dung heap to gather the remains of her friend.

Time went by, and Yeh-Shen, who was often left alone, took comfort in speaking to the bones of her fish. When she was hungry, which happened quite often, Yeh-Shen asked the bones for food. In this way, Yeh-Shen managed to live from day to day, but

she lived in dread that her stepmother would discover her secret and take even that away from her.

So the time passed and spring came. Festival time was approaching: It was the busiest time of the year. Such cooking and cleaning and sewing there was to be done! Yeh-Shen had hardly a moment's rest. At the spring festival young men and young women from the village hoped to meet and to choose whom they would marry. How Yeh-Shen longed to go! But her stepmother had other plans. She hoped to find a husband for her own daughter and did not want any man to see the beauteous Yeh-Shen first. When finally the holiday arrived, the stepmother and her daughter dressed themselves in their finery and filled their baskets with sweetmeats. "You must remain at home now, and watch to see that no one steals fruit from our trees," her stepmother told Yeh-Shen, and then she departed for the banquet with her own daughter.

As soon as she was alone, Yeh-Shen went to speak to the bones of her fish. "Oh, dear friend," she said, kneeling before the precious bones, "I long to go to the festival, but I can not show myself in these rags. Is there somewhere I could borrow clothes fit to wear to the feast?" At once she found herself dressed in a gown of azure blue, with a cloak of kingfisher feathers draped around her shoulders. Best of all, on her tiny feet were the most beautiful slippers she had ever seen. They were

woven of golden threads, in a pattern like the scales of a fish, and the glistening soles were made of solid gold. There was magic in the shoes, for they should have been quite heavy, yet when Yeh-Shen walked, her feet felt as light as air.

"Be sure you do not lose your golden shoes," said the spirit of the bones. Yeh-Shen promised to be careful. Delighted with her transformation, she bid a fond farewell to the bones of her fish as she slipped off to join in the merrymaking.

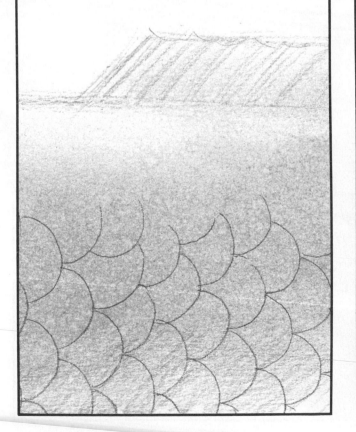

That day Yeh-Shen turned many a head as she appeared at the feast. All around her people whispered, "Look at that beautiful girl! Who can she be?"

But above this, Stepsister was heard to say, "Mother, does she not resemble our Yeh-Shen?"

Upon hearing this, Yeh-Shen jumped up and ran off before her stepsister could look closely at her. She raced down the mountainside, and in doing so, she lost one of her golden slippers. No sooner had the shoe fallen from her foot than all her fine clothes turned back to rags.

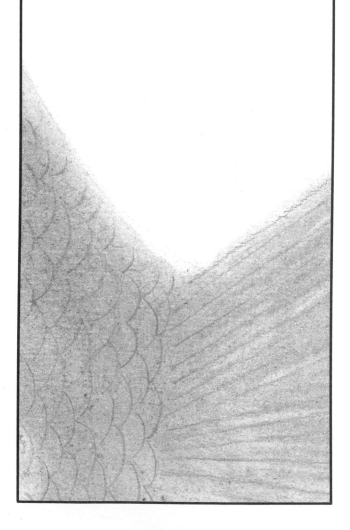
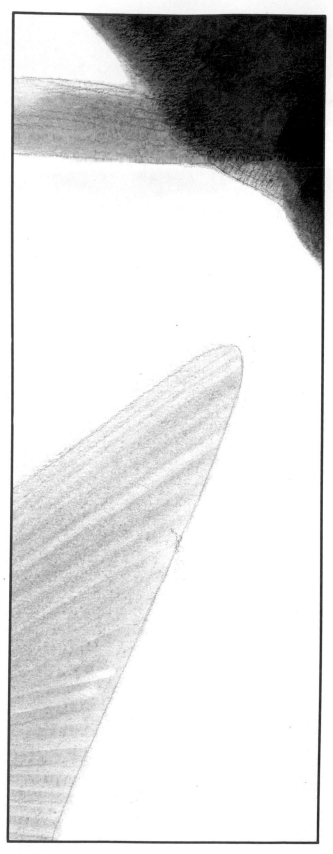

Only one thing remained—a tiny golden shoe. Yeh-Shen hurried to the bones of her fish and returned the slipper, promising to find its mate. But now the bones were silent. Sadly Yeh-Shen realized that she had lost her only friend. She hid the little shoe in her bedstraw, and went outside to cry. Leaning against a fruit tree, she sobbed and sobbed until she fell asleep.

The stepmother left the gathering to check on Yeh-Shen, but when she returned home she found the girl sound asleep, with her arms wrapped around a fruit tree. So thinking no more of her, the stepmother rejoined the party. Meantime, a villager had found the shoe. Recognizing its worth, he sold it to a merchant, who presented it in turn to the king of the island kingdom of T'o Han.

The king was more than happy to accept the slipper as a gift. He was entranced by the tiny thing, which was shaped of the most precious of metals, yet which made no sound when touched to stone. The more he marveled at its beauty, the more determined he became to find the woman to whom the shoe

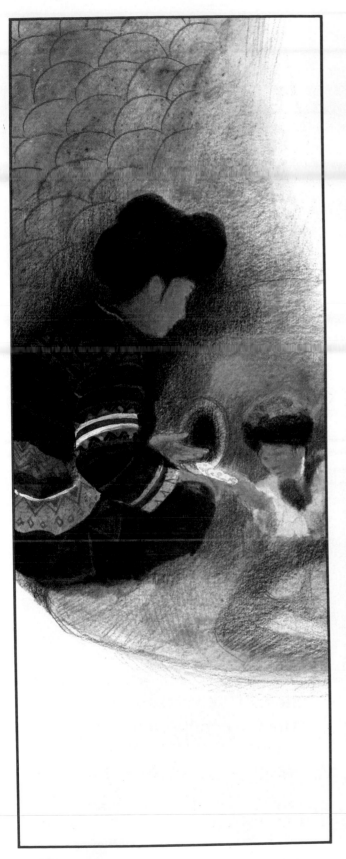

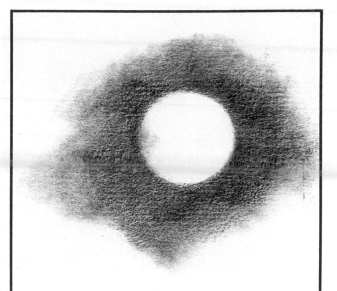

belonged. A search was begun among the ladies of his own kingdom, but all who tried on the sandal found it impossibly small. Undaunted, the king ordered the search widened to include the cave women from the countryside where the slipper had been found. Since he realized it would take many years for every woman to come to his island and test her foot in the slipper, the king thought of a way to get the right woman to come forward. He ordered the sandal placed in a pavilion by the side of the road near where

it had been found, and his herald announced that the shoe was to be returned to its original owner. Then from a nearby hiding place, the king and his men settled down to watch and wait for a woman with tiny feet to come and claim her slipper.

All that day the pavilion was crowded with cave women who had come to test a foot in the shoe. Yeh-Shen's stepmother and stepsister were among them, but not Yeh-Shen—they had told her to stay home. By day's end, although many women had eagerly tried to put on the slipper, it still had not been worn. Wearily, the king continued his vigil into the night.

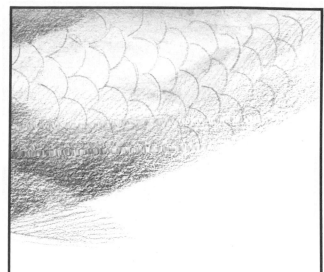

It wasn't until the blackest part of night, while the moon hid behind a cloud, that Yeh-Shen dared to show her face at the pavilion, and even then she tiptoed timidly across the wide floor. Sinking down to her knees, the girl in rags examined the tiny shoe. Only when she was sure that this was the missing mate to her own golden slipper did she dare pick it up.

At last she could return both little shoes to the fish bones. Surely then her beloved spirit would speak to her again.

Now the king's first thought, on seeing Yeh-Shen take the precious slipper, was to throw the girl into prison as a thief. But when she turned to leave, he caught a glimpse of her face. At once the king was struck by the sweet harmony of her features, which seemed so out of keeping with the rags she wore. It was then that he took a closer look and noticed that she walked upon the tiniest feet he had ever seen.

With a wave of his hand, the king signaled that this tattered creature was to be allowed to depart with the golden slipper. Quietly, the king's men slipped off and followed her home.

All this time, Yeh-Shen was unaware of the excitement she had caused. She had made her way home and was about to hide both sandals in her bedding when there was a pounding at the door. Yeh-Shen went to see who it was—and found a king at her doorstep. She was very frightened at first, but the king spoke to her in a kind voice and asked her to try the golden slippers on her feet. The maiden did as she was told, and as she stood in her golden shoes, her rags were transformed once more into the feathered cloak and beautiful azure gown.

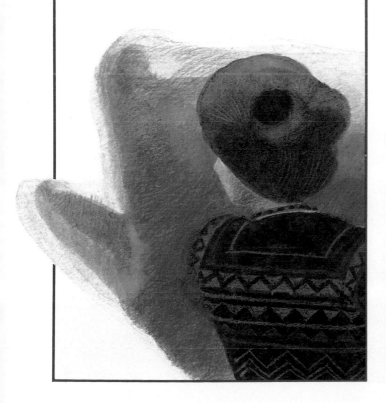
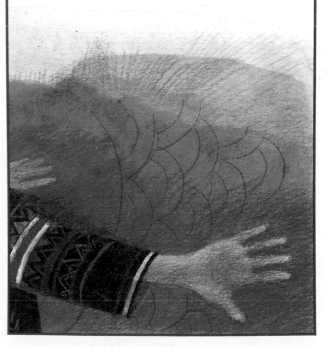

Her loveliness made her seem a heavenly being, and the king suddenly knew in his heart that he had found his true love.

Not long after this, Yeh-Shen was married to the king. But fate was not so gentle with her stepmother and stepsister. Since they had been unkind to his beloved, the king would not permit Yeh-Shen to bring them to his palace. They remained in their cave home, where one day, it is said, they were crushed to death in a shower of flying stones.

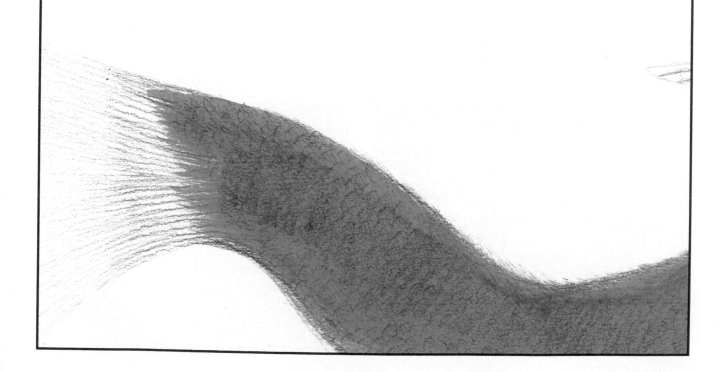

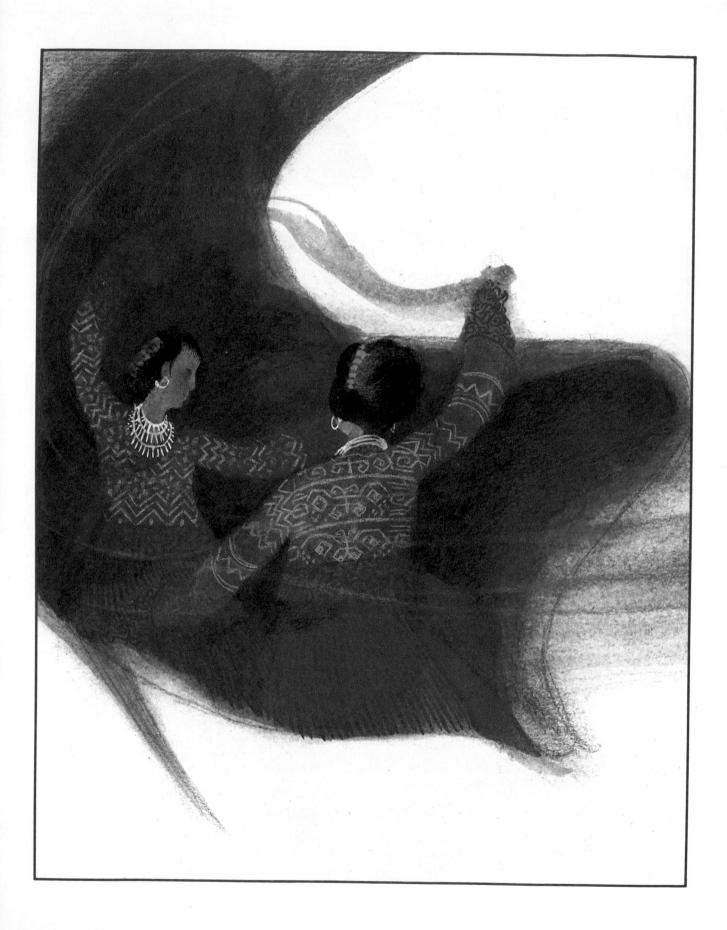

Meet Ed Young

In Shanghai, China, where Ed Young grew up, his father would entertain the family by reading and spinning endless tales. Young still remembers some of the scenes he imagined as he listened. He made his own drawings, too. "I drew everything that happened to cross my mind: airplanes, people, a tall ship. . . . I have always been happiest doing my own thing."

In some of his books, Young combines his love of storytelling and drawing. One of his best-known books, *Lon Po Po*, is his retelling of a Chinese Little Red-Riding Hood story, for which he won the Caldecott Medal. For both *Lon Po Po* and *Yeh-Shen*, Young set his art in colorful panels like those of Chinese folding screens. He also created hidden images. In *Lon Po Po*, the wolf's image is cleverly hidden in some drawings. Looking closely at the drawings in *Yeh-Shen*, you will see Yeh-Shen's fish hidden in the panels.

Meet Ai-Ling Louie

Books have always been a part of Ai-Ling Louie's life. "When I was a girl, it seemed I always had my nose in a book," she says. Ai-Ling Louie's career as a teacher brought out her desire to write. "I used to love to write stories to tell the children."

Louie wrote down *Yeh-Shen: A Cinderella Story from China* for one of her classes. She learned the story from her mother, who first heard it as a child in China.

IN SEARCH OF CINDERELLA

From dusk to dawn,
From town to town,
Without a single clue,
I seek the tender, slender foot,
To fit this crystal shoe.
From dusk to dawn,
I try it on
Each damsel that I meet.
And I still love her so, but oh,
I've started hating feet.

Shel Silverstein

INVITATION

If you are a dreamer, come in,
If you are a dreamer, a wisher, a liar,
A hope-er, a pray-er, a magic bean buyer...
If you're a pretender, come sit by my fire
For we have some flax-golden tales to spin.
Come in!
Come in!

Shel Silverstein

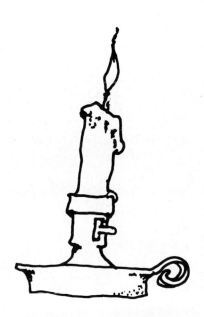

An Interview with Storyteller
WON-LDY PAYE
by Margaret H. Lippert

In a classroom filled with
curious children, Won-Ldy Paye
tells a story of the trickster
Anansi. Paye becomes Anansi,
sneaking as Anansi sneaks,
dancing as Anansi dances. Soon
everyone in the audience is
drumming, dancing, or both.
Afterward, Ms. Lippert, who
lives in Washington near Paye,
interviewed him.

Lippert: You are a master story-teller and drummer. How did you develop these talents?

Paye: I grew up in rural Liberia, a country on the West Coast of Africa. I am from the Dan tribe, which is known for its artistic abilities, especially mask making and traditional dancing. I am an actor and a musician; storytelling is like a one-person play to me.

Lippert: How did you learn the art of storytelling?

Paye: I come from a family of "Griots"—storytellers. We tell stories when we work on the rice farm, at bedtime, or when the kids get together. My grandmother would tell us stories every evening. Before Grandmother would tell her story, she might say, "Won-Ldy, it's your turn to tell a story." As I repeated the story, she and the other kids would correct me. After a while, I learned the stories and added my own style and fun and movement to them. By seventh grade, I was already telling stories to big crowds. People would say, "The kid's a good storyteller."

Lippert: What makes a good story-teller?

Paye: You must be able to make people listen—that is the true quality of a storyteller. Just because people ask you to tell a story doesn't guarantee that they're going to sit and listen to you all night. . . . Storytelling is a profession—something that you learn, and study, and devote a lot of time to, and go to great people to learn from. I've learned storytelling because others have shared with me. It's important to me to tell my stories. So, anybody who wants to hear my story, I will tell them the story.

The Three Little Pigs and the Fox

WILLIAM H. HOOKS

ILLUSTRATED BY
S. D. SCHINDLER

AUTHOR'S NOTE

The art of storytelling is alive and well in Appalachia. It has flourished there since the earliest English, Scottish, and Irish settlers arrived more than three centuries ago. The classic folk and fairy tales have been preserved, but gradually in the telling they have changed until they seem to spring not from some fanciful, faraway place, but from the mountains and hollows of Appalachia itself.

Each storyteller is unique, adding local color and regional language to capture and enchant an audience. This rendition of The Three Little Pigs *is based on several oral versions I have heard over the years in the Great Smoky Mountains. In keeping with one of the truest roles of the storyteller, I have added a few flourishes of my own.*

This story happened a long time ago, way back when the animals could still talk around these parts. Back then they could say a whole lot more than *baa-baa, moo-moo, oink-oink,* and stuff like that. They could talk just like human folks.

Back then there was this humongous mama pig. She built herself a house out of rocks in a pretty green holler over Black Mountain way. As soon as she'd finished, she moved into her fine rock house with her three piglets.

The oldest piglet, Rooter, was a fair-sized shoat.
The middle piglet, Oinky, was a real mama's boy.
The baby piglet was a tiny little girl runt named
Hamlet.

Now, Rooter and Oinky and Hamlet had the finest
pig house in the holler. They even had a wallowing
hole right in the front yard. But all Rooter and Oinky
wanted to do was eat, eat, eat!

Baby Hamlet liked to eat, too—but not all the
time. Hamlet liked to roll around in the delicious mud

in the wallowing hole and look up at the pretty blue sky. She was a right smart piglet with more on her mind than eating.

It wasn't long 'fore Rooter and Oinky got so fat they just about filled up the whole house. What a squeeze it was to fit everybody in.

Finally it got so tight that Mama Pig spoke to Rooter. "Rooter, you're the oldest. Time's come for you to go out and seek your fortune."

"Oh, no!" Rooter squealed. "I'm still a piglet!"

"Look in that mud hole," said Mama Pig. "What do you see?"

Rooter looked in the muddy water. "I see a great big fat pig," he said.

"That big fat pig is you, Rooter. Time's come to go out and seek your fortune."

Well, Rooter hemmed and hawed and had an extra big helping of his mama's baked beans to settle his nerves. Oinky had some, too, just to keep Rooter company.

Meanwhile, Mama Pig gathered up some hoecakes and turnips, along with some dried beans and corn. She packed them in a big tow sack for Rooter to take along.

"Now, son," said Mama Pig, "you'll be fine if you remember three things."

"That's a lot to remember," said Rooter.

"Stop chewing and listen careful," said Mama Pig.

Rooter gulped. "I'm listening."

"One: You got to watch out for that mean, tricky old drooly-mouth fox.

"Two: Build yourself a safe, strong house out of rocks.

"Three: Come home to see your mama every single Sunday."

Mama and Oinky and baby Hamlet kissed Rooter on his fat, round jowls. And for good luck they kissed him again on his pink, trembly snout.

Then Rooter trotted on down the road, dragging his tow sack behind him. He walked and he walked. And what did all that walking do? It made him mighty hungry.

He didn't think about any mean, tricky old drooly-mouth fox.

He didn't think about any safe, strong rock house.

He didn't think about visiting his mama come Sunday.

All he could think about was the food his mama had put into the tow sack. So he set himself down on a rock and opened up the sack.

"Hoecakes!" He squealed and started gobbling them up.

Rooter felt a tap on the shoulder. He didn't look around, and he didn't miss a chew, just said between bites, "Don't bother me. I'm busy eating."

But the tapping went on. Rooter swallowed a big chunk of hoecake and looked around. There was mean, tricky old drooly-mouth fox grinning at him.

"Have some hoecake," said Rooter, real scared.

"Don't like hoecake," said the fox.

"Well, how about some turnips or corn?" said Rooter.

"Don't like none of them," said the fox.

"Well, what can I offer you?" asked Rooter.

"I love barbecued pig!" cried the fox. And he grabbed the tow sack and stuffed Rooter into it.

"Please don't eat me up," Rooter pleaded.

"I won't eat you right now," said mean, tricky old drooly-mouth fox. "I'm going to save you up for a cold winter's day. Nothing like hot barbecue on a cold winter's day."

So he took poor Rooter off to his den and locked him up.

Sunday rolled around. All day Mama Pig and baby Hamlet looked for Rooter to come visiting, while Oinky spent the Sabbath eating a double share of rutabagas and corn dumplings. But the night came on without Rooter ever showing up.

A month of Sundays passed, and they didn't see snout or tail of Rooter. Meanwhile, Oinky was growing so big the house was getting crowded again. They were having a hard time fitting in.

Finally Mama Pig said, "Oinky, it's time you set out to seek your fortune."

"No, Mama!" Oinky squealed. "I'm too little to leave my mama."

"Look in that mud hole and tell me what you see," said Mama Pig.

Oinky looked in the muddy water and saw how huge he had grown. He knew his mama was right.

Oinky didn't say a word, but two big tears rolled down his plump jowls.

Mama Pig said, "No need for tears, Oinky. All you have to do is remember three things.

"One: Watch out for that mean, tricky old drooly-mouth fox.

"Two: Build yourself a safe, strong house out of rocks.

"Three: Come home to see your mama every single Sunday."

Mama packed Oinky a tow sack full of his favorite food, rutabagas and corn dumplings.

Then baby Hamlet and Mama Pig kissed Oinky on his fat, round jowls. And for good luck they kissed him again on his pink, trembly snout.

Oinky went slowly on down the road till he was out of sight. He walked and he walked. And he kept thinking how much he was going to miss his mama. He felt so sad, he sat down on a rock to have a little nourishment and cheer himself. He didn't think once about the mean fox or building a safe house, although he did long for Sunday to visit his mama.

Oinky was just easing a tooth into a crusty, golden corn dumpling when he felt a tap on the shoulder. He whirled around so fast he dropped the dumpling. There was mean, tricky old drooly-mouth fox grinning at him.

"Would you like some of my dumplings?" stammered Oinky, scared to death.

"Never eat 'em," said the fox.

"How about some rutabagas?" asked Oinky.

"Can't stand the smell of 'em," said the fox.

"Well, what do you like?" asked Oinky.

"Pork with lima beans!" said the fox. And he snatched up the tow sack and stuffed poor Oinky inside.

"Please don't eat me," begged Oinky. "Please! Please! Please!"

"Oh, shut up," said mean, tricky old drooly-mouth fox. "I'm not going to eat you right now. I'm going to save you for a rainy day. There's nothing better than pork and beans on a rainy day."

So the fox took Oinky to his den and locked him up.

Sunday rolled around. Mama and baby Hamlet got up early and cooked a big mess of collard greens and wild onions. They wanted to have something special in case Rooter and Oinky remembered to come see their mama. But the night came on without either Rooter or Oinky ever showing up.

A month of Sundays passed, and they didn't see snout or tail of Rooter or Oinky. The leaves turned all red and gold, and the nights got real nippy.

Baby Hamlet—who didn't look so much like a little runt anymore—was getting restless. One day she spoke to her mama. "Mama, it's high time I set out to seek my fortune."

"No, no!" Mama Pig cried. "You're too young to leave your mama! Besides, none of my children ever come back to visit me on Sundays."

"Now, stop your worrying, Mama," said Hamlet. "I can take care of myself. All I've got to do is remember three things.

"One: Watch out for that mean, tricky old drooly-mouth fox.

"Two: Build myself a safe, strong house out of rocks.

"Three: Come home and visit my dear, sweet mama every Sunday."

So Mama Pig packed a tow sack with sweet potato pone, Hamlet's favorite food. She kissed baby Hamlet on her fat, round jowls, and for luck kissed her again on her pink, trembly snout.

Hamlet skipped on down the road. She walked and she walked. She looked all around to make sure no mean fox was sneaking up on her. She got tired and set herself down on a rock to rest.

"I think I'll just have a nibble on this sweet potato pone," she said.

Suddenly she felt a tap on the shoulder. It was mean, tricky old drooly-mouth fox grinning at her.

"What a surprise!" exclaimed Hamlet. She was thinking fast and stalling for time.

"I've got a real big surprise for you," said the fox.

"I mentioned *surprise* first," said Hamlet. "This tow sack is full of surprises."

The fox reached inside the sack and pulled out some sweet potato pone. "Umm," he mumbled, chewing away. "Only one thing I like better than sweet potato pone."

"What's that?" asked Hamlet.

"Pork chops to go with it!" cried the fox, grabbing for baby Hamlet.

But Hamlet was too sharp for him. She slapped the tow sack over the fox and tied it tight with a hard knot. Then she left that old fox rolling and squirming around on the ground inside the sack.

Hamlet skipped on down the road till she found a place with a fine bunch of rocks. She made herself a safe little rock house with a nice fireplace to keep warm by.

No sooner had Hamlet settled in than that mean, tricky old drooly-mouth fox came knocking at her door. "Please let me in, little pig," he begged. "I'm near freezing to death."

"Not on the fuzz of your bushy tail will I let you in," said Hamlet.

"Please, have mercy on a poor old fox. My nose is about frozen off. Just open the door a crack to let me warm my nose," he pleaded.

Hamlet cracked the door a mite. The fox shoved his nose in the crack.

Slam! Hamlet banged the door shut.

The fox thought his nose would really drop off, it hurt so. But he was thinking what nice pork chops Hamlet would make.

"My nose is warmer now," he called, "but my ears are freezing. Please open the door a little wider so I can warm my ears."

Hamlet opened the door a little more. The fox tried to push all the way in.

Slam! Hamlet banged the door shut, pretty

near knocking the breath out of mean, tricky old drooly-mouth fox.

But the fox still had his mind set on pork chops.

"Oh, that was much better, little pig." He gasped. "Now, if you would open the door a little bit more and let me get my hind feet warmed, I'll be on my way."

Hamlet opened the door wide. The fox sprang inside. But that smart little pig was too fast for him. *Slam!* She shut the door on his tail and stopped him in his tracks.

"Oh, oh, my tail!" cried mean, tricky old drooly-mouth fox.

"Shut up!" said Hamlet. "You're making so much racket I can't hear what's going on outside."

The fox lowered his voice to a moan. "Please, my tail. My tail."

"Just what I thought I heard," said Hamlet. "Dogs barking."

"Dogs? What kind of dogs?" asked the fox.

"Hunting dogs. I'm sure they're fox-hunting dogs, from the way they're barking."

"Please hide me," cried the fox. "Don't let the hounds catch me!"

Hamlet was thinking fast and sharp.

"I'll hide you if you tell me what you've done with Rooter and Oinky."

"They're locked up in my den. Please, hurry. Those dogs will be here any minute."

"First tell me where I can find your den."

Mean, tricky old drooly-mouth fox hated to give that away. But his tail was killing him, and the dogs were hot on his trail.

"It's under the big, rusty-colored rock over in Rattlesnake Holler." He groaned.

"Here, jump into this churn," said Hamlet. She pushed the door off mean, tricky old drooly-mouth fox's tail and lifted the lid from the big wooden churn.

The fox squeezed inside. Hamlet slammed the lid down on the churn and latched it tight.

"Are the dogs getting closer?" the fox mumbled from inside the churn.

"What dogs?" asked baby Hamlet. "I don't hear any dogs."

The old fox knew he'd been tricked. He gnashed his teeth and rattled and raved and shook the churn. But he couldn't get out.

Baby Hamlet rolled the churn down to the creek and right into the water. Downstream it floated like an ark. And that was the last mean, tricky old drooly-mouth fox was seen around the hollers of Black Mountain.

Baby Hamlet hurried on down to Rattlesnake Holler and searched all around till she found the fox den with her brothers, Rooter and Oinky.

It just happened to be on Sunday when she found them and set them free. So they all trotted right over to Mama Pig's house. And there was snorting and eating, and kissing and eating, and wallowing in the mud hole and more eating, the likes of which you've never seen.

Meet
WILLIAM H. HOOKS

As a youngster growing up in the North Carolina countryside, William H. Hooks heard many tales that the country folk had told for generations. Hooks has woven memories of those tales into the many books he has written for children.

During a visit to the Smokey Mountains of Tennessee, Hooks heard an old Appalachian version of *The Three Little Pigs*. Hooks turned that story into his book *The Three Little Pigs and the Fox*.

Hooks has this advice for youngsters who want to write: "Write. Do it. Keep doing it. It will get better and better."

Érase Una Vez

Érase una vez
un lobito bueno

al que maltrataban
todos los corderos.

Y había también
un príncipe malo,

una bruja hermosa
y un pirata honrado.

Todas estas cosas
había una vez
cuando yo soñaba
un mundo al revés.

Juan Goytisolo

Once Upon a Time

Once upon a time
there was a good little wolf

that all the sheep
used to bother.

And at the same time
there was an evil prince,

a beautiful witch
and an honest pirate.

And all of these things
were once upon a time
in a world of my dreams
that was upside down, it seems.

ANCESTRY

I splash in the ocean
My big brother watches me
We sing,
    "Wade in the water
    Wade in the water, children."

Mom and Dad
Teaching us spirituals
Reading us African tales
Singing songs
Telling stories
Reminding us
Of our ancestry

On the beach
Other children
Dig to China
I dig
To Africa

Ashley Bryan

Illustration by Ashley Bryan from *Sing to the Sun*.

Meet John Steptoe

When John Steptoe wanted to write a book about his African ancestors, he decided to write a version of the Cinderella story. As he prepared to write by talking to Africans and reading about Africa, he found many reasons to be proud of his ancestors. Steptoe discovered that people of a thousand years ago behaved much the same as people do today. "My ancestors were probably very like my own family," he said. "Telling the story was easy once I knew who my characters were."

Mufaro's Beautiful Daughters is Steptoe's African Cinderella story. He used members of his family as models for some of the characters.

Steptoe hoped his books would lead children, especially African-American children, "to accomplish the dreams I know are in their hearts."

Mufaro's Beautiful Daughters

An African Tale

Written and Illustrated by John Steptoe

*M*ufaro's
Beautiful Daughters
*was inspired by
an African
folktale
published in
1895. Details of
the illustrations were
inspired by the ruins of an
ancient city found in Zimbabwe,
and the flora and fauna of that
region. The names of the characters
are from the Shona language:
Mufaro (moo-FAR-oh) means
"happy man"; Nyasha
(nee-AH-sha) means
"mercy"; Manyara
(mahn-YAR-ah)
means "ashamed";
and Nyoka
(nee-YO-kah)
means "snake."*

A LONG TIME AGO, in a certain place in Africa, a small village lay across a river and half a day's journey from a city where a great king lived. A man named Mufaro lived in this village with his two daughters, who were called Manyara and Nyasha. Everyone agreed that Manyara and Nyasha were very beautiful.

$\mathcal{M}$anyara was almost always in a bad temper.
She teased her sister whenever their father's back was
turned, and she had been heard to say, "Someday,
Nyasha, I will be a queen, and you will be a servant
in my household."

"If that should come to pass," Nyasha responded, "I
will be pleased to serve you. But why do you say such
things? You are clever and strong and beautiful. Why are
you so unhappy?"

"Because everyone talks about how kind *you* are, and they praise everything you do," Manyara replied. "I'm certain that Father loves you best. But when I am a queen, everyone will know that your silly kindness is only weakness."

Nyasha was sad that Manyara felt this way, but she ignored her sister's words and went about her chores. Nyasha kept a small plot of land, on which she grew millet, sunflowers, yams, and vegetables. She always sang as she worked, and some said it was her singing that made her crops more bountiful than anyone else's.

One day, Nyasha noticed a small garden snake resting beneath a yam vine. "Good day, little Nyoka," she called to him. "You are welcome here. You will keep away any creatures who might spoil my vegetables." She bent forward, gave the little snake a loving pat on the head, and then returned to her work.

From that day on, Nyoka was always at Nyasha's side when she tended her garden. It was said that she sang all the more sweetly when he was there.

*M*ufaro knew nothing of how Manyara treated Nyasha. Nyasha was too considerate of her father's feelings to complain, and Manyara was always careful to behave herself when Mufaro was around.

Early one morning, a messenger from the city arrived. The Great King wanted a wife. "The Most Worthy and Beautiful Daughters in the Land are invited to appear before the King, and he will choose one to become Queen!" the messenger proclaimed.

Mufaro called Manyara and Nyasha to him. "It would be a great honor to have one of you chosen," he said. "Prepare yourselves to journey to the city. I will call together all our friends to make a wedding party. We will leave tomorrow as the sun rises."

"But, my father," Manyara said sweetly, "it would be painful for either of us to leave you, even to be wife to the king. I know Nyasha would grieve to death if she were parted from you. I am strong. Send me to the city, and let poor Nyasha be happy here with you."

Mufaro beamed with pride. "The king has asked for the most worthy and the most beautiful. No, Manyara, I cannot send you alone. Only a king can choose between two such worthy daughters. Both of you must go!"

That night, when everyone was asleep, Manyara stole quietly out of the village. She had never been in the forest at night before, and she was frightened, but her greed to be the first to appear before the king drove her on. In her hurry, she almost stumbled over a small boy who suddenly appeared, standing in the path.

"Please," said the boy. "I am hungry. Will you give me something to eat?"

"I have brought only enough for myself," Manyara replied.

"But, please!" said the boy. "I am so *very* hungry."

"Out of my way, boy! Tomorrow I will become your queen. How dare you stand in my path?"

After traveling for what seemed to be a great distance, Manyara came to a small clearing. There, silhouetted against the moonlight, was an old woman seated on a large stone.

The old woman spoke. "I will give you some advice, Manyara. Soon after you pass the place where two paths cross, you will see a grove of trees. They will laugh at you. You must not laugh in return. Later, you will meet a man with his head under his arm. You must be polite to him."

"How do you know my name? How dare you advise your future queen? Stand aside, you ugly old woman!" Manyara scolded, and then rushed on her way without looking back.

Just as the old woman had foretold, Manyara
came to a grove of trees, and they did indeed seem
to be laughing at her.

"I must be calm," Manyara thought. "I will *not* be
frightened." She looked up at the trees and laughed
out loud. "I laugh at you, trees!" she shouted, and she
hurried on.

It was not yet dawn when Manyara heard the sound
of rushing water. "The river must be up ahead," she
thought. "The great city is just on the other side."

But there, on the rise, she saw a man with his head
tucked under his arm. Manyara ran past him without
speaking. "A queen acknowledges only those who please
her," she said to herself. "I will be queen. I will be
queen," she chanted, as she hurried on toward the city.

Nyasha woke at the first light of dawn. As she put on her finest garments, she thought how her life might be changed forever beyond this day. "I'd much prefer to live here," she admitted to herself. "I'd hate to leave this village and never see my father or sing to little Nyoka again."

Her thoughts were interrupted by loud shouts and a commotion from the wedding party assembled outside. Manyara was missing! Everyone bustled about, searching and calling for her. When they found her footprints on the path that led to the city, they decided to go on as planned.

As the wedding party moved through the forest, brightly plumed birds darted about in the cool green shadows beneath the trees. Though anxious about her sister, Nyasha was soon filled with excitement about all there was to see.

They were deep in the forest when she saw the small boy standing by the side of the path.

"You must be hungry," she said, and handed him a yam she had brought for her lunch. The boy smiled and disappeared as quietly as he had come.

Later, as they were approaching the place where the two paths crossed, the old woman appeared and silently pointed the way to the city. Nyasha thanked her and gave her a small pouch filled with sunflower seeds.

The sun was high in the sky when the party came to the grove of towering trees. Their uppermost branches seemed to bow down to Nyasha as she passed beneath them.

At last, someone announced that they were near their destination.

Nyasha ran ahead and topped the rise before the others could catch up with her. She stood transfixed at her first sight of the city. "Oh, my father," she called. "A great spirit must stand guard here! Just look at what lies before us. I never in all my life dreamed there could be anything so beautiful!"

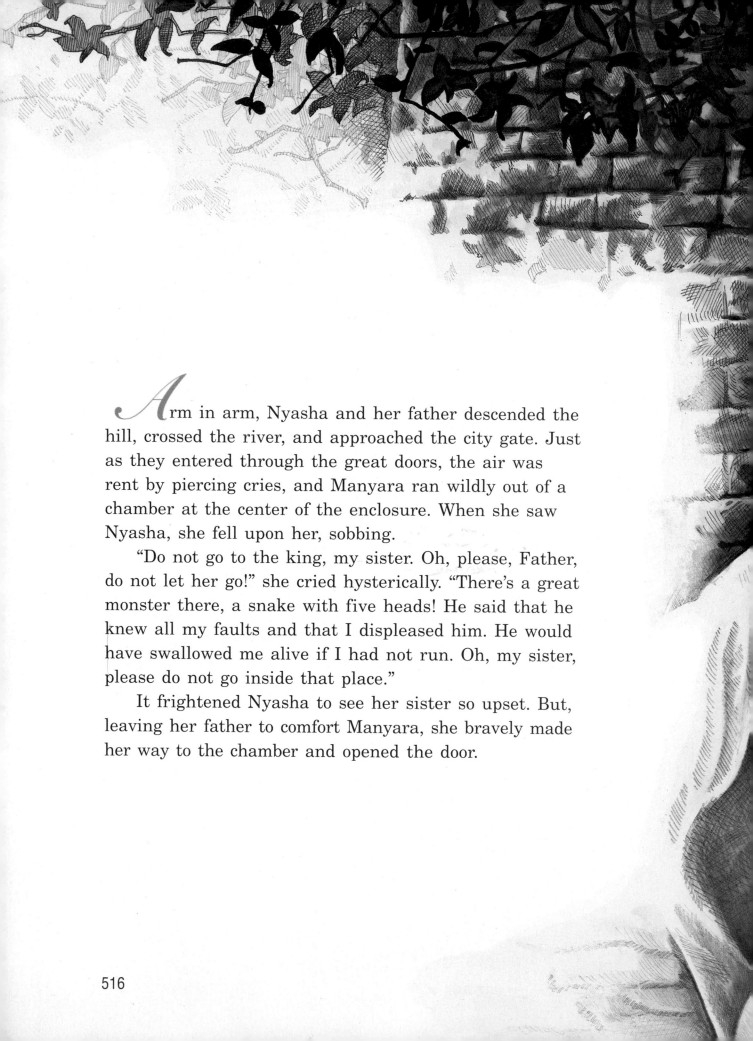

Arm in arm, Nyasha and her father descended the hill, crossed the river, and approached the city gate. Just as they entered through the great doors, the air was rent by piercing cries, and Manyara ran wildly out of a chamber at the center of the enclosure. When she saw Nyasha, she fell upon her, sobbing.

"Do not go to the king, my sister. Oh, please, Father, do not let her go!" she cried hysterically. "There's a great monster there, a snake with five heads! He said that he knew all my faults and that I displeased him. He would have swallowed me alive if I had not run. Oh, my sister, please do not go inside that place."

It frightened Nyasha to see her sister so upset. But, leaving her father to comfort Manyara, she bravely made her way to the chamber and opened the door.

On the seat of the great chief's
stool lay the little garden snake.
Nyasha laughed with relief and joy.

"My little friend!" she exclaimed.
"It's such a pleasure to see you, but
why are you here?"

"I am the king," Nyoka replied.

And there, before Nyasha's eyes,
the garden snake changed shape.

"I am the king. I am also the hungry boy with whom you shared a yam
in the forest and the old woman to
whom you made a gift of sunflower
seeds. But you know me best as Nyoka.
Because I have been all of these, I
know you to be the Most Worthy and
Most Beautiful Daughter in the Land.
It would make me very happy if you
would be my wife."

And so it was that, a long time ago, Nyasha agreed to be married. The king's mother and sisters took Nyasha to their house, and the wedding preparations began. The best weavers in the land laid out their finest cloth for her wedding garments. Villagers from all around were invited to the cele-bration, and a great feast was held. Nyasha prepared the bread for the wedding feast from millet that had been brought from her village.

Mufaro proclaimed to all who would hear him that he was the happiest father in all the land, for he was blessed with two beautiful and worthy daughters—Nyasha, the queen; and Manyara, a servant in the queen's household.

Mother Goose Tales, by Palmer Hayden, about 1935.

GIVE

Your World is Alive with Rhymes and Stories.

It's 1935. You live in Harlem, in New York City—the most exciting black neighborhood there is. You're home from school, reading *Mother Goose:*

> *"If all the world was apple pie*
> *And all the sea was ink . . ."*

You know every page of this old book. Jack and Jill, pigs and kings, blackbird pies . . . These rhymes have existed for hundreds of years, recited by people in lands far away—recited over and over till one day someone wrote them down.

You hear rhymes and songs and stories all the time in Harlem, too.

Outside your window, the streets are alive with men singing, grandmothers telling tales, peddlers calling:

> *"I got vegetables today, so*
> *don't go away.*
>
> *Stick around, and you'll*
> *hear me say:*
>
> *Buy 'em by the pound,*
> *put 'em in a sack.*
>
> *Hurry up and get 'em, cause*
> *I'm not coming back."*

You stop reading and listen to the song. What a book it would make if someone wrote these street rhymes down, too! Listen well, remember all you hear, and maybe it will be you.

THE Stonecutter

An Indian folk tale retold and illustrated by Pam Newton

Once there was a poor stonecutter who lived in a small hut in the forest on the side of a mountain.

Every morning while the sun was still a yellow ribbon of promise in the eastern sky, the stonecutter picked up his tools and climbed the mountain path until he arrived at a big rock in the side of the mountain. Along the way trees waved morning greetings and calling birds soared across the mountainside. A tiger, hidden in his cave, yawned and curled up for a nap.

Before the stonecutter began to work he prayed to the mountain spirit for blessing and protection. Then he hammered and chipped and smoothed and polished the building blocks he made from the stones he took out of the mountain.

Although he worked hard and his days were long, he never minded until the day he delivered some blocks of stone to repair a wall at the home of a rich man.

The stonecutter had never seen such splendor. He looked at the luxury surrounding him and marveled. From then on, the stonecutter spent his days wishing for comfort and his nights dreaming of wealth.

It grew harder and harder to be a poor stonecutter. Every morning he climbed the mountain path on feet heavy as stones. One day as he neared the big rock he threw down his tools and prayed to the mountain spirit. But this time he cried out for more. His angry demands and cries of discontent shook the forest, scattering the birds into the air. The sleeping tiger, hidden in his cave, rolled over and opened one great golden eye.

Deep within the mountain the spirit heard the stonecutter's cries and decided to grant his prayers.

The spirit stilled the trees and calmed the birds and soothed the tiger back to sleep. The stonecutter's heart was filled with hope so that when he raised his hammer and began to work, he believed his prayers would soon be answered.

The next day, as he walked to the city to deliver some blocks of stone, the stonecutter saw a merchant leading camels heaped high with silks and spices for the market. He stood by the side of the road and watched.

"A stonecutter is nothing compared to a rich merchant," he said, sighing, and squeezed his eyes shut against the dust.

"If only I were a rich merchant," he cried, as he covered his ears to keep out the shouts of the camel drivers. "Then I could be truly happy."

Far away inside the mountain, the spirit heard his wish and made it true.

When the stonecutter opened his eyes, his blocks of stone had disappeared and in their place stood all the wealth of a merchant. He bowed his richly turbaned head and murmured his gratitude.

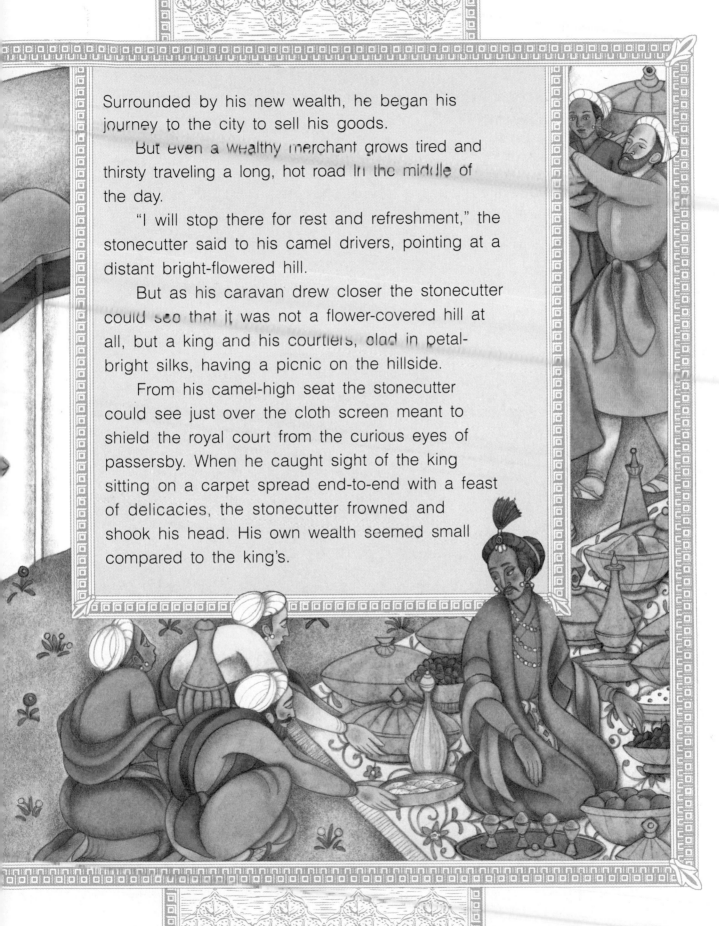

Surrounded by his new wealth, he began his journey to the city to sell his goods.

But even a wealthy merchant grows tired and thirsty traveling a long, hot road in the middle of the day.

"I will stop there for rest and refreshment," the stonecutter said to his camel drivers, pointing at a distant bright-flowered hill.

But as his caravan drew closer the stonecutter could see that it was not a flower-covered hill at all, but a king and his courtiers, clad in petal-bright silks, having a picnic on the hillside.

From his camel-high seat the stonecutter could see just over the cloth screen meant to shield the royal court from the curious eyes of passersby. When he caught sight of the king sitting on a carpet spread end-to-end with a feast of delicacies, the stonecutter frowned and shook his head. His own wealth seemed small compared to the king's.

"A merchant is nothing compared to a king," he said. "If only I were a king, then I could be truly happy."

The words were barely spoken when—wonder of wonders—the stonecutter became a king!

A servant offered him a tray of sherbets. The sweet pink ices cooled his dry throat. Perfumed courtiers hovered like butterflies, filling the air with the scent of roses and sandalwood. The stonecutter kicked off his slippers and settled into his cushions, nibbling first from one tray of delights and then another.

Though his every desire was fulfilled, the afternoon sun burned down on the hillside and the stonecutter began to feel hot. His beard glistened with sweat and his skin blistered and itched.

Shielding his eyes with his hand, the stonecutter tried to look heavenward. High above, the sun blazed powerful and brilliant, too great for even a king to gaze upon.

"I was wrong," moaned the stonecutter, wiping his brow with a silk scarf. "A king is nothing compared to the sun. If only I were the sun, then I could be truly happy."

His wish spoken, the stonecutter at once became the scorching sun, whirling red-hot across the heavens, and dazzling the world with his fiery strength.

"Now there is nothing more glorious than I am," he declared, seeing each flower's face turn to him and every tree reach up, up to embrace him.

"Even a powerful king cannot stop me from burning his skin," declared the stonecutter, as his thousand wheeling arms searched the earth for a king.

Just then a small cloud drifted across the sky and passed between the sun and the earth. The stonecutter cried out, for his face was hidden from the earth.

He was utterly powerless.

"I was wrong," he groaned. "The sun is nothing compared to a cloud. If only I were a cloud, then I could be truly happy."

And so saying, the stonecutter was transformed into a pale gossamer cloud, with the sun scowling at his back, the earth spread below, and the sky all around. He had nothing better in the world to do but float along effortlessly, puffed up with the pride and power of his new position.

But not for long.

As quickly as the cloud had covered the sun, a wind arrived and swept the cloud away.

"Oh-h-h," sobbed the stonecutter, as the wind's icy breath tore him apart. "A cloud is nothing compared to the wind. If only I were the wind, then I could be truly happy."

At once the stonecutter became the wind, tossing the clouds across the sky as he rushed to earth.

"Whee-e-e-e!" He blew over the ocean making waves.

"Whir-r-r-r!" He rolled across the fields, bending flowers and grasses.

"Who-o-o-sh!" He rustled through the trees, snapping branches.

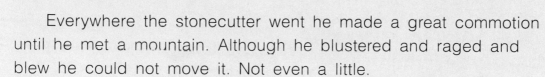

Everywhere the stonecutter went he made a great commotion until he met a mountain. Although he blustered and raged and blew he could not move it. Not even a little.

"The wind is nothing compared to a mountain," huffed the stonecutter. "If only I were a mountain, then I could be truly happy."

"Now," boasted the stonecutter as once again his wish was granted, "a wind cannot move me."

"A cloud cannot cover me."

"The sun cannot burn me."

"A king cannot equal my majesty."

"And surely a merchant is nothing compared to a mountain."

But as he spoke, a man climbed up the side of the mountain. He carried a hammer, and when he began to pound, pound, pound, the stonecutter cried out: "I am the mountain and there is nothing on earth or in the heavens as powerful as I am."

The man continued to hammer and chip and smooth and polish, making building blocks from the stones he took out of the mountain.

"Oh-h-h, no-o-o," wailed the stonecutter. "I was wrong."

544

"Stone by stone, even a mountain is nothing compared to a stonecutter. If only I were a stonecutter, then I would be truly happy."

His wish spoken, he found himself standing on the side of the mountain. He was a stonecutter once again.

As he climbed his well-worn path, trees waved and birds soared and sang. The tiger slumbered in his cave.

The stonecutter offered a prayer of thanks to the mountain spirit. A feeling of contentment settled over him.

"At last I am happy to be a stonecutter—truly happy."

Then he began to hammer and chip and smooth and polish, making building blocks from the stones he took out of the mountain.

Meet Pam Newton

Pam Newton says, "I knew from kindergarten that I wanted to be an artist. I liked to draw horses." As a child, Newton also liked to read. Her favorite stories were fairy tales by the Brothers Grimm and Hans Christian Andersen. She still spends all her extra time reading.

Today, as Newton reads, she looks for folk tales and myths that she can retell and illustrate. Newton chooses folk tales very carefully. She knows the story is good, she says, "if it makes pictures in your head."

The Stonecutter began not with a picture in her head but with one outside a window. When she and her family lived in Turkey, she awakened one morning to see a camel caravan passing by. Years later, Newton read the tale about the stonecutter and realized she had found a place for the long-remembered caravan.

The Story Song

Where do stories come from? Tell me if you know.
Where do stories come from, and where do stories go?
Stories come from deep inside, then they travel far and wide—
That's where stories come from, that's where stories go.

Where do stories come from? Tell me if you can.
Where do stories come from? History of man, and woman.
Stories come from me to you, travel on to who knows who—
That's where stories come from, that's where stories go.

If you like my stories, tell them to a friend.
Keep the chain a-growing, stories never end.
From a golden story box, turn the key, unlock the locks—
That's where stories come from, that's where stories go.

That's where stories come from . . . that's where stories go!

Marcia Lane

READING RESOURCES

CONTENTS

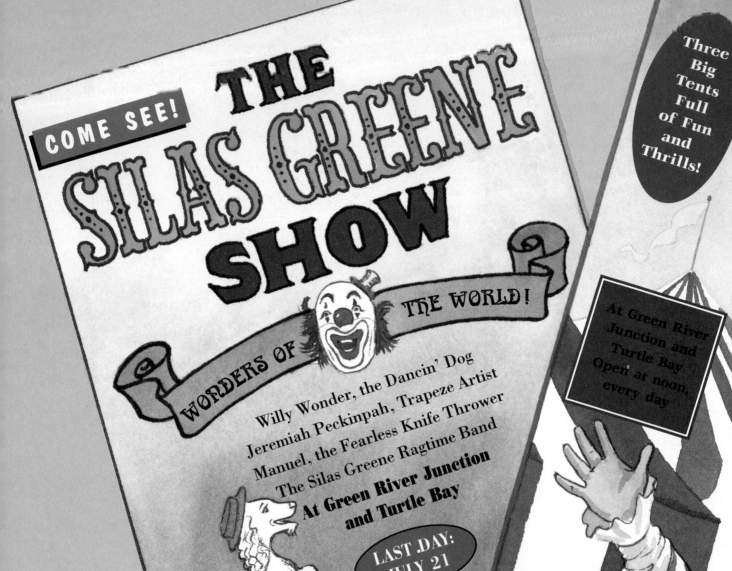

COME SEE! **THE SILAS GREENE SHOW**

WONDERS OF THE WORLD!

Willy Wonder, the Dancin' Dog
Jeremiah Peckinpah, Trapeze Artist
Manuel, the Fearless Knife Thrower
The Silas Greene Ragtime Band
At Green River Junction and Turtle Bay

LAST DAY: JULY 21

ADMISSION
Adults 25 Cents
Children 10 Cents
Refreshments Available

OPEN AT NOON - EVERY DAY!

Three Big Tents Full of Fun and Thrills!

At Green River Junction and Turtle Bay Open at noon, every day

Admission:
25 cents ADULTS
10 cents CHILDREN
Refreshments Available

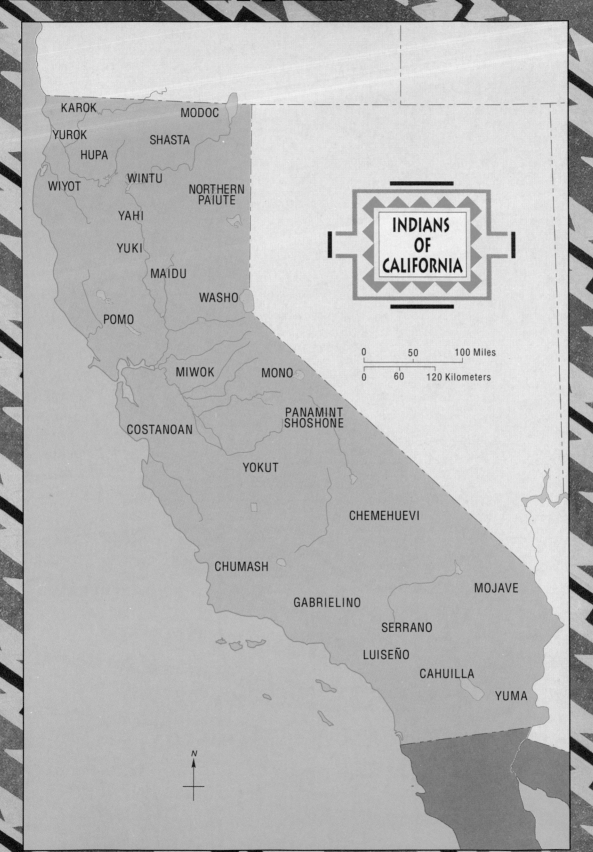

KAROK
MODOC
YUROK
SHASTA
HUPA
WIYOT
WINTU
NORTHERN
PAIUTE
YAHI
YUKI
MAIDU
WASHO
POMO
MIWOK
MONO
COSTANOAN
PANAMINT
SHOSHONE
YOKUT
CHEMEHUEVI
CHUMASH
MOJAVE
GABRIELINO
SERRANO
LUISEÑO
CAHUILLA
YUMA

INDIANS OF CALIFORNIA

0   50   100 Miles
0   60   120 Kilometers

N

ATLAS

OREGON

IDAHO

CASCADE RANGE

GOOSE LAKE

Crescent City

Klamath Mountains

Klamath R.

Mount Shasta
14,162 ft.
(4,317 m.)

Pit R.

EAGLE LAKE

Humboldt Bay

Trinity R.

SHASTA LAKE

Eureka

Mad R.

Cape Mendocino

Redding

Lassen Peak
10,457 ft.
(3,187 m)

HONEY LAKE

COAST

Sacramento R.

SACRAMENTO VALLEY

Chico

SIERRA

CLEAR LAKE

Point Arena

Russian R.

Feather R.

LAKE TAHOE

Sacramento

American R.

Santa Rosa

Mokelumne R.

NEVADA

Sonora Peak
11,429 ft.
(3,484 m)

MONO LAKE

Point Reyes

Stockton

Stanislaus R.

Tuolumne R.

San Francisco

Oakland

San Joaquin R.

Modesto

Merced R.

Boundary Peak
13,145 ft. (4,006 m)

San Francisco Bay

San Jose

Mount Lyell
13,095 ft.
(3,991 m)

Owens R.

NEVADA

Santa Cruz

RANGES

Madera

Monterey Bay

Fresno R.

Fresno

Salinas

SAN JOAQUIN VALLEY

DEATH VALLEY

Monterey

Salinas R.

Mount Whitney
14,494 ft.
(4,418 m)

OWENS LAKE

282 ft. (86 m)
below sea level

Point Sur

Hanford

Telescope Peak
11,045 ft. (3,367 m)

Tulare

TulareBasin

Kern R.

San Luis Obispo

Bakersfield

MOJAVE DESERT

SODA LAKE

Buena Vista
Lake Reservoir

Tehachapi Mountains

Mojave R.

PACIFIC

Lompoc

Point Conception

Santa Barbara

San Bernardino Mountains

San Miguel

Santa Cruz

Oxnard

Pasadena

San Gorgonio Mountain
11,502 ft. (3,506 m)

Los Angeles

San Bernardino

Santa Rosa

Long Beach

Anaheim

Palm Springs

OCEAN

San Clemente

SALTON SEA

Santa Catalina

Oceanside

San Nicolas

Gulf of Santa Catalina

Escondido

IMPERIAL VALLEY

COLORADO DESERT

Colorado R.

San Clemente

San Diego

El Centro

Point Loma

ARIZONA

N

MEXICO

CALIFORNIA
Landforms

★ State Capital
• Other City
▨ Mountains
▨ Hills
▨ Plateaus
▨ Plains

0   50   100 Miles

0   60   120 Kilometers

BROCHURES

Welcome ~to~ Yosemite National Park

Welcome to Yosemite National Park! You're about to discover a magnificent landscape that compelled explorer John Muir to petition to make Yosemite a national park in 1880. Today, 3.5 million visitors come annually to marvel at the natural beauty that is Yosemite National Park.

A Few Basic Facts

Size of the Park: 1,189 sq. mi. (3080 sq. km.)

Highest Point: Cloud's Rest 1 mi. (1.6 km.)

Location of the Park: 200 mi. (320 km.) east of San Francisco, 320 mi. (515 km.) northeast of Los Angeles

Main Roads to the Park: Routes 140, 41, and 120

Admission:
$3.00 if you enter by foot, bicycle, or bus
$5.00 by car

Park Services

General Park Information: 209-372-0265
Yosemite Valley Visitors Center: 209-372-0265
Tuolumne Meadows Visitors Center:
209-372-0263

Nature Trails

Bridalveil Falls—¼ mi. (402 m.)—easy
Mirror Lake Loop—3 mi. (4.8 km.)—easy
Cathedral Lakes—4 mi. (6.4 km.)—moderate
Nevada Fall/Mist Trail—7 mi. (11.3 km.)—difficult
Upper Yosemite Falls Trail—7.2 mi. (11.6 km.)—very difficult

Car Routes

Tioga Road: Sights include Tuolumne Meadows, Tenaya Lake, El Capitan, Bridalveil Falls, Yosemite Falls, Sentinel Dome, Half Dome
Glacier Point: Sights include Half Dome, Vernal Falls, Nevada Falls, Mariposa Grove

Don't Miss These Sights ▲▲▲

Bridalveil Falls
southern Yosemite Valley
height: 620 feet (189 meters)

Nevada Falls
"The Twisted Falls"
height: 594 feet (181 meters)

Half Dome
height: 8.852 feet
(2,698 meters)

Cloud's Rest
height: 1 mile
(1.6 km.)

BROCHURES

Map of the Park

GRAND CANYON OF
THE TUOLUMNE RIVER

120

Tioga Pass
Entrance

N
W ← → E
S

Tioga Rd.

Tenaya
Lake

Tuolumne Meadows
Visitors Center

Cathedral
Lakes

John Muir
Trail

Big Oak Flat Entrance
(Info Station)

Cloud's Rest

CATHEDRAL
RANGE

120

Valley
Visitors
Center

Yosemite
Falls

Half
Dome

Vernal Fall

El Capitan

Nevada
Fall

Mirror Lake

CLARK
RANGE

Arch Rock
Entrance

Cathedral
Rocks

140

Glacier
Point Rd.

Bridalveil
Fall

SIERRA
NATIONAL FOREST

SIERRA
NATIONAL
FOREST

Mariposa Grove

South
Entrance

To Fresno

41

5 miles
0

5 kilometers
0

CARD CATALOG

J 643.51 A

Alexander, Sally Hobart

Mom's Best Friend. The daughter of a blind woman tells about life adjusting to Mom's new seeing-eye guide dog. Photographs by George Ancona. New York: Macmillan Publishing Company, 1992.

48 pages

AUTHOR CARD

Mom's Best Friend

J 643.51 A

Alexander, Sally Hobart
Mom's Best Friend. The daughter of a blind woman tells about life adjusting to Mom's new seeing-eye guide dog. Photographs by George Ancona. New York: Macmillan Publishing Company, 1992.

48 pages

TITLE CARD

DOGS, GUIDE   J 643.51 A

Alexander, Sally Hobart
Mom's Best Friend. The daughter of a blind woman tells about life adjusting to Mom's new seeing-eye guide dog. Photographs by George Ancona. New York: Macmillan Publishing Company, 1992.

48 pages
1. dogs, guide   2. blindness   3. dogs and people
I. Ancona, George, photo. II. title

SUBJECT CARD

CARD CATALOG

COMPUTERIZED FORM OF THE CARD CATALOG

You may search the catalog by one of the following

Author   To find authors, composers, performers, illustrators, editors, conferences, corporate authors

Title   To find a work by title
EXAMPLE: >>T = Mom's Best Friend

Subject   To find material on a subject
EXAMPLE: >>S + dogs, guide
>>S = blindness

Enter your search below, or press the (NextScreen) key for more information. >>

CARD CATALOG DRAWERS

A-Bi	D-Em	J-Ken	Pe-Q	Ta-Tim
Bj-Bz	En-F	Keo-L	R-Rom	Tin-V
C-Ch	G-Hos	M-Nos	Rom-Sm	Wa-Wis
Ci-Cz	Hot-I	Not-Pa	Sn-Sz	Wit-Z

NOISE POLLUTION

Source of Noise	Decibels*	Effects
Jet airplane takeoff at close range (250 feet or 75 meters)	150 160	Painful and possibly damaging to hearing
Rock music at close range	120	
Construction work and jackhammers	110+	
Subway train		
Heavy street traffic	100 100	
	90+	
Freeway traffic	80	
Vacuum cleaner	70	Annoying
Ordinary speech		
Residential street traffic	60 60	
Average living room	50-60	
	30-60	
Whispering		
Breathing	10-20	Acceptable
	5-10	
	0	

*A decibel is the unit for measuring the loudness of sounds.

CHARTS & TABLES

Names for Animals and Their Young			
Animal	**Male**	**Female**	**Young**
Bear	Boar	Sow	Cub
Cat	Tom	Queen	Kitten
Cattle	Bull	Cow	Calf
Chicken	Rooster	Hen	Chick
Deer	Buck	Doe	Fawn
Duck	Drake	Duck	Duckling
Goose	Gander	Goose	Gosling
Horse	Stallion	Mare	Foal
Lion	Lion	Lioness	Cub
Rabbit	Buck	Doe	Bunny
Sheep	Ram	Ewe	Lamb
Swan	Cob	Pen	Cygnet
Tiger	Tiger	Tigress	Cub
Whale	Bull	Cow	Calf

CHARTS & TABLES

MADE FROM STONE

Type of Stone	Name of Structure	Date When Built	Location
Limestone	pyramids	circa 2600 B.C.	Egypt
	Acropolis	circa 400 B.C.	Greece
	pyramids	circa A.D. 600	Mexico
	Empire State Building (outer surface)	1931	New York City
Marble	Taj Mahal	1650	Agra, India
	Washington Monument	1884	Washington, D.C.
	Jefferson Memorial	1943	Washington, D.C.
	Lincoln Memorial	1922	Washington, D.C.
Granite	Mount Rushmore	1941	South Dakota
	Vietnam Memorial	1982	Washington, D.C.
Bluestone and Sandstone	Stonehenge	circa 1500 B.C.	England

Did You Know?

The Washington Monument stands 555 feet (169 meters) tall and weighs 90,000 tons (28,000 metric tons). That's a lot of marble!

Did You Know?

Mount Rushmore took 14 years to make. Builders used dynamite to remove 450,000 tons of rock. That's a lot of granite!

Did You Know?

Nobody really knows why the rocks at Stonehenge were grouped as they are.

CHARTS & TABLES

Weather in Selected U.S. Cities

City	Avg. Jan. Temp. °F	Avg. July Temp. °F	Avg. Inches Precipitation (yearly)	Days of Precipitation (yearly)
Anchorage, AK	21.1	71.1	35.74	134
Atlanta, GA	41.9	78.6	48.61	115
Boston, MA	29.6	73.5	43.81	127
Chicago, IL	21.4	73.0	33.34	127
Cloveland, OH	25.5	71.6	35.40	156
Dallas, TX	44.0	86.3	20.16	78
Honolulu, HI	72.6	80.1	23.47	100
Houston, TX	51.4	83.1	44.76	105
Knoxville, TN	38.2	77.6	47.29	127
Little Rock, AK	39.9	82.1	49.20	104
Los Angeles, CA	56.0	69.0	12.08	36
Miami, FL	67.1	82.5	57.55	129
Minneapolis, MN	11.2	73.1	26.36	115
New Orleans, LA	52.4	82.1	59.74	114
New York, NY	31.4	76.4	42.82	119
Pittsburgh, PA	26.7	72.0	36.30	154
Portland, ME	21.5	68.1	43.52	128
Raleigh, NC	39.6	77.7	41.76	112
Reno, NV	32.2	69.5	7.49	51
Salt Lake City, UT	28.6	77.5	15.31	90
San Francisco, CA	48.5	62.2	19.71	63
Seattle, WA	39.1	64.8	38.60	158
Tuscon, AZ	51.1	86.2	11.14	52
Washington, D.C.	35.2	78.9	39.00	112
Wichita, KS	29.6	81.4	28.61	85

DIAGRAMS

A FOOD CHAIN

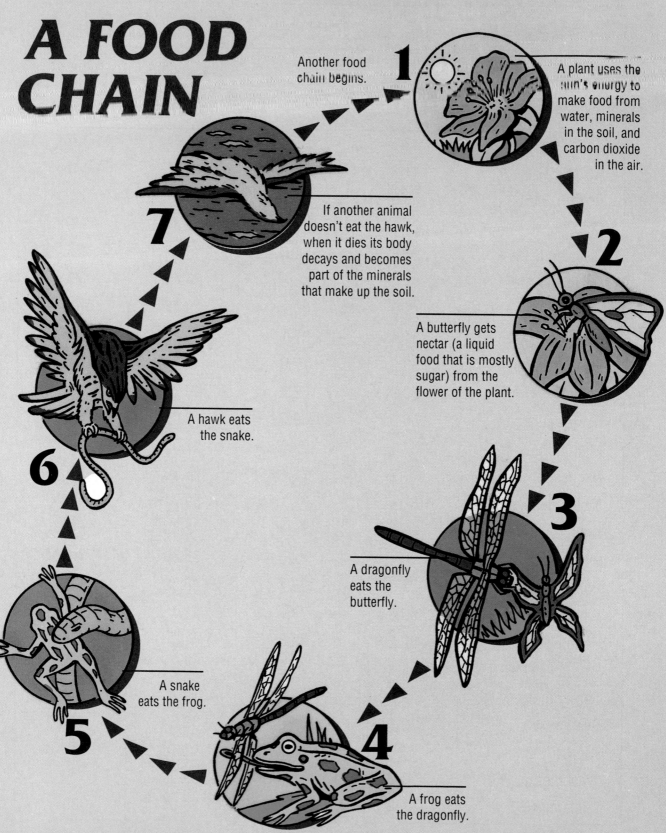

Another food chain begins.

1 A plant uses the sun's energy to make food from water, minerals in the soil, and carbon dioxide in the air.

2 A butterfly gets nectar (a liquid food that is mostly sugar) from the flower of the plant.

3 A dragonfly eats the butterfly.

4 A frog eats the dragonfly.

5 A snake eats the frog.

6 A hawk eats the snake.

7 If another animal doesn't eat the hawk, when it dies its body decays and becomes part of the minerals that make up the soil.

562

DIAGRAMS

ORIOLE PARK AT CAMDEN YARDS
home of the
BALTIMORE ORIOLES

Orioles Box Office
Ticket Prices

- ■ Club Box . . . . . $25.00 (Sec. No. 204–270)
- ■ Field Box . . . . . $20.00 (Sec. No. 14–58)
- ■ Lower Box . . . . $18.00 (Sec. No. 6–12, 60–64)
- ■ Left Field Club . . $16.00 (Sec. No. 272–288)
- ▨ Terrace Box . . . . $16.00 (Sec. No. 1–65)
- ■ Upper Box . . . . . $14.00 (Sec. No. 306–372)
- ■ Left Field Box . . $14.00 (Sec. No. 66–86)
- ■ Left Field
   Upper Box . . . . $12.00 (Sec. No. 374–388)

- ■ Upper Reserve . . . $9.00 (Sec. No. 306–372)
- ▨ Lower Reserve . . . $9.00 (Sec. No. 4, 7–87)
- ■ Left Field
   Upper Reserve . . $7.00 (Sec. No. 374–388)
- ▨ Bleachers . . . . . . $5.00 (Sec. No. 90–98)
- ☐ Standing Room . . $3.00

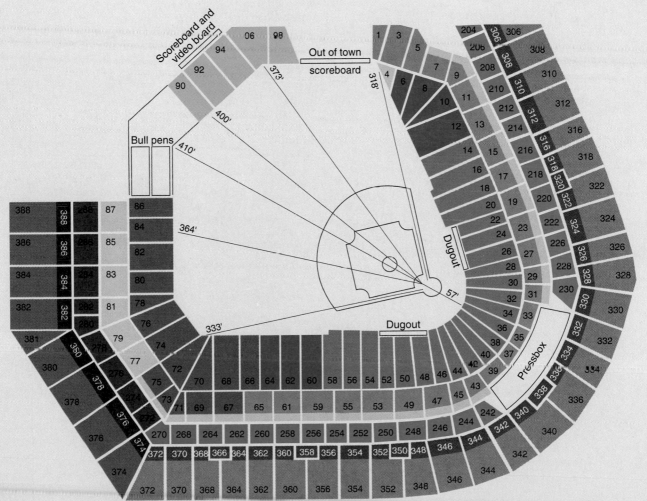

DICTIONARY

main entry

definition

pronunciation

illustration

compound word

itself. The dress hung in graceful *folds.* **2.** A mark or crease made by folding. Cut the paper along the *fold. Noun.*
    fold (fōld) *verb,* **folded, folding;** *noun,* *plural* **folds.**

fold² A pen or other closed in area for sheep. The farmer herded the sheep into the *fold* for the night.
    fold (fōld) *noun, plural* **folds.**

folder **1.** A holder for loose papers. A folder is often a folded sheet of thin cardboard. **2.** A booklet made up of folded sheets of paper. Before our trip to Europe, we got travel *folders* about all the places we wanted to see.
    fold·er (fōl′dər) *noun, plural* **folders.**

foliage The leaves on a tree or other plant.
    fo·li·age (fō′lē ij) *noun.*

folk **1.** People. City *folk* often take their vacations in the country. If you talk to the old *folks* who live here, you can learn a lot about the town's history. **2.** Family or relatives. My *folks* still live in a small town. *Noun.*
    —Coming from or belonging to the common people. Modern doctors have learned some interesting things from the *folk* medicine of China. *Adjective.*
    folk (fōk) *noun, plural* **folks** or **folk;** *adjective.*

folk dance **1.** A traditional dance that was originally invented by the common people of a region or country. **2.** The music for this kind of dance.

performing a **folk dance**

folklore The tales, beliefs, customs, or other traditions of a group of people that are handed down from one generation to the next.
    folk·lore (fōk′lôr′) *noun.*

folk music The traditional music of the common people of a region or country.

DICTIONARY

fold²/font

folk singer   A singer who sings folk songs.

folk song   **1.** A traditional song of a region or country that has been handed down among the common people.   **2.** A song imitating or in the style of a real folk song.

folktale   A traditional story that has been handed down among the common people.
folk·tale (fōk′tāl′) *noun, plural* **folktales.**

part of speech

follow   **1.** To go or come after, behind, or in back of. The lost dog *followed* us down the street. Spring *follows* winter.   **2.** To go along. *Follow* this road down the hill and turn left at the stop sign.   **3.** To act according to; obey. *Follow* the instructions on the package.   **4.** To pay attention to and understand. The listeners *followed* the story with interest. I didn't *follow* the teacher's explanation, so I asked for it to be repeated.   **5.** To make a living from. Most people along this coast *follow* the fishing trade.

example sentence

• **to follow up.**   To follow an action with something that strengthens its effect. I wrote a letter of complaint to the company, and I *followed up* with a phone call a few days later.
fol·low (fol′ō) *verb,* **followed, following.**

idiom

verb forms

follower   Someone who supports or admires a person or a set of beliefs. The *followers* of the religious leader gathered to listen to the sermon.
fol·low·er (fol′ō ər) *noun, plural* **followers.**

following   That comes after in order or time. We'll pack on Thursday evening and start on our trip the *following* morning. *Adjective.*
—A group of supporters. That author has a large *following. Noun.*
fol·low·ing (fol′ō ing) *adjective; noun, plural* **followings.**

syllable division

folly   A lack of good sense; foolishness. It is *folly* to think that you can drive anywhere in this blizzard.
fol·ly (fol′ē) *noun, plural* **follies.**

plural

fond   Liking or loving. I'm *fond* of my classmates.
fond (fond) *adjective,* **fonder, fondest.**

font   A basin used to hold water for baptism.
font (font) *noun, plural* **fonts.**

at; āpe; fär; câre; end; mē; it; ice; pîerce; hot; ōld; sông, fôrk; oil; out; up; ūse; rüle; pùll; tûrn; chin; sing; shop; thin; this; hw in white; zh in treasure. The symbol ə stands for the unstressed vowel sound in about, taken, pencil, lemon, and circus.

pronunciation key

DIRECTIONS

Planting Seeds

1

Fill the containers almost full of potting soil. Press the soil down slightly as you put it in.

SUPPLIES:
- containers with holes in them (peat pots)
- potting soil
- seeds
- stakes or popsicle sticks
- a watering can or plant sprayer

2

Put one (or two) seeds in each container. (Some seeds don't sprout. If both do, you can transplant one later.)

5

Set the containers in a pan of shallow, warm water. Leave them there until the water seeps up and moistens the soil.

3

Cover the seeds with more soil—just a thin layer. Pat the soil down.

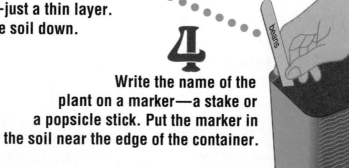

4

Write the name of the plant on a marker—a stake or a popsicle stick. Put the marker in the soil near the edge of the container.

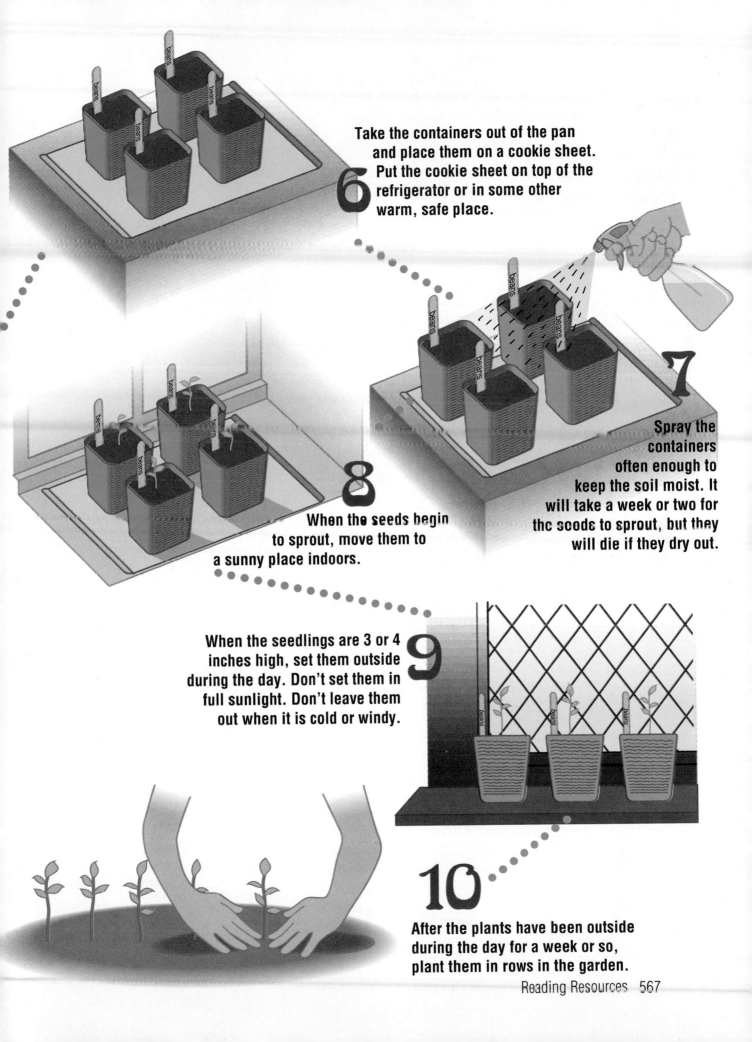

6 Take the containers out of the pan and place them on a cookie sheet. Put the cookie sheet on top of the refrigerator or in some other warm, safe place.

7 Spray the containers often enough to keep the soil moist. It will take a week or two for the seeds to sprout, but they will die if they dry out.

8 When the seeds begin to sprout, move them to a sunny place indoors.

9 When the seedlings are 3 or 4 inches high, set them outside during the day. Don't set them in full sunlight. Don't leave them out when it is cold or windy.

10 After the plants have been outside during the day for a week or so, plant them in rows in the garden.

558   Hiawatha

Hiawatha (hī'ə woth'ə), a 16th-century North American Indian chieftain credited with founding the Iroquois Confederacy of tribes in what is now New York State. Since every new chief of the Tortoise Clan of the Mohawk Indians inherited the name Hiawatha, the Iroquois hero is believed to have been a Mohawk. A disciple of the great Indian prophet Deganawidah, Hiawatha wanted to unite all North American tribes in universal peace. In about 1570 he and Deganawidah persuaded four nearby tribes to join the Mohawks in the Iroquois Confederacy, which dominated most Indians of the northeastern United States early in the 18th century. By that time, Iroquois legends described Hiawatha as a magical figure who had brought civilization to his people by teaching them agriculture, medicine, political cooperation, and the arts.

In the 19th century, scholars mistakenly attached Hiawatha's name to a group of legends about the mythical Chippewa hero Manabozho. Henry Wadsworth Longfellow based his famous *The Song of Hiawatha* on the Chippewa tales.

Frederick J. Dockstader

A hibernating ground squirrel is insensitive to touch.

hibernation (hī'bər nā'shən), also called winter sleep, a state of reduced activity that occurs in many animals during the winter. In cold weather most animals need relatively large amounts of food to carry on their normal body activities. In winter, however, food often becomes scarce, and many animals could not survive unless they hibernated. In the state of hibernation normal body activities are so greatly reduced that very little food is required. As a result, hibernating animals may survive for months on fat stored in the body.

Hibernation occurs in many mammals, including woodchucks, ground squirrels, hamsters, hedgehogs, and certain bats. It also occurs in most reptiles and amphibians, some insects, and a few fishes and birds. Although the condition varies slightly from one animal to the next, all hibernating animals undergo certain similar changes. The rate of metabolism is always greatly decreased, and the body temperature falls until it approaches the temperature of the animal's surroundings. Both the rate of breathing and the heartbeat slow down considerably. The animal is not sensitive to touch or sound, and it remains in a coma-like state of unconsciousness. Usually a rise in temperature arouses a hibernating animal. With the arrival of warm weather in spring, the body processes begin to speed up. Soon the animal awakens and becomes active again, searching for food that is once more available.

Mammals. Toward winter, many mammals seek out sheltered burrows or tree hollows in which to hibernate. Shortly after they fall asleep, their rate of metabolism and their body temperature fall. Breathing slows down to about the rate of one breath every five minutes, and the heart beats only four or five times a minute.

The length of time a mammal hibernates depends on the severity and length of the winter season. For example, some arctic animals hibernate for as long as eight months. Since hibernating animals live on stored body fat, mammals that hibernate for a long time may lose as much as one-third of their original weight.

Contrary to popular belief, bears do not hibernate. Although they enter a deep sleep and live on stored fat, their body temperature does not fall more than a few

degrees, and their rate of metabolism decreases very little. They remain sensitive to touch, and they can be awakened by prodding. Certain other mammals, including opossums, skunks, and raccoons, enter a deep sleep similar to that of bears. However, they do not really hibernate.

Reptiles and Amphibians. Unlike mammals, reptiles and amphibians are cold-blooded. They do not generate their own body heat, and they depend on their surroundings to provide the warmth needed to carry on their body activities. As winter approaches, many lizards and snakes enter burrows and crevices in the ground. Freshwater turtles spend the winter at the bottom of a lake or pond. Frogs, toads, and other amphibians hibernate by burying themselves in mud.

In hibernating reptiles and amphibians, the body temperature drops to only one or two degrees above that of the surroundings and sometimes almost to freezing. Almost no air is taken in, and no food is eaten.

Fishes, Insects, and Birds. Hibernation is rare in fishes. However, some freshwater species, such as the carp, move into deep water for the winter, and some freshwater eels bury themselves in mud. Certain kinds of insects, such as yellow jackets and some butterflies, also hibernate in winter. Hibernating insects usually crawl under bark or stones or into the ground.

Only a few kinds of birds are known to hibernate. Such birds include the poorwill, a small bird native to the western United States and Mexico, and some species of swifts and hummingbirds.

Lorus and Margery Milne

Hibernia (hī bėr'ni ə), the Latin name given to Ireland by the ancient Romans. It is derived from Ierne, the ancient Greek name. Today, Hibernia is occasionally used as a poetic name for Ireland. See also IRELAND.

Norman J. G. Pounds

ENCYCLOPEDIA

ENTRY
WORD

which was the strike force of Haganah, the underground Jewish army. During World War II he fought for the British in Lebanon and Syria. In the Israeli war for independence in 1948, he was deputy commander of the Palmach, and he commanded the brigade that kept the supply lines to Jerusalem open. Rabin remained in the army as a career soldier, eventually becoming chief of staff in 1964. He retired from the army in 1968 and served as ambassador to the United States from 1968 to 1973. He was minister of labor in early 1974.

Charles Radding

Raccolta (rə kōl′tə), in the Roman Catholic church, a collection of material describing the various ways of gaining indulgences, or reductions of the time a soul must pass in Purgatory. These include prayers, good works, and pilgrimages. The Raccolta was first published in 1807.

*Rev. Thomas H. McBrien, O.P.

raccoon (ra kün′), also called coon, a stout-bodied mammal with a pointed face and long bushy tail. Raccoon live in many regions throughout the continental United States, Mexico, and Central America. They are especially abundant in parts of southern Canada, and some raccoon are found as far south as the equator.

The raccoon's fur was used as money by early settlers in North America, and raccoon hats were often worn by explorers. Raccoon were also trapped and hunted for their tasty flesh. In some parts of the United States and Canada they are still hunted for their flesh and for their fur, which is used to make coats, collars, hats, pocketbooks, and other apparel. Raccoon from northern climates are widely used for these purposes because their coat is denser than that of raccoon living in southern areas.

Raccoon are often kept as pets, particularly in rural areas. However, it is not recommended that raccoon be taken into the home as pets. While the young are playful and mischievous, raccoon tend to become surly as they grow older.

Size and Appearance. When fully grown, large raccoon are about 2½ feet (75 cm) long, including their 9-inch-long (23-cm-long) tail. They range in weight from 10 pounds (4.5 kg) to more than 30 pounds (13.5 kg).

A raccoon's coat is usually one or more shades of gray, but it may range from yellow to black. Red, brown, and even pure-white coons are occasionally born. Across the eyes of the coon's face is a black band, which extends sideways like a mask. Another black band extends up from the tip of the nose and flares out into the gray fur that covers the head. The short rounded ears are light at the tips and edges, and the feet are also light in color. The tail is banded, usually with five bands of light gray.

Behavior. Most raccoon live in hollow trees. They may also live in holes in the ground, rocky ledges, beaver dams, or even abandoned houses. Usually they remain in the nest during the day and leave only at night to search for food. Raccoon are completely omnivorous. They eat crayfish, fish, worms, and rabbits, as well as plant products, such as nuts and corn and other grains.

Contrary to popular belief, raccoon do not wash their food before eating. A raccoon may dip its food in water, but it never washes anything. The belief

Raccoons live in many regions of North America and Central America. They are skillful climbers, and they frequently escape from their predators by rapidly ascending a tree.

that it washes its food has arisen because the raccoon has a keen sense of touch and investigates objects by feeling them. Because it can feel moist objects better than dry ones, it frequently dips objects in any available water, whether it is clean or dirty. The feeling motions made by the coon are often mistaken for washing, but the animal also makes the same feeling motions with dry objects.

Like many other animals, raccoon slow down their activities during the cold winter months. They do not hibernate, but they do enter a deep sleep from which they are difficult to rouse. They are nourished through this period by deposits of fat, which they store in the body in the fall.

Reproduction. The mating season usually occurs during February and March, and the young, called cubs, are born about 61 days later. A litter generally consists of four cubs, but there may be as few as one or as many as eight. The newborn young, which are about 4 inches (10 cm) long and weigh about 6 ounces (170 gm) remain with the mother until they are about 6 months old. Raccoon mature at about the age of 8 months, but they continue to grow for 18 months. The first litter is born to females in the second year of life. Raccoon may live as long as 20 years, but the average life-span is 9 or 10 years.

Coon Hunting. On fall and early winter nights, coon hunters and their dogs invade the areas where coons are known to live. The dogs are usually a kind of hound that has been bred for hunting, but sometimes they are crosses between hounds and other breeds.

In a typical coon hunt, a party of hunters walks through the woods until a dog crosses a raccoon's track. The dog follows the trail to the tree that the animal has climbed and barks steadily until the hunters arrive to shoot the coon. Some dogs are trained to run ahead of a hunter's slow-moving automobile. When the dog crosses a coon's trail, the hunters park the car and follow the dog through the woods until it trees the coon. After a hunt, raccoon are often eaten.

The raccoon, *Procyon lotor*, is classified in the order Carnivora, family Procyonidae.

Leon F. Whitney

FORMS & APPLICATIONS

If you enjoyed **Folktales of the United States**, you may want to read some of the other books included in WORLD-WIDE PUBLISHERS' series FOLKTALES OF THE WORLD. Use the handy order form below to receive copies.

— — — — — — — — — — — — — — — DETACH HERE — — — — — — — — — — — — — — — —

ORDER FORM

Folktales of China	#1002 $4.95	**Folktales of England**	#1007 $4.95
Folktales of Africa	#1003 $4.95	**Folktales of Australia**	#1008 $4.95
Folktales of Mexico	#1004 $4.95	**Folktales of Canada**	#1009 $4.95
Folktales of South America	#1005 $4.95	**Folktales of Greece**	#1010 $4.95
Folktales of France	#1006 $4.95	**Folktales of the Pacific**	#1011 $4.95

Please Print

NAME Douglas Montero

ADDRESS 732 West Alameda

CITY Goshen   STATE Ala.   ZIP 00000

PHONE (000) 555-7231

ITEM #	QTY.	NAME OF BOOK	ITEM PRICE	TOTAL	POSTAGE ($.50 per item)	TOTAL ITEM CHARGES
1006	2	Folktales of France	$4.95	$9.90	$1.00	$10.90
1007	1	Folktales of England	4.95	4.95	.50	5.45
1008	1	Folktales of Australia	4.95	4.95	.50	5.45
1010	1	Folktales of Greece	4.95	4.95	.50	5.45

PAYMENT METHOD (check one)

☑ CHECK

❏ MONEY ORDER

(SORRY – NO CREDIT CARDS)

Price & Postage TOTAL	$27.25
Special handling ($.50 per item)	
Tax: 5% for residents of Iowa	
TOTAL	$27.25

SEND TO: WORLD-WIDE PUBLISHERS
Folktales of the World
2200 North Mississippi
Chanticlere, Iowa 00000

ALLOW 3-4 WEEKS FOR DELIVERY

LAKESIDE LIBRARY
APPLICATION FOR LIBRARY CARD

PLEASE PRINT

NAME _____Lung Wei_____

ADDRESS _____439 Coolidge_____
number and street   apt. # if applicable

HOME PHONE _____555-7019_____

MAILING ADDRESS _____
(only if different from above address)   number and street

_____Privet Point,_____   _____Michigan_____   _____00000_____
city   state   zip

PARENT/GUARDIAN NAME _____Ying Wei_____

SCHOOL _____Garrison Elementary_____
(if attending)

EMPLOYER NAME _____

EMPLOYER ADDRESS _____
number and street

_____
city   state   zip

WORK PHONE _____ EXT. _____

**I AGREE TO FOLLOW ALL LIBRARY RULES AND BE
RESPONSIBLE FOR ALL MATERIALS THAT ARE CHARGED
TO THIS CARD.**

X _____Lung Wei_____
signature of patron

X _____Ying Wei_____
signature of parent/guardian if patron is under 18

The library requests your VOLUNTARY assistance in providing
information in order to select materials, plan services and
programs, and apply for possible grants. This information is
confidential. **PLEASE CIRCLE THE APPROPRIATE LETTERS:**

BORN BETWEEN:
A. BEFORE 1900   D. 1921-1930   G. 1951-1960   (J.) 1981-2000
B. 1901-1910   E. 1931-1940   H. 1961-1970
C. 1911-1920   F. 1941-1950   I. 1971-1980

CIRCLE YOUR PRIMARY READING LANGUAGE:
A. Arabic   E. German   I. Maltese   M. Tagalog
(B) Chinese   F. Italian   J. Portuguese N. Tongan
(C) English   G. Japanese   K. Russian   O. Vietnamese
D. French   H. Korean   L. Spanish   P. Other _____

THANK YOU FOR YOUR COOPERATION

STAFF USE ONLY

DATE: _____

INIT/LIB: _____

BAR CODE #: _____

OTHER ID: _____

MAIL CODE:
1   2   3

AGE: _____

READ. LANG: _____

_____

DATE ENTERED:
_____

INITIALS: _____

GRAPHS

Wonderful

Sizing Them Up

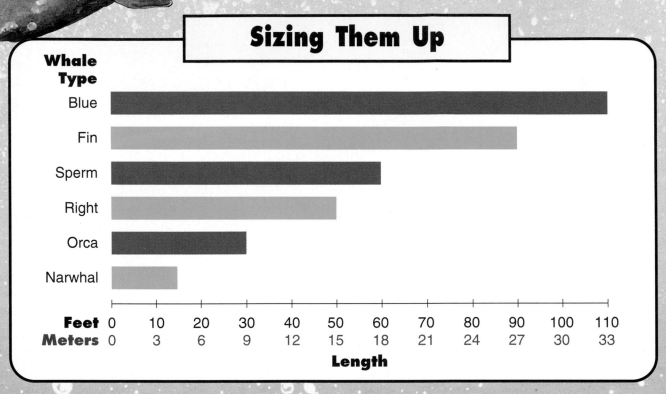

Whale Type

Whale Type	Length
Blue	
Fin	
Sperm	
Right	
Orca	
Narwhal	

Feet	0	10	20	30	40	50	60	70	80	90	100	110
Meters	0	3	6	9	12	15	18	21	24	27	30	33

Length

A Weighty Whale

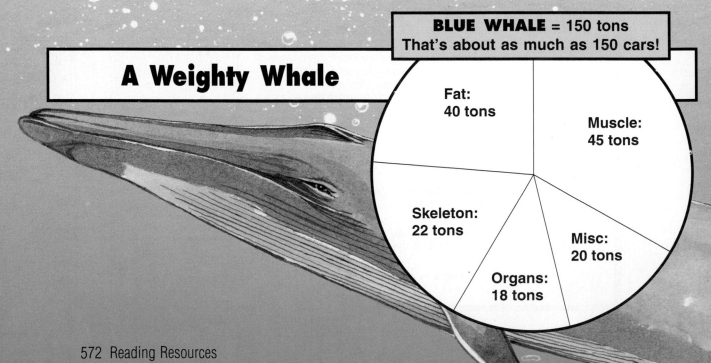

BLUE WHALE = 150 tons
That's about as much as 150 cars!

Fat: 40 tons

Muscle: 45 tons

Skeleton: 22 tons

Misc: 20 tons

Organs: 18 tons

GRAPHS

Whales

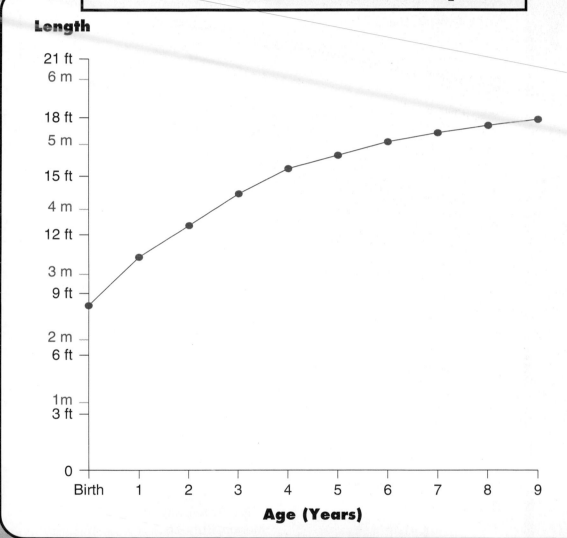

A Killer Whale Grows Up

Length

21 ft
6 m

18 ft
5 m

15 ft
4 m

12 ft

3 m
9 ft

2 m
6 ft

1m
3 ft

0

Birth   1   2   3   4   5   6   7   8   9

Age (Years)

INDEX

115

PETPURE
Insect-Killing Mist

Kills fleas, ticks, and lice on dogs or cats for up to 2 weeks

Active Ingredient: D-trans Allethrin 1%
Inert Ingredients 99%

CAUTION: Some animals may be sensitive to this spray. Do not use on sick animals. Keep away from eyes of animals and humans. Wear protective clothing.

KEEP OUT OF REACH OF CHILDREN

Eyes: If spray comes into contact with eyes, flush with plenty of water. Get medical attention.

Skin: If spray comes into contact with skin, wash with soap and water. Get medical attention if irritation develops.

Environmental Hazards: This product is toxic to marine life. Keep out of lakes, streams, and ponds.

Do not reuse empty container.

DIRECTIONS:
It is a violation to use this product in a manner inconsistent with its labeling.
Shake Well Before Using. Spray animal from a distance of about 12 inches. For long-haired animals, part hair for good penetration. Spray entire animal, from back of neck to tail. Avoid facial area. Spray until coat is moist.

PET PURE INDUSTRIES

Do Not Use If Plastic Wrap Is Broken

Infants' Fruit-Flavored Acetaminophen Drops

Usage: for temporary relief of fever, discomfort, or pain due to colds, flu, or teething.

Dosage: Repeat every 4 hours up to 4 times daily.

Age	Weight (lb)	Dose
Under 2	*Under 24*	*Consult Your Doctor*
2–3	24–35	2 Dropperfuls

Fill dropper to marked level. Squeeze slowly into child's mouth. Can also be mixed with juices or formula.

Each dropperful (0.8 mL) contains 80 mg acetaminophen
Inactive Ingredients: Citric Acid, Artificial Flavoring, Glycerin, Propylene Glycol, Saccharin, Purified Water

Warning: Keep this and all medication out of the reach of children. In case of accidental overdosage, contact a physician or poison control center.

Consult your physician if fever persists for more than 3 days or if pain continues for more than 5 days.

See bottom panel for expiration date.

Do not use with other pain-killers or other products that contain acetaminophen without consulting your physician.

Migration Route of the Harp Seal

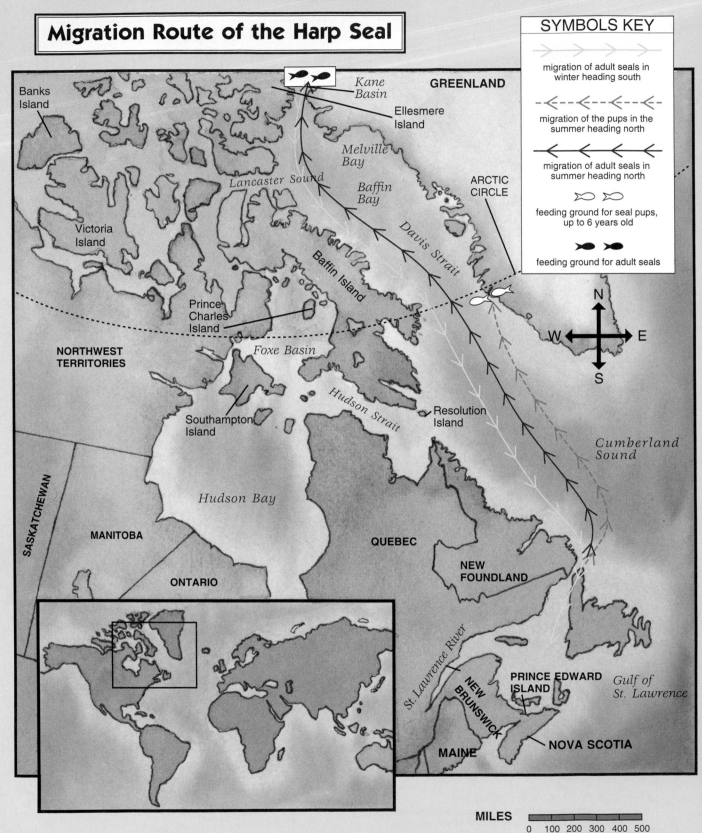

SYMBOLS KEY

migration of adult seals in winter heading south

migration of the pups in the summer heading north

migration of adult seals in summer heading north

feeding ground for seal pups, up to 6 years old

feeding ground for adult seals

GREENLAND

Banks Island

Kane Basin

Ellesmere Island

Melville Bay

Baffin Bay

Lancaster Sound

ARCTIC CIRCLE

Davis Strait

Victoria Island

Baffin Island

Prince Charles Island

NORTHWEST TERRITORIES

Foxe Basin

Cumberland Sound

Southampton Island

Hudson Strait

Resolution Island

SASKATCHEWAN

MANITOBA

Hudson Bay

QUEBEC

ONTARIO

NEW FOUNDLAND

St. Lawrence River

NEW BRUNSWICK

PRINCE EDWARD ISLAND

Gulf of St. Lawrence

MAINE

NOVA SCOTIA

MILES
0 100 200 300 400 500

KILOMETERS
0 100 200 300 400 500

N
W — E
S

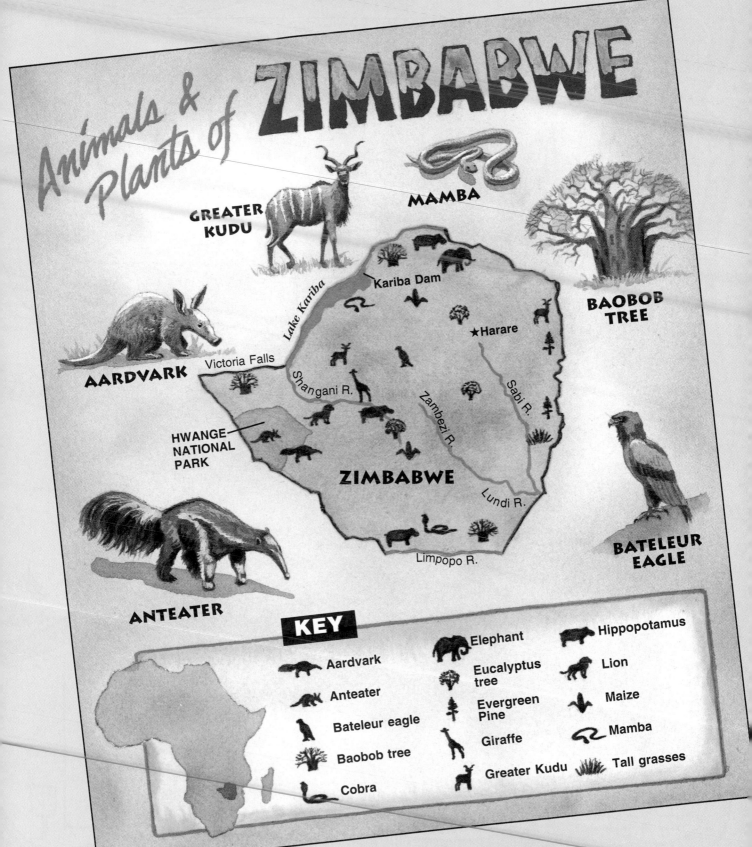

Animals & Plants of ZIMBABWE

GREATER KUDU

MAMBA

BAOBOB TREE

AARDVARK

Lake Kariba

Kariba Dam

Victoria Falls

Shangani R.

★Harare

Sabi R.

Zambezi R.

HWANGE NATIONAL PARK

ZIMBABWE

Lundi R.

ANTEATER

Limpopo R.

BATELEUR EAGLE

KEY

Aardvark

Anteater

Bateleur eagle

Baobob tree

Cobra

Elephant

Eucalyptus tree

Evergreen Pine

Giraffe

Greater Kudu

Hippopotamus

Lion

Maize

Mamba

Tall grasses

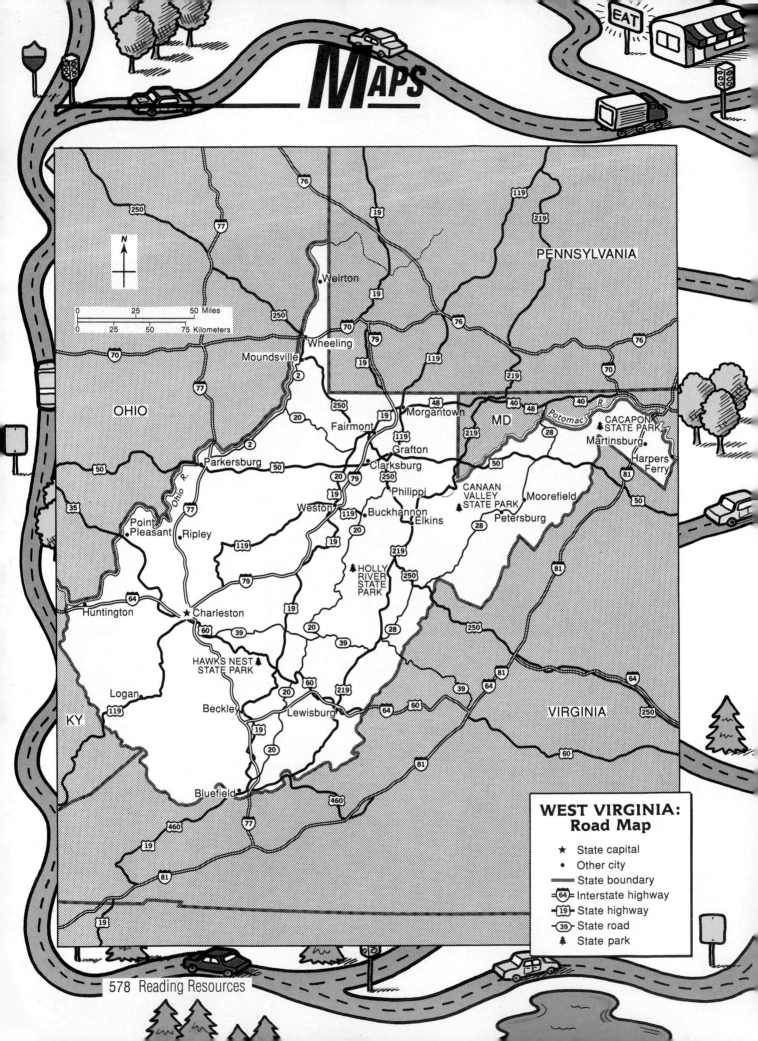

Maps

WEST VIRGINIA: Road Map

★ State capital
• Other city
━━━ State boundary
🛡64🛡 Interstate highway
🛡19 State highway
🛡39 State road
🌲 State park

Locations

PENNSYLVANIA

Weirton
Wheeling
Moundsville
Morgantown
Fairmont
Grafton
Clarksburg
Philippi
Weston
Buckhannon
Elkins

OHIO

Parkersburg
Point Pleasant
Ripley

Huntington
Charleston

HAWKS NEST STATE PARK

Logan
Beckley
Lewisburg

KY

Bluefield

HOLLY RIVER STATE PARK

CANAAN VALLEY STATE PARK

Moorefield
Petersburg

MD

CACAPON STATE PARK
Martinsburg
Harpers Ferry

VIRGINIA

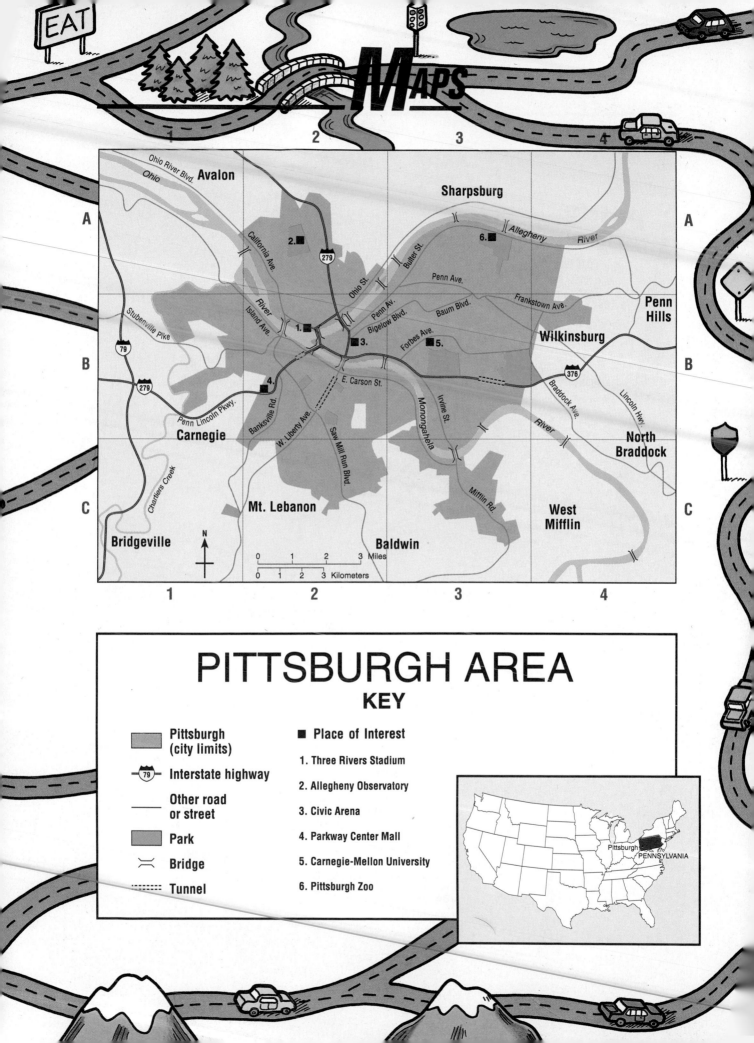

PITTSBURGH AREA
KEY

Pittsburgh (city limits)

Interstate highway

Other road or street

Park

Bridge

Tunnel

■ Place of Interest

1. Three Rivers Stadium
2. Allegheny Observatory
3. Civic Arena
4. Parkway Center Mall
5. Carnegie-Mellon University
6. Pittsburgh Zoo

Pulao
A Rice Dish from India

Pulao (pronounced POU-low), is made with special rice called basmati (bah-SMAH-tee). It has a delicious nutty flavor. Try to find some to use for this recipe. If not, long-grain wild rice will work also. You will also need a variety of spices to make this recipe from northern India come alive. (Serves 6–8.)

Ingredients

½ cup vegetable or peanut oil

½ medium onion, thinly sliced

5 whole cloves

½ stick cinnamon

5 cardamom pods

½ teaspoon ground coriander

1 cup basmati or other long-grain rice, rinsed and well drained

2 cups boiling water

½ teaspoon salt

1 tablespoon butter or margarine

¼ cup raisins

2 tablespoons blanched, slivered almonds or cashews

Steps

1. Pour the oil into a medium saucepan and heat over a medium-high flame.

2. Add the onion and cook for 5 minutes.

3. Stir in the cloves, cinnamon, cardamom, and coriander. Reduce heat and cook for 1 minute.

4. Now add the uncooked rice. Fry until the rice has been well covered with oil.

5. Pour in the water, add salt, and bring to a boil.

6. Lower the heat, cover, and cook for 15 minutes until the water has been absorbed and the rice is tender.

7. In a separate pan, heat the butter; then add in the raisins and nuts to brown.

8. Now mix the rice with the nuts and raisins. Make sure you remove the cloves, cinnamon stick, and cardamom pods.

9. Eat right away!

SCHEDULES

4th GRADE CLASS SCHEDULE

TIME / DAY	MONDAY	TUESDAY	WEDNESDAY	THURSDAY	FRIDAY
8:00-8:10	Flag Salute, Announcements	Flag Salute, Announcements	Flag Salute, Announcements	Flag Salute, Announcements	Flag Salute, Announcements
8:10-9:50	Language Arts	Language Arts	Language Arts	Language Arts	Language Arts
9:50-10:10	P.E.	P.E.	P.E.	P.E.	P.E.
10:10-11:10	Social Studies	Social Studies	Social Studies	Social Studies	Social Studies
11:10-11:50	Lunch & Recess	Lunch & Recess	Lunch & Recess	Lunch & Recess	Lunch & Recess
11:50-12:15	Independent Reading	Independent Reading	Independent Reading	Independent Reading	Independent Reading
12:15-1:00	Math	Math	Math	Math	Math
1:00-1:30	Health	Health	Health	Health	Health
1:30-1:45	Recess	Recess	Recess	Recess	Recess
1:45-2:20	Science	Science	Science	Science	Science
2:20-2:45	Art	Music	Art	Music	Art
2:45	D I S M I S S A L				

Drawing with the Computer

A User's Manual

Using the Paint Tools

This is the paint tools palette.

Just like tools in the real world, each paint tool creates a different effect. Experimenting with the tools is the best way to find out how they work. Follow these simple steps to get started.

The Pencil Tool

The pencil tool draws thick and thin lines. It's good for outlines and rough sketches.

The Paint Bucket Tool

The paint bucket tool fills a space with whatever color and pattern you have chosen. First click the paint bucket. Then click a solid color or pattern on the color palette.

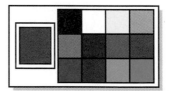

Then click the area you want to fill with that color. We chose a different color for each fruit.

TECHNOLOGY

 ## The Line Tool

The line tool draws straight lines. Just click-and-drag between two points.

The line tool is good for tables, buildings, and windows. What other objects can you think of to draw with straight lines?

 ## The Spray Can Tool

The spray can tool sprays a color into an area, but it doesn't completely fill the area. It's good for adding texture to your drawing.

 ## The Eraser Tool

The eraser tool is for getting rid of mistakes. Just like an eraser on a chalkboard, it will erase whatever you drag it across.

Exploring the paint tools is easy, especially if you don't worry too much about your first few drawings. Just experiment with all the tools to see what works best for you. And remember, if you make a mistake, you can just erase it!

Emergency 1

EMERGENCY NUMBERS

Blairtown

Fire	**555-2323**
Police (Alternate number 555-2616)	**555-2452**
Sheriff (Night 555-2412)	**555-2501**
Ambulance	**555-2104**

Grenfell

Fire	**911**
Police	**911**
Sheriff	**555-6180 or 555-3822**
Ambulance	**911**

San Ruiz

Fire	**555-2123**
Police	**555-3031**
Sheriff (Night 555-2412)	**555-2501 or 555-2940**
Ambulance	**555-2104**

Other Emergency Numbers

Police Control Center	**1 + 800-555-6633**
Highway Patrol	**1 + 555-2562**
FBI	**1 + 555-555-8181**
If no answer call	**1 + 555-555-6100**

For Other Helpful Numbers see page 14

On the

TELEPHONE DIRECTORY

Kreel Floyd 519 S Burr.............................555-1665
Kreen Mae 418 W 1 555-2644
Kruger Al 215 N Spencer..........................555-2936
Kruger Burt Rt 1.....................................555-3428
Kruger John 202 Lebow...........................555-3952

L

L & S Hardware 101 Webster 555-3400
Lamb Otto 560 Benton 555-2857
LARSON GRAIN CO Hwy 44......................555-4000
Lee K T 110 N Burr..................................555-2242
Leery Jacob 811 E 10 555-2901
Lemon Alice 806 Lebow 555-2865
Lester Betty L 112 W 1 555-5254

Lucas Ben 220 S Adams 555-9778
Lumis Roger Rt 1 555-2705
Lunez Martin 502 N Spencer 555-2345
Lyman C E 519 Lebow.............................555-3143
Lymann Carl 820 Webster 555-6167
Lyon Margaret 113 S Spencer.................555-7881
Lyons Ed 220 Benton 555-5274
Lyons Frances 531 E 2 555-5201
Lyons Juanita 1555 N Adams..................555-2667
Lyons Max 117 Benton............................555-3788

M

Macer Tim 333 W 7 555-6778
Mac_____ 609 S Denison 555-4287

Farm Equipment

Bane Bros Farms Inc
620 Lebow Blairtown...................555-5500

FARMER AND RANCH INC

| Combines | Tractors | Irrigation Equipment |

Hwy 44 San Ruiz......................**555-6666**

Gard Farm Supply Rte 1..............555-4646

FARM EQUIPMENT

Tractors new and used
Forage tools
Combines and other harvest machines

Parts • Service • Finance

JUSTIN FARM SUPPLY
555 6700

FEDERAL OFFICES - See Government-United States

Feed Dealers

Argo Agri Services
Blairtown 555-7990
BLAIRTOWN FEED AND SEED
W Hwy 37....................................555-7855

CENTERTOWN COOP

Feed and Fertilizer Supply
Equipment to Lease

201 W 23............................**555-4488**

Midway Suppliers
E Hwy 37.....................................555-8345
Sutton Feed & Fertilizer Supply
3400 W Jackson San Ruiz................555-6652
WESTERN SUPPLY
1616 N Burr San Ruiz 555-3435

WILLIAMS EQUITY EXCHANGE

Liquid & Dry
Fertilizer

209 E 17 Grenfell.....................**555-2562**

GLOS

This glossary can help you to pronounce and find out the meanings of words in this book that you may not know.

The words are listed in alphabetical order. Guide words at the top of each page tell you the first and last words on the page.

Each word is divided into syllables. The way to pronounce each word is given next. You can understand the pronunciation respelling by using the key at right. A shorter key appears at the bottom of every other page.

When a word has more than one syllable, a dark accent mark (′) shows which syllable is stressed. In some words, a light accent mark (′) shows which syllable has a less heavy stress.

Glossary entries are based on entries in *The Macmillan/McGraw-Hill School Dictionary 1.*

a	at, bad	d	dear, soda, bad
ā	ape, pain, day, break	f	five, defend, leaf, off, cough, elephant
ä	father, car, heart	g	game, ago, fog, egg
âr	care, pair, bear, their, where	h	hat, ahead
e	end, pet, said, heaven, friend	hw	white, whether, which
ē	equal, me, feet, team, piece, key	j	joke, enjoy, gem, page, edge
i	it, big, English, hymn	k	kite, bakery, seek, tack, cat
ī	ice, fine, lie, my	l	lid, sailor, feel, ball, allow
îr	ear, deer, here, pierce	m	man, family, dream
o	odd, hot, watch	n	not, final, pan, knife
ō	old, oat, toe, low	ng	long, singer, pink
ô	coffee, all, taught, law, fought	p	pail, repair, soap, happy
ôr	order, fork, horse, story, pour	r	ride, parent, wear, more, marry
oi	oil, toy	s	sit, aside, pets, cent, pass
ou	out, now	sh	shoe, washer, fish, mission, nation
u	up, mud, love, double	t	tag, pretend, fat, button, dressed
ū	use, mule, cue, feud, few	th	thin, panther, both
ü	rule, true, food	<u>th</u>	this, mother, smooth
u̇	put, wood, should	v	very, favor, wave
ûr	burn, hurry, term, bird, word, courage	w	wet, weather, reward
ə	about, taken, pencil, lemon, circus	y	yes, onion
b	bat, above, job	z	zoo, lazy, jazz, rose, dogs, houses
ch	chin, such, match	zh	vision, treasure, seizure

absolutely Completely. He is *absolutely* right about wearing the proper sneakers when running.
ab•so•lute•ly (ab'sə lüt'lē *or* ab'sə lüt'lē) *adverb*.

Abuelita A Spanish word for "Grandmother."
A•bue•li•ta (ä'bwā lē'tä) *noun*.

acquaint To make familiar. All swimmers must *acquaint* themselves with the rules of the swimming pool.
ac•quaint (ə kwānt') *verb*, **acquainted, acquainting.**

admiration A feeling of approval or respect. The astronauts have earned the *admiration* of the whole country.
ad•mi•ra•tion (ad'mə rā'shən) *noun*.

advertise To make known to the public the good qualities of. That company *advertises* its toothpaste on television, on the radio, and in magazines.
ad•ver•tise (ad'vər tīz') *verb*, **advertised, advertising.**

altitude The height that something is above the ground or above sea level. The plane flew at an *altitude* of 1 mile (1.6 kilometers).
al•ti•tude (al'ti tüd' *or* al'ti tūd') *noun*, *plural* **altitudes.**

Word History

The word **altitude** comes from the Latin word *altus*, meaning "high" or "deep." When an airplane gains altitude, it flies higher.

---

annoy To bother or disturb. The sound of that loud radio *annoys* me.
an•noy (ə noi') *verb*, **annoyed, annoying.**

antarctic An ice-covered region surrounding the South Pole.
ant•arc•tic (ant ärk'tik *or* ant är'tik) *noun*.

Antarctic

Appalachia A region of the United States that includes the Appalachian Mountains. *Appalachia* extends from southern New York to central Alabama.
Ap•pa•la•chi•a (ap'ə lā'chē ə) *noun*.

arctic An ice-covered region surrounding the North Pole.
arc•tic (ärk'tik *or* är'tik) *noun*.

assignment Something that is given out or appointed as a task. My arithmetic *assignment* is to do ten multiplication problems.
as•sign•ment (ə sīn'mənt) *noun*, *plural* **assignments.**

assure To give confidence to. We *assured* the child that the dog was friendly.
as•sure (ə shur') *verb*, **assured, assuring.**

astronaut A person trained to fly in a spacecraft. The *astronauts* landed safely on the moon.
    as•tro•naut (as′trə nôt′) *noun, plural* **astronauts.**

Word History

The word **astronaut** is made up of two Greek words that mean "star" and "sailor." An astronaut is thought of as sailing among the stars.

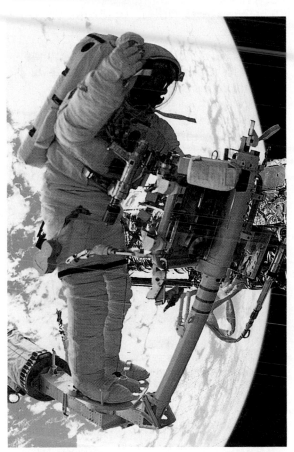

astronaut

audition A short performance that demonstrates the ability of an actor, singer, or other performer. If I give a successful *audition,* I might be asked to play in the band.
    au•di•tion (ô dish′ən) *noun, plural* **auditions.**

B

Baja California A long, narrow strip of land in northern Mexico, separating the Gulf of California from the Pacific Ocean.
    Ba•ja Cal•i•for•nia (bä′hə kal′ə fôr′nyə) *noun.*

ballerina A woman or girl who dances ballet.
    bal•le•ri•na (bal′ə rē′nə) *noun, plural* **ballerinas.**

Barents Sea The part of the Arctic Ocean north of Norway and the Soviet Union.
    Bar•ents Sea (bar′ənts sē) *noun.*

blizzard A heavy snowstorm with very strong winds. We missed the party because we couldn't drive in the *blizzard.*
    bliz•zard (bliz′ərd) *noun, plural* **blizzards.**

blowhole A breathing hole of certain whales, dolphins, and other similar animals, often located at the top of the head.
    blow•hole (blō′hōl′) *noun, plural* **blowholes.**

blubber A layer of fat under the skin of whales, seals, and some other sea animals. The oil made from whale *blubber* used to be burned in lamps.
    blub•ber (blub′ər) *noun, plural* **blubbers.**

---

at; āpe; fär; câre; end; mē; it; īce; pîerce; hot; ōld; sông; fôrk; oil; out; up; ūse; rüle; půll; tûrn; chin; sing; shop; thin; <u>th</u>is; hw in white; zh in treasure. The symbol ə stands for the unstressed vowel sound in about, taken, pencil, lemon, and circus.

braille A system of printing for blind people. The letters of the alphabet in *braille* are formed by raised dots. Blind people read *braille* by touching the dots with their fingers.
braille (brāl) *noun*.

brilliant Very bright; sparkling. The diamond shone with a *brilliant* light.
bril•liant (bril′yənt) *adjective*.

bulge To swell out. The bag *bulged* with groceries.
bulge (bulj) *verb*, **bulged, bulging.**

burrow A hole dug in the ground by an animal. Rabbits, gophers, woodchucks, and other animals use *burrows.* ▲Other words that sound like this are **borough** and **burro.**
bur•row (bûr′ō) *noun, plural* **burrows.**

C

Caleb (kā′ləb).

Canada A country in North America that is north of the United States.
Can•a•da (kan′ə də) *noun*.

captivity The state of being held by force as a prisoner. Animals in a zoo live in *captivity.*
cap•tiv•i•ty (kap tiv′i tē) *noun, plural* **captivities.**

cast 1. To pick the actors who will take different roles in a play. They *cast* me as the wicked magician in the class play. **2.** To send or put. Each student *cast* a vote in the election for class president.
cast (kast) *verb*, **cast, casting.**

celebration The ceremonies and other activities that are carried on to observe or honor a special day or event. All the members of the winning team were at the victory celebration.
cel•e•bra•tion (sel′ə brā′shən) *noun, plural* **celebrations.**

Chandra (chän′drə *or* shän′drə).

Charlottetown The capital and largest city of Prince Edward Island, Canada, a port on the southern coast of the province.
Char•lotte•town (shär′lət toun′) *noun*.

chemical A substance made by or used in chemistry. Ammonia is a *chemical* used in household cleansers.
chem•i•cal (kem′i kəl) *noun, plural* **chemicals.**

chessboard A square board marked off into sixty-four alternately colored squares, used in playing chess or checkers.
chess•board (ches′bôrd) *noun, plural* **chessboards.**

chessboard

Chuku (chü′kü).

circulate To pass from person to person. Bills and coins *circulate.*
cir•cu•late (sûr′kyə lāt′) *verb*, **circulated, circulating.**

clasp To hold or grasp close or tight. The young child *clasped* the cup with both hands.
clasp (klasp) *verb*, **clasping, clasped.**

coil Anything wound into rings. Wind the hose into a *coil* when you finish watering the flowers.
    coil (koil) *noun, plural* **coils.**

collapse 1. To lose strength or health. The heat caused some of the marchers in the parade to *collapse.* 2. To fall in; break down or fail. The force of the explosion caused the house to *collapse.*
    col•lapse (kə laps′) *verb,* **collapsed, collapsing.**

commercial Having to do with business or trade. He worked on a *commercial* fishing boat but enjoyed fishing for pleasure on the weekends.
    com•mer•cial (kə mûr′shəl) *adjective.*

commotion A noisy confusion; disorder. There was a *commotion* at the stadium as the crowd booed the referee's decision.
    com•mo•tion (kə mō′shən) *noun, plural* **commotions.**

companion A person who often goes along with another; friend; comrade. We three students were constant *companions* at camp last summer.
    com•pan•ion (kəm pan′yən) *noun, plural* **companions.**

compass An instrument for showing directions. A *compass* has a magnetic needle that points to the north. Airplane pilots, ship captains, and many other people use *compasses.*
    com•pass (kum′pəs) *noun, plural* **compasses.**

compass

considerate Thoughtful of other people and their feelings. It's *considerate* to leave some peanuts for the rest of the family.
    con•sid•er•ate (kən sid′ər it) *adjective.*

Consuela (kōn swä′lä).

crackle To make slight, sharp, snapping sounds. Dry leaves *crackle* when you walk on them. Some breakfast cereals *crackle* when you pour on milk.
    crack•le (krak′əl) *verb,* **crackled, crackling.**

creation The formation of the world and all the things in it.
    cre•a•tion (krē ā′shən) *noun, plural* **creations.**

crumple To press or crunch into wrinkles or folds. We *crumpled* sheets of newspaper to start the fire.
    crum•ple (krum′pəl) *verb,* **crumpled, crumpling.**

D

dart To jump or move suddenly and quickly. We watched the rabbit *dart* into the bushes.
    dart (därt) *verb,* **darted, darting.**

at; āpe; fär; câre; end; mē; it; īce; pîerce; hot; ōld; sông; fôrk; oil; out, up; ūse; rüle; pull; tûrn; chin; sing; shop; thin; **this**; hw in **wh**ite; **zh** in treasure. The symbol ə stands for the unstressed vowel sound in about, taken, pencil, lemon, and circus.

dazzle **1.** To make almost blind by too much light. The bright sun on the beach *dazzled* our eyes. **2.** To impress with something very showy or brilliant. The acrobat's spectacular tricks *dazzled* the audience.
> **daz•zle** (daz′əl) *verb*, **dazzled, dazzling.**

descend To move or come down from a higher place to a lower one. They rode up the hill in a cable car but *descended* on skis.
> **de•scend** (di send′) *verb*, **descended, descending.**

destination A place to which a person is going or a thing is being sent. I told the train conductor that my *destination* was New York City.
> **des•ti•na•tion** (des′tə nā′shən) *noun, plural* **destinations.**

detect To find out; discover. I called the fire department after I *detected* smoke coming from the garage.
> **de•tect** (di tekt′) *verb*, **detected, detecting.**

devour To eat; consume. The lion *devoured* the deer.
> **de•vour** (di vour′) *verb*, **devoured devouring.**

dogwood A tree or shrub that has small flowers with a greenish yellow center and pink or white leaves that look like petals.
> **dog•wood** (dôg′wu̇d′) *noun, plural* **dogwoods.**

dogwood

editor A person who edits. The *editor* made changes in the book after talking with its author.
> **ed•i•tor** (ed′i tər) *noun, plural* **editors.**

eerie Strange in a scary way; making people frightened or nervous. The sound of the tree branches hitting the house is *eerie*.
> **ee•rie** (îr′ē) *adjective*, **eerier, eeriest.**

encounter To meet, usually unexpectedly. I *encountered* an old friend on my way to the library.
> **en•coun•ter** (en koun′tər) *verb*, **encountered, encountering.**

exist To be real. We all know her imaginary friend doesn't *exist*.
> **ex•ist** (eg zist′) *verb*, **existed, existing.**

expand To make larger or become larger. Metal *expands* when it is heated.
> **ex•pand** (ek spand′) *verb*, **expanded, expanding.**

explanation A reason or meaning. My parents wanted an *explanation* for why the vase was broken.
> **ex•pla•na•tion** (ek′splə nā′shən) *noun, plural* **explanations.**

expose To make something known; reveal. The police *exposed* a gang of thieves who were stealing cars.
> **ex•pose** (ek spōz′) *verb*, **exposed, exposing.**

extraordinary Very unusual; remarkable. The art teacher said that I have *extraordinary* talent.
> **ex•traor•di•nar•y** (ek strôr′də ner′ē *or* ek′strə ôr′də ner′ē) *adjective*.

fade To become gradually weaker, fainter, or dimmer. The sound of the footsteps *faded* away.
    fade (fād) *verb*, **faded, fading.**

festival A celebration or holiday. Many religious *festivals* take place throughout the year.
    fes•ti•val (fes′tə vəl) *noun, plural* **festivals.**

festival

fiery Containing or made up of fire. The *fiery* furnace provides heat and hot water for the entire house.
    fier•y (fīr′ē *or* fī′ə rē) *adjective*, **fierier, fieriest.**

flue The hollow inside part of a chimney that draws the smoke from a fireplace out of the room and into the outside air. ▲ Other words that sound like this are **flew** and **flu.**
    flue (flü) *noun, plural* **flues.**

fluke[1] Either of the two fins of a whale's tail.
    fluke (flük) *noun, plural* **flukes.**

fluke[2] An unexpected turn of luck; chance happening. By a *fluke*, we saw our friends in the large crowd at the parade.
    fluke (flük) *noun, plural* **flukes.**

foolishness Actions or behavior that do not show good sense. It is *foolishness* to dive into a lake without knowing how deep it is.
    fool•ish•ness (fü′lish nis) *noun.*

formation The way in which the members or units of a group are arranged. The band lined up in parade *formation.*
    for•ma•tion (fôr mā′shən) *noun, plural* **formations.**

foul 1. Very unpleasant or dirty. There was a *foul* odor in the air when the sewer pipes broke. **2.** Cloudy, rainy, or stormy. *Foul* weather delayed the ship. **3.** Very bad, evil. The villain in the story had committed all sorts of *foul* deeds. ▲ Another word that sounds like this is **fowl.**
    foul (foul) *adjective*, **fouler, foulest.**

Fuentes (fwen′tes).

furnace A large, enclosed metal box where heat is produced. A *furnace* is used to heat a building or to melt metal.
    fur•nace (fûr′nis) *noun, plural* **furnaces.**

---

at; āpe; fär; câre; end; mē; it; īce; pîerce; hot; ōld; sông; fôrk; oil, out; up; ūse; rüle; pull; tûrn; chin; sing; shop; thin; **this**; hw in white; zh in treasure. The symbol ə stands for the unstressed vowel sound in about, taken, pencil, lemon, and circus.

G

glorious Full of great praise, honor, or beauty; grand; magnificent. A *glorious* sunset filled the sky.
glo•ri•ous (glôr′ē əs) *adjective.*

glum Gloomy or sullen. She looked *glum* when she realized her bicycle tire had a leak.
glum (glum) *adjective,* **glummer, glummest.**

gnaw To bite again and again in order to wear away little by little. The dog *gnawed* a hole through the fence.
gnaw (nô) *verb,* **gnawed, gnawing.**

Greene, Silas (grēn, sī′ləs).

Greenland A Danish island northeast of the mainland of North America, lying mostly within the Arctic Circle. It is the largest island in the world.
Green•land (grēn′lənd) *noun.*

grieve To feel great sorrow. The entire nation *grieved* at the death of their president.
grieve (grēv) *verb,* **grieved, grieving.**

grizzly bear A very large and powerful bear. It has long claws and usually brown or gray fur. *Grizzly bears* live in western North America.
griz•zly bear (griz′lē bâr) *noun, plural* **grizzly bears.**

Gulf of St. Lawrence An arm of the Atlantic, on the eastern coast of Canada, at the mouth of the St. Lawrence River.
Gulf of St. Law•rence (gulf uv sānt lôr′əns) *noun.*

H

harbor A sheltered place along a coast. Ships and boats often anchor in a harbor.
har•bor (här′bər) *noun, plural* **harbors.**

harbor

harness The straps, bands, and other gear used to attach a work animal to a cart, plow, or wagon.
har•ness (här′nis) *noun, plural* **harnesses.**

Hassan (hə son′).

haze Mist, smoke, or dust in the air. The bridge was hidden in the morning *haze.*
haze (hāz) *noun, plural* **hazes.**

herb A plant whose leaves, stems, seeds, or roots are used in cooking for flavoring, in medicines, or because they are fragrant. Mint and parsley are *herbs.*
herb (ûrb *or* hûrb) *noun, plural* **herbs.**

hibernation The act of spending the winter in a deep sleep. Many animals such as bears, squirrels, and snakes, a few fish and birds, and some insects go into *hibernation* in the winter.
hi•ber•na•tion (hī'bər nā'shən) *noun.*

Word History

The word **hibernation** comes from the Latin word *hibernare,* meaning "to pass the winter." An animal that hibernates passes the winter by sleeping.

---

historical Having to do with an account or record of what has happened in the past. This book has *historical* information, such as how our town began, how it changed, and who its leaders have been.
his•tor•i•cal (hi stôr'i kəl) *adjective.*

honeycomb A wax structure made by bees to store their eggs and honey in. A *honeycomb* is made up of layers of cells that have six sides.
hon•ey•comb (hun'ē kōm') *noun, plural* **honeycombs.**

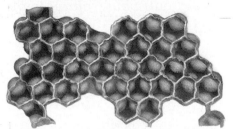
honeycomb

horizon The line where the sky and the ground or the sea seem to meet. We could see a rocky island on the *horizon.*
ho•ri•zon (hə rī'zən) *noun, plural* **horizons.**

horror A feeling of great fear and dread. They watched with *horror* as the passenger ship sank.
hor•ror (hôr'ər) *noun, plural* **horrors.**

huddle To gather close together in a bunch. The scouts *huddled* around the campfire to keep warm.
hud•dle (hud'əl) *verb,* **huddled, huddling.**

I

identify To find out or tell exactly who a person is or what a thing is; recognize. Can you *identify* this strange object?
i•den•ti•fy (ī den'tə fī') *verb,* **identified, identifying.**

ignite To set on fire. We *ignited* the sticks for the campfire with a match.
ig•nite (ig nīt') *verb,* **ignited, igniting.**

ignore To pay no attention to. I tried to *ignore* the noise of the subway as I read my book.
ig•nore (ig nôr') *verb,* **ignored, ignoring.**

image A picture or other likeness of a person or a thing. A penny has an *image* of Abraham Lincoln on one side of it.
im•age (im'ij) *noun, plural* **images.**

---

at; āpe; fär; câre; end; mē; it; īce; pîerce; hot; ōld; sông; fôrk; oil; out; up; ūse; rüle; pull; tûrn; chin; sing; shop, thin; **this**; hw in white; zh in treasure. The symbol ə stands for the unstressed vowel sound in about, taken, pencil, lemon, and circus.

---

impress 1. To have a strong effect on the mind or feelings of. The height of the skyscraper *impressed* me. **2.** To fix in the mind. Our parents tried to *impress* a sense of right and wrong on each of us.
    im•press (im pres′) *verb,* **impressed, impressing.**

independence Freedom from the control of another or others. The American colonies fought to win *independence* from England.
    in•de•pend•ence (in′di pen′dəns) *noun.*

India A country in southern Asia.
    In•di•a (in′dē ə) *noun.*

inspect To look at closely and carefully. The official *inspected* our car and declared that it was safe to drive.
    in•spect (in spekt′) *verb,* **inspected, inspecting.**

inspire To move to action. What *inspired* you to take up stamp collecting?
    in•spire (in spīr′) *verb,* **inspired, inspiring.**

instinct A way of acting or behaving that a person or animal is born with and does not have to learn. Birds build nests by *instinct.*
    in•stinct (in′stingkt′) *noun, plural* **instincts.**

instructor A person who instructs; teacher. We are taking lessons from the swimming *instructor* at the town pool.
    in•struct•or (in struk′tər) *noun, plural* **instructors.**

investigate To look into carefully in order to find facts and get information. The police are responsible for *investigating* the bank robbery.
    in•ves•ti•gate (in ves′ti gāt′) *verb,* **investigated, investigating.**

jagged Having sharp points that stick out. Some eagles build nests on *jagged* cliffs.
    jag•ged (jag′id) *adjective.*

jagged

jealous Having envy of a person, or what a person has or can do. I used to be *jealous* of my friend's ability to play football well.
    jeal•ous (jel′əs) *adjective.*

jowl Heavy, loose flesh hanging from or under the lower jaw.
    jowl (joul) *noun, plural* **jowls.**

Kaiserslautern A small city located in the Rhine Valley region of western Germany.
    Kai•ser•slau•tern (Kī zərz′lau tərn) *noun*

Keija (kē′ja).

knapsack A bag made of canvas, leather, or other material that is used for carrying clothes, equipment, or other supplies. A *knapsack* is strapped over the shoulders and carried on the back.
> **knap•sack** (nap′sak′) *noun, plural* **knapsacks.**

Labrador (lab′rə dor).

launch 1. To start something. The company *launched* its store by having a big sale. **2.** To start in motion; send off. The scientists at the space center will *launch* a rocket.
> **launch** (lônch) *verb,* **launched, launching.**

linger To stay on as if not wanting to leave; move slowly. The fans *lingered* outside the stadium to see the players on the team.
> **lin•ger** (ling′gər) *verb,* **lingered, lingering.**

loft 1. A large, open room in a building. The owner of the building divided the *loft* into three apartments. **2.** The upper floor, room, or space in a building. Use the *loft* for storing hay.
> **loft** (lôft) *noun, plural* **lofts.**

loop To make a rounded shape by crossing a string, wire, rope, or anything similar. You *loop* the laces when you tie your shoes. As the dog ran, the chain *looped* around the tree.
> **loop** (lüp) *verb,* **looped, looping.**

Maidu A Native American tribe from the Sacramento Valley area of California.
> **Mai•du** (mī′du) *noun.*

Maldonado, Felicidad (mäl′dō nä′dō, fə lē′sē däd′).

mammal A kind of animal that is warm-blooded and has a backbone. Female *mammals* have glands that produce milk to feed their young. Most *mammals* are covered with fur or have some hair. Human beings, cattle, dogs, cats, and whales are *mammals.*
> **mam•mal** (mam′əl) *noun, plural* **mammals.**

mammal

at; āpe; fär; câre; end; mē; it; īce; pîerce; hot; ōld; sông; fôrk; oil, out; up; ūse; rüle; pull; tûrn; chin; sing; shop; thin; **th**is; hw in white; zh in treasure. The symbol ə stands for the unstressed vowel sound in about, taken, pencil, lemon, and circus.

mammoth Very large; gigantic; huge. Building that cabin was a *mammoth* job.
　mam•moth (mam'əth) *adjective.*

marine Having to do with or living in the sea. Whales are *marine* animals.
　ma•rine (mə rēn') *adjective.*

marketplace A place where food and other products are bought and sold. In old towns the *marketplace* was often found in a square.
　mar•ket•place (mär'kit plās') *noun, plural* **marketplaces.**

marketplace

marvel To feel wonder and astonishment. We *marveled* at the acrobat's skill.
　mar•vel (mär'vəl) *verb,* **marveled, marveling.**

master To become expert in. That student *mastered* French easily.
　mas•ter (mas'tər) *verb,* **mastered, mastering.**

mature Having reached full growth or development; ripe. The farmer harvested the corn when it was *mature.*
　ma•ture (mə chür' *or* mə tür' *or* mə tyür') *adjective.*

Mercado (mer kä'dō).

merchant A person whose business is buying goods and selling them for profit. My grandparents were clothing *merchants.*
　mer•chant (mŭr'chənt) *noun, plural* **merchants.**

Methuselah A biblical character believed to have lived 969 years.
　Me•thu•se•lah (mə thü'zə lə) *noun.*

mill A building where there are machines to make raw materials into finished products. Steel *mills* make steel.
　mill (mil) *noun, plural* **mills.**

Misha (mē'shə).

Mount Everest A mountain in the Himalayas; the highest mountain peak in the world (29,028 feet, or 8,848 meters).
　Mount Ev•er•est (mount ev'ər əst *or* mount ev'rəst) *noun.*

mutter To speak in a low, unclear way with the mouth almost closed. I *muttered* to myself that I would be late if I didn't hurry.
　mut•ter (mut'ər) *verb,* **muttered, muttering.**

N

Newfoundland An island off the east coast of Canada; part of the province of Newfoundland and Labrador.
　New•found•land (nü'fənd lənd *or* nü'fənd lənd) *noun.*

nippy Cold or chilly in a sharp biting way. The air is *nippy* in November.
　nip•py (nip'ē) *adjective,* **nippier, nippiest.**

nursery A place where young children are taken care of during the day.
> **nurs•er•y** (nûr′sə rē) *noun, plural* **nurseries.**

O

obedience The act of carrying out the orders, wishes, or instructions of. The strict teacher expected *obedience* from her students.
> **o•be•di•ence** (ō bē′dē əns) *noun*

obstacle A person or thing that stands in the way or blocks progress. The heavy snowstorm was an *obstacle* to traffic.
> **ob•sta•cle** (ob′stə kəl) *noun, plural* **obstacles.**

obstacle

old-fashioned No longer in fashion. The hat in the attic is *old-fashioned.*
> **old-fash•ioned** (ōld′fash′ənd) *adjective*

opponent A person who is against another in a fight, contest, or discussion. He beat his *opponent* and won the championship.
> **op•po•nent** (ə pō′nənt) *noun, plural* **opponents.**

organization A group of people joined together for a particular purpose. I belong to an *organization* that does work for various charities.
> **or•gan•i•za•tion** (ôr′gə nə zā′shən) *noun, plural* **organizations.**

orphan A child whose parents are dead.
> **or•phan** (ôr′fən) *noun, plural* **orphans.**

outstanding So good as to stand out from others of its kind.
> **out•stand•ing** (out′stan′ding) *adjective.*

P

peninsula A piece of land that sticks out into the water from a larger body of land. The southern part of Florida is a *peninsula.*
> **pen•in•su•la** (pə nin′sə lə *or* pə nin′syə lə) *noun, plural* **peninsulas.**

Word History

The word **peninsula** comes from two Latin words, *paene,* meaning "almost," and *insula,* meaning "island." A *peninsula* is a strip of land surrounded by water on three sides, so it is almost an island.

---

at; āpe; fär; câre; end; mē; it; īce; pîerce; hot; ōld; sông; fôrk; oil; out; up; ūse; rüle; pùll; tûrn; chin; sing; shop; thin; **th**is; hw in white; zh in treasure. The symbol ə stands for the unstressed vowel sound in about, taken, pencil, lemon, and circus.

pesky Troublesome or annoying. The *pesky* mosquitoes bit me.
  pes•ky (pes′kē) *adjective*,
  peskier, peskiest.

pesticide A chemical substance used to kill insects, rats, or other animal pests.
  pest•i•cide (pes′tə sīd′) *noun*, *plural* **pesticides.**

petition A formal request that is made to a person in authority. I signed a *petition* asking the city to put up a stop sign on the corner.
  pe•ti•tion (pi tish′ən) *noun*, *plural* **petitions.**

physical Having to do with the body. An elephant has great *physical* strength.
  phys•i•cal (fiz′i kəl) *adjective*.

Pittsburgh A city in southwestern Pennsylvania, the leading center of iron and steel production in the United States.
  Pitts•burgh (pits′bûrg) *noun*.

plead To make a sincere request; beg. I *pleaded* with my friend not to swim near the rocks.
  plead (plēd) *verb*, **pleaded** *or* **pled, pleading.**

poisonous Containing or having the effects of a drug or other substance that harms or kills by chemical action. Many household cleaning products are *poisonous*.
  poi•son•ous (poi′zə nəs) *adjective*.

poncho A cloak made of one piece of cloth or other material. It has a hole in the middle for the head.
  pon•cho (pon′chō) *noun*, *plural* **ponchos.**

potion A drink mixture, especially one believed to have magical power. When the princess drank the magic *potion* she turned into a frog.
  po•tion (pō′shən) *noun*, *plural* **potions.**

prairie Flat or rolling land covered with grass. A *prairie* has few or no trees.
  prai•rie (prâr′ē) *noun*, *plural* **prairies.**

prairie

praise To express high regard and approval of. The teacher *praised* the student's fine drawing.
  praise (prāz) *verb*, **praised, praising.**

prance To spring forward on the hind legs. The colt *pranced* and leaped about the field.
  prance (prans) *verb*, **pranced, prancing.**

prejudice Hatred or unfair treatment of a particular group, such as members of a race or religion. Because of *prejudice*, the owners of the company only hired workers of their own religion.
  prej•u•dice (prej′ə dis) *noun*, *plural* **prejudices.**

preparation The act of making something ready, or the condition of being made ready. The cook was busy with the *preparation* of dinner.
  prep•a•ra•tion (prep′ə rā′shən) *noun*, *plural* **preparations.**

preserve To keep from being lost, damaged, or decayed; protect. It is important that we *preserve* our freedoms in this country.
> **pre•serve** (pri zûrv′) *verb,* **preserved, preserving.**

Prince Edward Island The smallest province of Canada, consisting of an island in the Gulf of St. Lawrence.
> **Prince Ed•ward Is•land** (prins ed′wərd ī′lənd) *noun.*

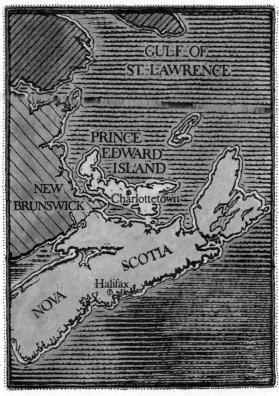

Prince Edward Island

property 1. A piece of land. We bought some *property* near the ocean. **2.** A characteristic of something. Heat is a *property* of fire.
> **prop•er•ty** (prop′ər tē) *noun,* *plural* **properties.**

protection The keeping of someone or something from harm. Our state has game preserves for the *protection* of wild animals.
> **pro•tec•tion** (prə tek′shən) *noun.*

R

rage To talk or act in a violent way. I *raged* at the bullies who had hurt my dog.
> **rage** (rāj) *verb,* **raged, raging.**

rajah A ruler or prince in India or the East Indies.
> **ra•jah** (rä′jə) *noun,* *plural* **rajahs.**

ravine A deep, narrow valley.
> **ra•vine** (rə vēn′) *noun,* *plural* **ravines.**

recite To repeat something from memory. Can you *recite* the names of all the fifty states and their capitals?
> **re•cite** (ri sīt′) *verb* **recited, reciting.**

reference 1. A person or thing that is referred to; source of information or help. The encyclopedia was the *reference* for my report. **2.** A statement that calls or directs attention to something. The authors made a *reference* to their other book.
> **ref•er•ence** (ref′ər əns *or* ref′rəns) *noun,* *plural* **references.**

refreshment Food and drink. What *refreshments* will you serve at the party?
> **re•fresh•ment** (ri fresh′mənt) *noun,* *plural* **refreshments.**

at; āpe; fär; câre; end; mē; it; īce; pîerce; hot; ōld; sông; fôrk; oil; out; up; ūoo; rüle; půll; tûrn; chin; sing; shop; thin; this; hw in white; zh in treasure. The symbol ə stands for the unstressed vowel sound in about, taken, pencil, lemon, and circus.

rein 1. One of two or more narrow straps that are attached to a horse's headgear. *Reins* are used to guide and control a horse. **2.** Any means of control. I kept a tight *rein* on my temper. ▲ Other words that sound like this are **rain** and **reign**.
rein (rān) *noun, plural* **reins.**

related Belonging to the same family. You and your sisters, brothers, cousins, aunts, uncles, and grandparents are all *related*.
re•lat•ed (ri lā′tid) *adjective.*

relieve To free from discomfort or pain; comfort, help, or aid. The good news *relieved* us of our worries.
re•lieve (ri lēv′) *verb,* **relieved, relieving.**

resound To be filled with sound. The stadium *resounded* with cheers from the fans.
re•sound (ri zound′) *verb,* **resounded, resounding.**

revolve To depend on. My whole life *revolves* around my family and my work.
re•volve (ri volv′) *verb,* **revolved, revolving.**

romp To play in a lively and noisy way. The children *romped* in the waves.
romp (romp) *verb,* **romped, romping.**

rubble Rough, broken pieces of stone, rock, or other solid material. The rescue workers searched through the *rubble* of the bombed building and were able to save many lives.
rub•ble (rub′əl) *noun.*

Russia An independent country in eastern Europe and northern Asia bordering on the Arctic and Pacific oceans, and on the Baltic and Black seas.
Rus•sia (rush′ə) *noun.*

S

sage[1] A very wise person, usually also old and very respected. The village consulted the *sage* for advice.
sage (sāj) *noun, plural* **sages.**

sage[2] A small plant whose leaves are used to flavor food.
sage (sāj) *noun.*

sage

scenery The painted pictures or objects that are used to make the setting of a play or movie. The *scenery* looked realistic
scen•er•y (sē nə rē) *noun, plural* **sceneries**

schedule The time at which something is supposed to happen. The train was running behind *schedule* because of the weather.
sched•ule (skej′ül) *noun, plural* **schedules.**

scientific Having to do with or used in science. All of the students in our class had to plan and carry out a *scientific* experiment.
sci•en•tif•ic (sī′ən tif′ik) *adjective.*

script 1. The written text of a play, movie, or television or radio show. We hope to say our lines without looking at the *script.* **2.** Handwriting in which the letters are joined together.
script (skript) *noun, plural* **scripts.**

segregation The practice of setting one racial group apart from another. There are laws against the *segregation* of black children and white children in the public schools.
seg•re•ga•tion (seg'ri gā'shən) *noun.*

shift A group of workers, or the time that they work. My cousin works during the day *shift* at the factory.
shift (shift) *noun, plural* **shifts.**

shriek To utter a loud sharp cry or sound.
shriek (shrēk) *verb,* **shrieked, shrieking.**

Sierra Nevada Mountains A mountain range in eastern California.
Si•er•ra Ne•vad•a Mount•ains (sē er'ə nə vad'ə moun'tənz *or* sē er'ə nə vä'də moun'tənz) *noun.*

sketch To make a quick, rough drawing. I *sketched* an old barn for my art class.
sketch (skech) *verb,* **sketched, sketching.**

skillet A shallow frying pan with a handle. A *skillet* is used for frying.
skil•let (skil'it) *noun, plural* **skillets.**

slick Smooth and shiny. The horse had a *slick* brown coat.
slick (slik) *adjective,* **slicker, slickest.**

smog A combination of smoke and fog in the air. *Smog* is found especially over cities where there are factories and many cars.
smog (smog) *noun.*

Word History

The word **smog** was made using the first two letters of the word *smoke* and the last two letters of the word *fog.*

---

snicker To laugh in a sly, disrespectful way. The student *snickered* during the boring speech.
snick•er (snik'ər) *verb,* **snickered, snickering.**

soar 1. To fly high in the air. The birds *soared* in the sky. **2.** To go very high. The price of food *soared* this year. ▲ Another word that sounds like this is **sore.**
soar (sôr) *verb,* **soared, soaring.**

soot A black greasy powder that forms when fuels such as wood, coal, and oil are burned.
soot (sut *or* süt) *noun.*

span To extend over or across. The fallen log *spanned* the mountain creek.
span (span) *verb,* **spanned, spanning.**

Word History

The word **span** comes from the Dutch word *spannen,* which means "to stretch."

---

spice The seeds or other parts of certain plants that are used to flavor food. Pepper, cloves, and cinnamon are *spices.*
spice (spīs) *noun, plural* **spices.**

spice

---

at; āpe; fär; câre; end; mē; it; īce; pîerce; hot; ōld, sông; fôrk; oil; out; up; ūse; rüle; pull; tûrn; chin; sing; shop; thin; this; hw in white; zh in treasure. The symbol ə stands for the unstressed vowel sound in about, taken, pencil, lemon, and circus.

---

sprout To begin to grow. The seeds that I planted a week ago have just *sprouted*.
    sprout (sprout) *verb*, **sprouted, sprouting.**

squall A strong gust of wind that arises very suddenly. *Squalls* often bring rain, snow, or sleet.
    squall (skwôl) *noun, plural* **squalls.**

squeal To make a loud, shrill cry or sound. The child *squealed* with delight upon seeing all the presents.
    squeal (skwēl) *verb*, **squealed, squealing.**

squirm To turn or twist the body; wriggle. The children were bored and began to *squirm* in their seats.
    squirm (skwûrm) *verb*, **squirmed, squirming.**

stable¹ A building where cattle or horses are kept and fed. A stable often has stalls for the animals that are kept there.
    sta•ble (stā′bəl) *noun, plural* **stables.**

stable

stable² Not easily moved, shaken, or changed. After the earthquake, only *stable* buildings were left standing.
    sta•ble (stā′bəl) *adjective*.

stall To delay or prevent. The neighborhood wants a traffic light placed at this corner, but the city has been *stalling*.
    stall (stôl) *verb*, **stalled, stalling.**

stammer To speak or say with difficulty, such as to repeat the same sound several times when trying to say a word. I sometimes *stammer* when I'm nervous.
    stam•mer (stam′ər) *verb*, **stammered, stammering.**

stoop¹ A small porch with stairs at the entrance of a house or other building.
    stoop (stüp) *noun, plural* **stoops.**

stoop² **1.** To bend forward and downward. The teacher *stooped* to pick up the pencil. **2.** To stand or walk with the head or shoulders bent forward. I *stoop* when I walk because my back hurts. **3.** To lower or degrade oneself to do something. I would never *stoop* to cheating.
    stoop (stüp) *verb*, **stooped, stooping.**

support A person or thing that holds up or provides for someone or something else. The center pole is the main *support* of the tent. *Noun.*
—To hold up. The columns *support* the roof. *Verb.*
    sup•port (sə pôrt′) *noun, plural* **supports;** *verb*, **supported, supporting.**

survive To continue to exist. These plants need water to *survive*.
    sur•vive (sər vīv′) *verb*, **surviving, survived.**

swarm A group of bees that leave their hive to start a new colony.
    swarm (swôrm) *noun, plural* **swarms.**

T

teammate A person who is a member of the same team. Many of my baseball *teammates* have become my friends.
  team•mate (tēm′māt′) *noun, plural* **teammates.**

Tío Jorge Spanish for "Uncle George."
  Tí•o Jor•ge (tē′ō hôr′hā) *noun.*

tradition A custom or belief that is passed on from parents or other relatives to their children. A picnic in the park on the 4th of July is a family *tradition.*
  tra•di•tion (trə dish′ən) *noun, plural* **traditions.**

trail 1. To lessen gradually (usually with *off* or *away*). Conversation *trailed off* as the evening wore on. **2.** To follow behind. The children *trailed* the parade. *Verb.*
—**1.** A path through an area that is wild or not lived in. The hikers followed the *trail* through the woods. **2.** A mark, scent, or path made by a person or animal. The hunters followed the bear's *trail.* *Noun.*
  trail (trāl) *noun, plural* **trails;** *verb,* **trailed, trailing.**

tremendous Very large or great; enormous. A *tremendous* clap of thunder shook the house.
  tre•men•dous (tri men′dəs) *adjective.*

tribal Having to do with a group of people who have the same ancestors, social customs, and other characteristics. We studied African *tribal* customs in my class.
  trib•al (trī′bəl) *adjective.*

twine A strong string made of two or more strands twisted together. I used *twine* to tie the package.
  twine (twīn) *noun, plural* **twines.**

twirl To spin around quickly. A drum majorette *twirled* a baton at the head of the parade.
  twirl (twûrl) *verb,* **twirled, twirling.**

twirl

U

unconscious Not conscious. I was knocked *unconscious* when I fell out of the tree and hit my head.
  un•con•scious (un kon′shəs) *adjective.*

uproar A noisy and excited disturbance. The crowd was in an *uproar* when the player hit a home run.
  up•roar (up′rôr′) *noun, plural* **uproars.**

---

at; āpe; fär; câre; end; mē; it; īce; pîerce; hot; ōld; sông; fôrk; oil; out; up; ūse; rüle; pull; tûrn; chin; sing; shop; thin; this; hw in white; zh in treasure. The symbol ə stands for the unstressed vowel sound in about, taken, pencil, lemon, and circus.

utensil An object or tool that is useful or necessary in doing or making something. I keep all my cooking *utensils* in a drawer.
u•ten•sil (ū ten′səl) *noun, plural* **utensils.**

weariness Fatigue or tiredness. In my *weariness* after our long hike I fell asleep before eating dinner.
wea•ri•ness (wîr′ē nes) *noun.*

wildlife Wild animals that live naturally in an area.
wild•life (wîld′līf′) *noun.*

vow A solemn promise or pledge. The soldiers took a *vow* of loyalty to the government.
vow (vou) *noun, plural* **vows.**

Yeh-Shen (yā′shən′).

Yellowstone National Park A national park in northwestern Wyoming and neighboring sections of Montana and Idaho.
Yel•low•stone Na•tion•al Park (yel′ō stōn nash′ə nəl pärk) *noun.*

waddle To walk or move with short steps, swaying the body from side to side. The duck *waddled* across the yard.
wad•dle (wod′əl) *verb,* **waddled, waddling.**

Zimbabwe A country in south-central Africa.
Zim•bab•we (zim bäb′wē *or* zim bäb′wā) *noun.*

waddle

at; āpe; fär; câre; end; mē; it; īce; pîerce; hot; ōld; sông; fôrk; oil; out; up; ūse; rüle; pu̇ll; tûrn; chin; sing; shop; thin; this; hw in white; zh in treasure. The symbol ə stands for the unstressed vowel sound in about, taken, pencil, lemon, and circus.

ACKNOWLEDGMENTS

The publisher gratefully acknowledges permission to reprint the following copyrighted material:

"The Ages Flow" from FESTIVAL IN MY HEART by Ikenaga Eri, translated by Bruno Narasky. Copyright © 1993 by Harry N. Abrams, Inc. Published by Harry N. Abrams, Inc. Reprinted by permission.

"Ancestry" from SING TO THE SUN by Ashley Bryan. Copyright © 1992 by Ashley Bryan. Published by HarperCollins Publishers Children's Books. Reprinted by permission.

Entire text and art and cover of CITY GREEN by DyAnne DiSalvo-Ryan. Copyright (c) 1994 by DyAnne DiSalvo-Ryan. By permission of Morrow Junior Books, a division of William Morrow and Company, Inc.

"Creation of a California Tribe: Grandfathers's Maidu Indian Tales" is from CREATION OF A CALIFORNIA TRIBE: GRANDFATHER'S MAIDU INDIAN TALES by Lee Ann Smith-Trafzer & Clifford E. Trafzer. Copyright © 1988 by Lee Ann Smith-Trafzer and Clifford F. Trafzer. Published by Sierra Oaks Publishing Co. Reprinted by permission.

"Do Not Disturb: The Mysteries of Animal Hibernation and Sleep" from DO NOT DISTURB: THE MYSTERIES OF ANIMAL HIBERNATION AND SLEEP by Margery Facklam. Text Copyright © 1989 by Margery Facklam; Illustrations Copyright © 1989 by Pamela Johnson. By permission of Little, Brown and Company.

"Dousing the Flames" from KIDS DISCOVER, January 1994, Volume 4, Issue 1. Copyright © 1994 by Kids Discover. Reprinted by permission.

"Draw!: 3-D Doodles and Shading Doodles" from DRAW! by Kim Solga. Copyright © 1991 by F & W Publications, Inc. Published by North Light Books. Reprinted by permission.

"Dreams" from THE DREAM KEEPER AND OTHER POEMS by Langston Hughes. Copyright © 1932 by Alfred A. Knopf, Inc. and renewed 1960 by Langston Hughes. Reprinted by permission of the publisher.

Cover permission for EL CHINO by Allen Say. Copyright © 1990 by Allen Say. Reprinted by permission of Houghton Mifflin Company. All rights reserved.

"Endangered Species Make Comebacks" reprint permission and copyright © 1994 by Weekly Reader Corporation. All Rights Reserved.

"Érase Una Vez"/"Once Upon a Time" by Juan Goytisolo from EXPRESION ORAL INFANTIL compiled, selected, and arranged by Noe Solchaga Zamudio and Luisa Aurora Solchaga Peña. Copyright © by Editorial Avante, S.A. and used with their permission.

Cover permission for the Trophy edition of THE FACTS AND FICTIONS OF MINNA PRATT by Patricia MacLachlan. Used by permission of HarperCollins Publishers.

"The Falling Star" reprinted with permission of Simon & Schuster, Inc. from COLLECTED POEMS OF SARA TEASDALE. Copyright 1930 by Sara Teasdale Filsinger, renewed 1958 by Guaranty Trust Co. of N.Y.

"Felita" is from FELITA by Nicholasa Mohr. Copyright © 1979 by Nicholasa Mohr. Used by permission of Dial Books for Young Readers, a division of Penguin Books USA Inc.

"Frog School Competing" by Shiki. Copyright © 1964 by Harry Behn. © renewed 1992 by Prescott Behn, Pamela Behn Adams, and Peter Behn. Reprinted by permission.

"Good Intentions Lead to Good Inventions" Application form: The 54th Westinghouse Science Talent Search. Article: "Here's How She Made Money Talk" by Hildebrand from Newsday (Nassau Edition), March 14, 1995. Reprinted by permission.

"Grandmother's Brook" reprinted with permisson of Simon & Schuster Books for Young Readers from POEMS by Rachel Field. Copyright 1934 by Macmillan Publishing Company, renewed 1962 by Arthur S. Pederson.

"The Great Pretenders" by Nature's Images Inc. from FALCON Nov/Dec 1994 issue. Copyright 1994 Falcon Press Publishing, Helena, MT, 59601. Reprinted by permission of the publisher.

"Hail Polluters" from STREET POEMS by Robert Froman. Copyright © 1971 by Robert Froman. Reprinted by permission of the author.

Cover permission for HAVE A HAPPY . . . by Mildred Pitts Walter with illustrations by Carole Byard. (Lothrop, Lee & Shepard). Text copyright © 1989 by Mildred Pitts Walter. Illustrations copyright © by Carole Byard. Cover use by permission of Marie Brown Associates.

"Her Dreams" is the text and art from UNDER THE SUNDAY TREE by Eloise Greenfield, illustrated by Mr. Amos Ferguson. Text copyright © by Eloise Greenfield. Paintings copyright © by Mr. Amos Ferguson. Reprinted by permission of HarperCollins Publishers.

"How?" from FEATHERED ONES AND FURRY by Aileen Fisher. Originally published in INSIDE A LITTLE HOUSE by Aileen Fisher, published by McBridge, New York. Copyright © 1938 by Aileen Fisher. Copyright renewed 1966 by Aileen Fisher. Reprinted by permission of the author.

"I Wonder" reprinted by permission of Curtis Brown Ltd. Copyright © 1972 by Flora Hood. First appeared in THE TURQUOISE HORSE published by G.P. Putnam's Sons.

"If once you have slept on an island" copyright (c) 1926 by The Century Company from TAXIS AND TOADSTOOLS by Rachel Field. . Used by permission of Bantam Doubleday Dell Books for Young Readers.

"Imagine" adapted from American Girl, vol. 2, number 5. © 1994 by Pleasant Company. Reprinted by permission of Pleasant Company.

"In Search of Cinderella" is the text and art of the work from A LIGHT IN

THE ATTIC by Shel Silverstein. Copyright © 1981 by Evil Eye Music, Inc. Reprinted by permission of HarperCollins Publishers.

"Invitation" is the text and art of the work from WHERE THE SIDEWALK ENDS by Shel Silverstein. Copyright © 1974 by Evil Eye Music, Inc. Reprinted by permission of HarperCollins Publishers.

"Just a Dream" is from JUST A DREAM by Chris Van Allsburg. Copyright © 1990 by Chris Van Allsburg. Reprinted by permission of Houghton Mifflin Company.

"Justin and the Best Biscuits in the World" is from JUSTIN AND THE BEST BISCUITS IN THE WORLD by Mildred Pitts Walter. Copyright © 1986 by Mildred Pitts Walter. Published by Lothrop, Lee & Shepard Books and reprinted by permission of William Morrow & Company, Inc., Publishers, New York.

"A Kettle of Hawks and Other Wildlife Groups" is from A KETTLE OF HAWKS AND OTHER WILDLIFE GROUPS by Jim Arnosky. Copyright © 1970 by Jim Arnosky. Published by Lothrop, Lee & Shepard Books and used by permission of William Morrow & Company, Inc./Publishers, New York.

"Landscape" from A SKY FULL OF POEMS by Eve Merriam. Copyright © 1964, 1970, 1973 by Eve Merriam. Reprinted by permission of Marian Reiner for the author.

"A Little Excitement" from A LITTLE EXCITEMENT by Marc Harshman, illustrated by Ted Rand. Text copyright © 1989 by Marc Harshman, copyright © 1989 by Ted Rand for illustrations. Used by permission of Cobblehill Books, an affiliate of Dutton Children's Books, a division of Penguin USA, Inc.

"The Lost Lake" is from THE LOST LAKE by Allen Say. Copyright © 1989 by Allen Say, Jacket art © 1989 by Allen Say. Reprinted by permission of Houghton Mifflin Co.

"A Lot of Kids" from THE BUTTERFLY JAR by Jeff Moss. Copyright © 1989 by Jeff Moss. Used by permission of Bantam Books, a division of Bantam Doubleday Dell Publishing Group, Inc.

"The Lucky Stone" is from THE LUCKY STONE by Lucille Clifton. Copyright © 1979 by Lucille Clifton. Used by permission of Delacorte Press, a division of Bantam Doubleday Dell Publishing Group.

"Memory" from WORDS WORDS WORDS by Mary O'Neill. Copyright © 1966 by Mary O'Neill. Used by permission of Doubleday, a division of Bantam Doubleday Dell Publishing Groups, Inc.

"Mom's Best Friend" by Sally Hobart Alexander, photographs by George Ancona. Text copyright (c) 1992 by Sally Hobart Alexander. Photographs copyright (c) 1992 by George Ancona. Reprinted with permission of Simon & Schuster Books for Young Readers, Simon & Schuster Children's Publishing Division.

Entire text and illustrations, MUFARO'S BEAUTIFUL DAUGHTERS: AN AFRICAN TALE by John Steptoe. Copyright (c) 1987 by John Steptoe. By permission of Lothrop, Lee & Shepard Books, a division of William Morrow & Company, Inc., with the approval of the Estate of John Steptoe.

"No Star Nights" is from NO STAR NIGHTS by Anna Egan Smucker, illustrated by Steve Johnson. Text copyright © 1989 by Anna Egan Smucker. Illustrations copyright © 1989 by Steven Johnson. Reprinted by permission of Alfred A. Knopf, Inc.

"Oath of Friendship" from TRANSLATIONS FROM THE CHINESE by Arthur Waley. Copyright 1919 and renewed 1947 by Arthur Waley. Reprinted by permission of Alfred A. Knopf, Inc. By permission also of Unwin Hyman of HarperCollins Publishers, Inc.

"The Old Plump Bullfrog" by Issa. Reprinted by permission of Charles E. Tuttle Co., Inc. of Tokyo, Japan.

"An Old Silent Pond" by Basho from CRICKET SONGS. Copyright © 1964 by Harry Behn. © renewed 1992 by Prescott Behn, Pamela Behn Adams, and Peter Behn. Reprinted by permission.

Cover permission for PARTNERS FOR LIFE: THE MYSTERIES OF ANIMAL SYMBIOSIS by Margery Facklam with illustrations by Pamela Johnson. Illustrations copyright © 1989 by Pamela Johnson. Reprinted by permission of Little, Brown and Company in association with Sierra Club Books.

"Pat Cummings: My Story" reprinted and recorded with the permission of Simon & Schuster Books for Young Readers from TALKING WITH ARTISTS compiled and edited by Pat Cummings. Jacket illustration copyright © 1992 Pat Cummings. Copyright © 1992 Pat Cummings.

Cover permission for THE POLAR EXPRESS by Chris Van Allsburg. Copyright © 1985 by Chris Van Allsburg. Reprinted by permission of Houghton Mifflin Company. All rights reserved.

"Rachel Carson: Protector of Planet Earth" by Virginia Evarts Wadsworth is from COBBLESTONE'S August 1989 issue: Environmentalism. Copyright © 1989 Cobblestone Publishing, Inc., 7 School St., Peterborough, NH 03458. Reprinted by permission of the publisher.

"The Rajah's Rice" from THE RAJAH'S RICE by David Barry, illustrated by Donna Perrone. Text copyright © 1994 by David Barry. Art copyright © 1994 by Donna Perrone. Used with permission of W. H. Freeman and Company.

"Sarah, Plain and Tall" text excerpt from SARAH PLAIN AND TALL by Patricia MacLachlan. Copyright © 1985 by Patricia MacLachlan. Reprinted by permission of HarperCollins Publishers. Cover permission for the Trophy Edition used by permission of HarperCollins Publishers.

Cover permission for THE SEA AROUND US by Rachel Carson. Copyright © 1950 by Oxford University Press renewed © 1979 by Roger Christie. Used by permission of Oxford University Press.